Advanced Play Therapy

Advanced Play Therapy

Essential Conditions, Knowledge, and Skills for Child Practice

Dee C. Ray

NEW YORK AND LONDON

Routledge
Taylor & Francis Group
605 Third Avenue,
New York, NY 10017

Routledge
Taylor & Francis Group
2 Park Square, Milton Park,
Abingdon, Oxon OX14 4RN

First issued in paperback 2021

Routledge is an imprint of Taylor & Francis Group, an Informa business

ISBN 13: 978-1-03-223755-8 (pbk)
ISBN 13: 978-0-415-88604-8 (hbk)

DOI: 10.4324/9780203837269

Publisher's Note
The publisher has gone to great lengths to ensure the quality of this reprint but points out that some imperfections in the original copies may be apparent.

Library of Congress Cataloging-in-Publication Data

Ray, Dee C.
Advanced play therapy : essential conditions, knowledge, and skills for child practice / Dee C. Ray.
p. ; cm.
Includes bibliographical references and index.
ISBN 978-0-415-88604-8 (hardcover : alk. paper)
1. Play therapy. I. Title.
[DNLM: 1. Play Therapy. 2. Child. WS 350.4]

RJ505.P6R39 2010
618.92'891653--dc22 2010037175

Visit the Taylor & Francis Web site at
http://www.taylorandfrancis.com

and the Routledge Web site at
http://www.routledgementalhealth.com

For Elijah and Noah

My most knowledgeable and caring play therapy teachers

For Russ

Who gave me my first person-centered relationship absent conditions of worth

Supplementary Resources Disclaimer

Additional resources were previously made available for this title on CD. However, as CD has become a less accessible format, all resources have been moved to a more convenient online download option.

You can find these resources available here: www.routledge.com/9780415886048

Please note: Where this title mentions the associated disc, please use the downloadable resources instead.

Contents

Foreword

Play therapy, just what is that really? The mental health field is still struggling with that question and has been unable to reach agreement on the fundamental questions of what play therapy is and what the essential elements of a play therapy relationship are. Dee Ray takes a forthright approach in providing specific, clear, and focused explanations to these questions. She is theoretically grounded and consistent in her approach to applying child-centered principles to the play therapy process.

This is not a book about techniques. This book is about the person of the child, the person of the therapist, and the essential child-centered play therapy skills that are necessary in the process of developing a relationship with children, a process that becomes a way of life for the child-centered play therapist. Dee provides a description of each skill and develops a "feeling" for the application of the skill by taking the reader into the world of children through case examples showing how the skills "look" in the interaction between the therapist and child. Her trademark in this book is a continual process of demonstrating the application of child-centered play therapy principles, concepts, and skills with children in play therapy. The reader will often react with an expression of "Oh, now I not only see how that works with children, I understand why it works." That is a rare quality in play therapy books.

Many readers will probably identify personally with Dee's open exploration of her journey in becoming a child-centered play therapist from rejecting the concepts to embracing the process. It is this kind of personal and professional sharing that is thought provoking. Play therapists should know what they believe about children and play therapy, be able to explain why they believe what they believe, and, perhaps most important, live out what they believe with passion.

This is a book about "being with" children in the playroom in a way that releases the innate, inner-directed, forward moving, self-healing capacity of children in such a way that children are free to be themselves. Dee draws on her years of experiences with children in play therapy to take the reader into the perceptually subjective inner world of play therapy in which principles and practices of the child-centered approach to children come alive as she shares her engaging interactions with children. Without having planned to do so, some readers will find issues, principles, and practices in this book becoming incorporated into their personal philosophies of play therapy.

Dee has written an all-encompassing text that explores a child-centered philosophy, process issues, consulting with parents, group play therapy, play therapy in schools, community agencies, and private practice and supervision in play therapy in such a clear way that the reader will be encouraged to return to this book from time to time to get grounded again in what is important in play therapy and to be reminded of the broad application of play therapy.

Garry L. Landreth
Regents Professor
Department of Counseling and Higher Education
University of North Texas

Preface

Play therapy is the preferred and developmentally appropriate intervention for children who are experiencing emotional, behavioral, and developmental problems. In 1947, Virginia Axline wrote her historically recognized book, *Play Therapy*, in which she presented the philosophy, concepts, and therapist actions that initiated the rise of child-centered play therapy (CCPT). From 1947 until 1991, CCPT, or nondirective play therapy as it was mostly referred to during this time, was researched and discussed in various prominent journals. In 1991, Dr. Garry Landreth published his book, *Play Therapy: The Art of the Relationship* (now in its second edition, 2002), describing CCPT in detail, including a concrete description of the CCPT approach. CCPT is currently the most utilized modality among professional play therapists and celebrates a rich history of empirical research to support its use.

In 1995, I had never heard of play therapy. Although I had received my master's degree in counseling years before and worked as a professional counselor with adolescents and adults, I had never worked with young children. When I was in graduate school, I was taught that children responded to behavioral techniques and that any existential or person-centered intervention would be fruitless with a young age group. From my early days of teaching adolescents, I discovered the inadequacies of behaviorism when helping people address chronic and serious emotional challenges. Hence, I concluded prior to receiving my master's degree that I would not be working with children because I simply did not believe in behaviorism and was unaware that another type of intervention was available. I returned to graduate school to gain my doctoral degree in counseling with an emphasis on adolescence.

It was at this time that I was introduced to play therapy. Inadvertently, I had chosen the University of North Texas because it had an excellent reputation in counseling. I did not know it was also the home of the Center for Play Therapy, the largest play therapy training center in the world. I had never heard of Garry Landreth, play therapy renowned author and founder of the Center for Play Therapy. I observed as fellow students facilitated play therapy with child clients and responded with skepticism to an intervention that not only did not embrace behaviorism, but also denied the necessity of its use with children. At one point in my career, I was play therapy's biggest critic. I was critical of the therapist's lack of directing the child. I was critical of the therapist's lack of emphasizing the need for the child to express emotions verbally. I was critical of the therapist's permissiveness in allowing child-directed play and verbalization. What good could possibly come from allowing a child to make the decisions? How could this possibly remediate the multitude of problems expressed by the parent regarding the child? Did these therapists not know that children need guidance and direction by adults? I resolved to stay as far away from play therapy and that Garry Landreth guy as possible.

As I made my resolution regarding play therapy and focused on my therapeutic training with adolescents and adults, I encountered Dr. Sue Bratton, current director of the Center for Play Therapy, in her role as my clinical supervisor and instructor. My slight leanings toward humanistic principles in working with clients grew into a full-blown belief system. Applying the person-centered approach to adolescent and adult clients became a natural way of working. Clients were growing and changing in the context of the therapeutic relationship. I, as a person, became my most effective tool in counseling as I helped facilitate conditions for growth, but trusted the client to move toward positive self-direction. At this point, Sue began to encourage me to take a class in play therapy. I refused, but she was tenacious. By this time, I had become aware of Garry Landreth's reputation and did not feel that I could assert my doubts to such a prestigious figure. I agreed that I would take the class on the one condition that I take it with Sue as an instructor. She was aware of my reservations and accepted me despite them, which was a powerful motivator for me. The other event that prompted my decision is that I had just had my first child. I was extremely fascinated with motherhood, child development, and parenting.

In this context, I took my first play therapy course. I admit that I was hooked from the first day. The readings from Axline and Landreth made perfect sense regarding how humanistic concepts fit in working with children. Sue's approach to answering every silly question and complaint by using her relational abilities always demonstrated the philosophy instead of an empty explanation. And it all seemed to fit with observing my own child in his first year of life. When I began to use CCPT with real clients,

I was amazed to watch it in action. Fifteen years later, I still observe play therapy as though it is magic. The most amazing thing about play therapy is that it works. I am shocked daily about this fact.

But the secret is that play therapy is not magic; it demands significant knowledge, training, supervision, consultation, awareness, personal investment, skills, and belief in children. Since the time that I started facilitating play therapy, I have enjoyed using the modality in school and clinic settings. I have worked extensively with individuals and groups of children, as well as a diversity of parents. I have conducted play therapy with multicultural populations spanning ethnicities within and outside the United States. The cynic in me still awaits the case where play therapy is ineffective, but I have yet to experience it.

There is no doubt that I am an avid believer in Landreth's approach to play therapy, and I have asked myself on several occasions if there is a need to write a book beyond the seminal *Play Therapy: Art of the Relationship.* I should note that after my initial play therapy course, I summoned the courage to take advanced play therapy courses with Garry Landreth and worked under his supervision. Under his tutelage, I experienced the relationship factors that he discusses in his work and I grew in my understanding and facilitation of CCPT. He is a true mentor. You will find his influence throughout these pages.

The purpose of this book is to serve as a companion to *Play Therapy: The Art of the Relationship.* Because Landreth does an exceptional job presenting CCPT, I summarize his work in a brief few pages. The reader is referred to Landreth (2002) for a complete presentation of the basics of CCPT. However, this book focuses on the advanced knowledge and skills needed to conduct CCPT in the current context of the mental health field. Learning the whys and hows of CCPT is only partially what is needed in today's market. Over the years as a clinic director and school counselor supervisor, I have accumulated a list of the challenges faced by play therapists after they are trained and enter the field. This book represents an attempt to address those challenges.

The first challenge is *knowledge.* Play therapy is based on three fields of knowledge, including psychology/therapy, play, and child development. Most play therapists are knowledgeable regarding the history of psychology and functions of therapy because they receive graduate degrees in mental health fields. However, play therapists often lack knowledge in the history and function of play, as well as a thorough understanding of child development. The lack of knowledge in these two areas limits the play therapist's ability to explain the importance of play therapy in working within the emotional world of children. This book will attempt to close this gap of knowledge by presenting chapters that specifically summarize the role and function of play, child development, and theory of play therapy. I attempt to integrate knowledge so that the chapters serve as a practical source for the play therapist in not only understanding how play therapy is linked to the whole child, but also acting as a primer for explanation with parents and other play therapy decision makers. Knowledge of play and child development is critical in understanding the emotional work of each child client.

The second challenge for practicing play therapists is *operationalizing* some of the general tasks they often are assigned but are not well defined. Specifically, through this book I attempt to operationalize parent consultation, working with play themes, and measuring progress. A chapter is dedicated to each of these tasks and presents a step-by-step method for immediate use by the play therapist. Methods were developed through my experience of working with and supervising literally thousands of children. This will be the first book to address theme work in play therapy in detailed description as developed by experiences with child clients.

And the third major challenge of practicing play therapists appears to be the recent focus on *accountability*. Accountability is required in many different ways across settings. Play therapists are accountable to parents to demonstrate measurable change. They are accountable to funding sources to demonstrate the effectiveness of services. They are accountable to third-party payers to describe and quantify progress. They are accountable to administrators to validate their work and continue employment. Throughout this book, I address individual accountability by presenting ways to measure change, collect data, and conduct treatment planning. In the final chapter of the book, I concentrate on the evidence provided by experimental research in play therapy. Finally, for those who are fully immersed in the evidence-based movement, I present the CCPT treatment manual in the Appendix to guide the exact facilitation of CCPT if demanded by those in authority, but mostly to be used for research purposes.

There are additional features throughout this book that will guide the reader's understanding. As in the typical person-centered tradition, I have attempted to use excerpts from actual sessions in the presentation of many therapeutic concepts. Through these transcripts, the reader will be able to visualize the approach in a real-life setting. I also address current special issues related to play therapy, such as the overwhelming task of working with children who are aggressive and make up a considerable number of child clients, as well as working with critics in both school and community settings. This book focuses on the toughest parts of play therapy, including children and parents who do not volunteer for play therapy, children who are difficult and challenging, parents who do not want to be involved, administrators who are critics, as well as many other common struggles faced by play therapists. For advanced play therapists, I have also included a chapter on supervision, hoping to provide a model to bring in new professionals.

For the benefit of implementing play therapy ideas and procedures provided throughout the book, a CD-ROM is included as a supplement for play therapists' use. The CD includes the electronic version of the CCPT Treatment Manual, along with multiple forms that can be used in clinical and school settings. Other forms include the Play Therapy Skills Checklist, Session Summary Form, Treatment Plan Form, Progress Worksheet, Sample School Counseling Consent Form, and Sample School Brochure.

My goal in writing this book is to support the beginning, practicing, and advanced play therapist. For those beginning play therapists, I summarize the why and how of CCPT. Previous books have addressed the how-to parts of play therapy but I am attempting to answer the "but what if…" questions regularly encountered by play therapists. What if the child won't follow the limit? What if the parent doesn't care? What if the child runs around my office screaming? What if the child doesn't seem to be making progress? What if I am personally frustrated with a child? These are the supervisory issues that I address in my daily practice as a clinical instructor. My hope is that this book will be a resource for play therapists who believe in CCPT but encounter real-life obstacles to its use. For experienced play therapists, I have attempted to provide a level of knowledge that is beneficial to continued practice and professional growth. What is the real meaning of congruence for the advanced play therapist, and how do we progress in the therapeutic conditions throughout a career? How do we keep the necessary conditions thriving over a lifetime so that we work at peak effectiveness?

As a play therapist, I find myself being challenged by external and internal forces. As the mental health field moves toward mechanistic ways of understanding and working with children, I am challenged to respond externally with knowledge, skills, and accountability. But more importantly, I am challenged to maintain my belief system in the unwavering trust in the human process of change. I respond to the challenge with an internal process of making contact with others and being reminded on a daily basis by colleagues, students, children, family, and friends that my relationships are enriched by an ability to remain aware and authentic. I am changed only through my relationships with others, which in turn facilitates change in them, releasing the self-actualizing tendency to its full potential.

Acknowledgments

My experience and knowledge in play therapy is attributed to persons with whom I have had the great honor to work, study under, teach, and develop relationships over a lifetime. My counseling journey began at Vanderbilt University as a young undergraduate taking graduate classes. I am immensely appreciative of my education at Vanderbilt under the leadership of the late Dr. Roger Aubrey and with counseling mentors Dr. Richard Percy, Dr. Julius Seeman, and Dr. Peggy Whiting. Under their guidance in my master's program, I learned how to stay attuned to my own awareness, develop relationships, and understand the impact of development over a lifetime. As a doctoral student at the University of North Texas (UNT), I had the great privilege of developing supervision relationships with Dr. Robert Berg, Dr. Garry Landreth, Dr. Sue Bratton, and Dr. Janice Holden. I grew immensely under their mentorship and further acknowledged the role of personal awareness in my ability to build counseling relationships.

My collegial relationships with faculty over the years have been invaluable to me and taught me the importance of extending meaningful relationships to students. I would like to thank Dr. Richard Lampe, Dr. Jerry Trusty, and Dr. Ruth Ann White for early mentorship in counselor education. And I thank Dr. Steve Armstrong who always serves as a support and sounding board. I would especially like to thank Dr. Denny Engels who served as a model for student relationships and advocacy. I feel extremely fortunate to work with my colleagues at UNT who facilitate an environment of challenge, growth, and sharing of ideas. Thank you to Dr. Carolyn Kern, Dr. Cynthia Chandler, Dr. Casey Barrio Minton, Dr. Delini Fernando, Dr. Natalya Edwards, Dr. Kerrie Fineran, Dr. Martin Gieda, Dr.

Leslie Jones, Dr. Janice Holden, Dr. Sue Bratton, Dr. Garry Landreth, and Dr. Denny Engels. I would also like to acknowledge the tremendous support I have received from Cathie McFarland who allows me the freedom to concentrate on play therapy daily.

I am grateful and humbled to work with the counseling students at UNT. Their commitment to growth and their desire to facilitate effective change for both adults and children are inspiring to me. This book is the result of countless discussions, supervision sessions, and daily interactions with students. I would specifically like to thank Dr. Ryan Foster and Kasie Lee who represented the typical dedication of UNT students by helping with the last-minute preparations of this book. As a team at UNT, we continue to search for meaning and best practice in play therapy.

Of course, I would not have made it into the world of counseling children without an inspired childhood. I thank my mother, Marilyn, who modeled independence and internal strength and my father, Jerry, who modeled leadership and quest for knowledge. I thank my brother, James, who facilitated my first experience in the world of mental health and started a trajectory of professional aspiration for me. And I thank my sister, Pam, who loved and nurtured me, plus taught me everything I know. I love you all and know that my childhood experiences allow me to understand others.

Most especially, I thank my husband, Russ, and my boys, Elijah and Noah. They have sacrificed much for me to give to the community and to my profession. They have taught me everything I know about relationships, including play therapy relationships. To Russ who provides me with unfailing support and love, even when I fall short of deserving it. To Noah who daily teaches me the importance of autonomy and emergence of an independent voice. To Elijah who gives love unconditionally and approaches the world with the same acceptance.

I thank God for being the first to offer the concept of unconditional love. I was reminded of His support throughout this writing process: "I can do all things through Him who strengthens me" (Philippians 4:13). And finally, I owe this book to each and every child with whom I have developed a relationship. Hours spent in one-on-one contact with children have been life changing and life affirming for me. Each play session has been an opportunity to enter the child's world on his or her terms and to emerge from that world with a new understanding of mine. It is only through children's acceptance of me that I am able to write about effective practices in working with them.

About the Author

Dee C. Ray, PhD, LPC-S, NCC, RPT-S, is associate professor in the Counseling Program and director of the Child and Family Resource Clinic at the University of North Texas. Dr. Ray has published more than 40 articles, chapters, and books in the field of play therapy, and more than 15 peer-reviewed research publications specifically examining the effects of Child-Centered Play Therapy. Dr. Ray is the author of the *Child-Centered Play Therapy Treatment Manual,* co-author of *Child-Centered Play Therapy Research: The Evidence Base for Effective Practice,* and former editor of the *International Journal of Play Therapy* (*IJPT*). She currently serves on the editorial board for the *IJPT* and on the Research Committee for the Association for Play Therapy. She is the recipient of the 2008 Outstanding Research Award for Association for Play Therapy, 2006 Outstanding Research Award for the Texas Counseling Association, and 2006 Nancy Guillory Award for Outstanding Service and Contribution to the Field of Play Therapy from the Texas Association for Play Therapy.

CHAPTER 1

History, Rationale, and Purpose of Play

Play therapy is a modality designed to serve children based on their most effective form of communication—play. Among play therapists, there are several statements that are routinely used to discuss the value of play, such as "play is the child's natural form of communication," "play bridges concrete experience to abstract thought," and "play is intrinsically motivated," among others. In fact, these statements are used so often that it is difficult to trace their origins. Certainly, Jean Piaget (1962), Swiss biologist and philosopher, is the most frequently cited contributor to a rationale for play in therapy. His exploration and explanation of how a child progresses through development using play as a form of assimilating the environment are the foundations of understanding the child's application of play in therapy. The history, research, and theories of play are rich with observation and discussion. The scholarly approach of Piaget and others is only one side of play inquiry. Play has been explored as an cultural phenomenon, instinctual drive, mode of education, economic influence, religious connotation, as well as its significant relationship with psychology and development—all of which have implications for the practice of play therapy.

History of Play

Play is depicted and discussed throughout the history of the world, mostly concentrated on its link to the experiences of childhood. Early views from the ancient Western world considered children as helpless, incapable, and having specials needs, such as the need to play (Hughes, 2010). Plato emphasized the use of play to build skills but also cautioned against too much adult supervision (Hughes, 2010; Smith, 2010). The rise of Christianity led to the belief that each child possessed a unique soul that was valued by God. The growing attitude of the individual value of each child, along with the belief that the child was innately sinful and unruly, led to a parental view of child's play as needing adult guidance and supervision. The adult role was to channel the play of the child into activities that were beneficial and productive.

Christianity led to the rise of Protestantism in England during the seventeenth and eighteenth centuries. A stricter approach to play was adopted in which play was seen as idle and mixed with instinctually negative motivations. John Locke of England (1632–1704) promoted the widely accepted philosophy that the child was born as a blank slate (*tabula rasa*) and the environment needs to be completely controlled by the parent to move children in the right direction. Chudacoff (2007), who traced the history of play in America, writes of Locke's influence on the early Puritan way of life:

> Locke was no modernist; his aim was to inculcate self-control, denial, and order in children's behavior, and the play that he most favored was the kind that a child could undertake under a teacher's careful supervision. Unstructured play, to him, was not appropriate (p. 27).

As a result, play was virtually suppressed by the middle and end of the eighteenth century (Hughes, 2010).

As Protestantism heavily influenced the view of children in England and America, a philosopher from France, Jean-Jacques Rousseau, published a novel, *Emile, or On Education* (1762), suggesting a positive nature of children. Rousseau believed that the natural state of children was movement toward taking in human virtue and goodness. Children needed to be appreciated, cared for, and allowed to operate naturally with little adult supervision. An outcome of this view of children was that play was accepted as an appreciated part of being young, embraced by adults as a celebration of childhood. Rousseau's philosophy ushered in a new, romantic perception of children that was quickly embraced by others throughout Europe, and eventually America. Friedrich Froebel (1782–1852) in Germany founded the kindergarten system based on his advocacy of play as a means of learning while Maria Montessori (1870–1952) in Italy integrated play into education as a means of learning about real life (Smith, 2010).

In America, the view of play was met with ambivalence. The early settlers were conflicted about a basic belief in submission to God, juxtaposed against a strong, growing sense of independence demanding freedom from human authority. Practically speaking, early America was an agricultural society that demanded a workforce consisting of all able bodies. Hence, children were viewed as independent, worthy of appreciation but vessels to be guided by adults to become productive members of a community, lest they give in to an innate sinful nature. The adult response to play was the concrete manifestation of this ambivalence. Play was allowed but only under conditions that it was not an idle waste of time and led to the child's development of religious and work ethics. Often, during this time, there was no delineation between adult and child play. Children and adults often played games together and played with the same toys, materials used by anyone for amusement. It was not until the mid-eighteenth century that toys began to be produced or viewed as materials belonging specifically to children (Chudacoff, 2007).

The beginning of the nineteenth century marked an emerging acceptance of childhood as a separate entity of development. In this acceptance, children were romanticized as innocent and playful, encouraging parents to delay the onset of adult responsibilities. This romanticism should also be viewed in the context of a growing industrialization in America where pre-adolescents labored in factories and workshops. The boundaries of childhood were limited to very young ages. Yet, by 1850, society recognized the playful rather than corrupt nature of children and not only tolerated but began to appreciate children's play (Chudacoff, 2007). The second half of the nineteenth century saw a rise in professional interest in play. Child study experts published manuals for parenting and child development, mostly concerned with the intellectual and moral growth of children, and mostly advocating a supervised approach to play. Philosophers continued to debate the purpose and use of play. Herbert Spencer (1820–1903), an English philosopher working within an evolutionary approach, described play as derived from excess energy developed in evolutionary higher species stimulated by highly developed nervous systems, referred to as surplus energy theory (Smith, 2010). Karl Groos (1861–1946), a German psychologist and author, argued that play was of functional significance and provided practice for skills needed for survival (Hughes, 2010; Smith, 2010). One of the first American psychologists interested in child development, G. Stanley Hall (1844–1924), countered what he saw as Groos' simplistic view of play. Hall observed that play was cathartic in nature and tied to the evolutionary progression of humans through playing out natural instincts from human history, referred to as recapitulation theory (Hughes, 2010; Smith, 2010). In America, this new and focused concentration on play translated behaviorally into the establishment of playgrounds, manufacturing of toys, and an adult focus on the initiation and supervision of children's play. Despite these adult efforts to encourage play, Chudacoff (2007) cited the psychology study of T.R. Crosswell in 1896 in which he surveyed 2,000 school children and concluded that free, unstructured play apart from work, school, or adult supervision was the most beneficial use of children's leisure time.

The advent of the twentieth century welcomed an explosion of interest in child development and child play. Psychologists turned their attention to the details involved in the psychological, intellectual, and educational nature of development. The use of play has always been closely aligned to an explanation of development, and authors of the twentieth century seemed attuned to this relationship. Sigmund Freud saw children as progressing through sexual stages of life, each one demanding a successful resolution. Children could use play to reduce anxiety, managing instinctual negative drives, through the stages of development. John Dewey advocated a progressive view of education that accepted the natural state of the child and promoted an appreciation of the child's own instincts, activities, and interests as the guide for education. The twentieth century was the child-centered era of adopting the structure of childhood as a separate and unique phase of human development. This child-centered era (not to be confused with child-centered play therapy or person-centered theory) was signified by an appreciation of childhood as a structure, a desire to study the uniqueness of the child's experience, and a need to generalize children's experiences into a coherent explanation of development. It is within this context, continued confusion over the role and purpose of play, that all theories and practices of play therapy developed.

The child-centered era in the twentieth century also generated what Smith (2010) refers to as the "play ethos" (p. 27). Smith noted that from the 1920s forward, educational thinking seemed to be impacted by an overarching view of the importance of play. He defined the play ethos as "a strong and unqualified assertion of the functional importance of play, namely that it is essential to adequate (human) development…" (p. 28). He further questioned the acceptance of the play ethos due to assumption of correctness and lack of empirical support.

There are two noticeable controversies emerging from a historical study of play. The first is most obvious and described throughout the literature, the conflict regarding the nature of the child. If a child is viewed as innately positive, born of the inherent good nature of humankind, then play is instinctively destined to move the child toward growth and should be trusted as a self-initiated element of childhood. However, if the child is born a blank slate or with an inclination toward a depraved nature, play will be an exercise in the child's lack of knowledge of what is good or practice in evil, thereby needing adult attention, supervision, and guidance. The second controversy regarding play appears to be a central theme in Chudacoff's (2007) historical review. Despite adult perspectives, actions, focus, guidance, initiation, and supervision of play, children will exert a need for autonomy away from the adult world to fully express their play. Chudacoff (2007) concluded from the period of 1850 to 1900, "… the breach of adult constraints signifies a vital dimension of children's play" (p.93). Later, he observed, "Dodging the control of parents has long been a part of growing up, but in the first half of the twentieth century resistance and the quest for autonomy flourished in ways that previously had not existed...about the mid-1950s, the nature of unstructured play, the places in which it occurred, and the peer-oriented culture of childhood promoted a type of behavior that, in varying degrees, signified children's freedom of action" (p. 151). In his observation of 1950 to present, he suggested, "The ways that children have used, and continue to use, toys rather than how grownups want toys to be used remains the most vital quality of children's autonomous play...children's manipulation of objects for their own purposes creates true play value" (pp. 197–198). In his final conclusions regarding the history of play in America, Chudacoff wrote, "Nevertheless, kids still want to be kids in their own way, and although they are generally willing to follow adult prescriptions, they also inhabit an independent, underground culture of self-devised play. And thus the two main continuities in children's play are the quest for autonomy and the demonstration of creativity" (p. 219).

Properties and Type of Play

Properties of Play

The definition of play is illusive, due to its various identified types and definitions. There is not just one definition, but theorists contend that there are many elements that help distinguish play from other activities. Garvey (1977) described five properties of play, including play must be pleasurable/ enjoyable, have no extrinsic goals, be spontaneous and voluntary, involve active engagement by the participant, and contain an element of make-believe. Although this description of play is cited often in the literature, it has limited use in understanding play therapy. Brown (2009) concurred with Garvey but offered more specificity in his list of elements. He noted that play is apparently purposeless, voluntary, inherently attractive (fun), provides freedom from time, diminished consciousness of self, improvisational potential, and a continuation desire. These representations of play construct a view of play as a fun activity with little purpose as acknowledged by the player.

Experienced play therapists would question whether the play observed in play therapy is always pleasurable to the child or whether it appears to be spontaneous and voluntary. Many children appear angry, sad, and confused when they play out certain scenes and sometimes appear as though they are being forced to carry through on play scenes that are painful for them, yet they keep playing, possibly looking for some end outside of their awareness. These kinds of actions in play therapy lead to further questions regarding the classification of certain behaviors in play therapy as play, or the proposal of a different definition of play. Concretely, when a child in the playroom screams angrily over and over at a doll because the doll knocked over a toy lamp, is this child playing or should this activity be labeled differently? Vygotsky (1966) claimed that the definition of play based on the pleasure it gives the child is incorrect for two reasons: (a) there are a number of activities that give a child more pleasurable experiences than play (such as sucking in an infant), and (b) there are games and play activities in which the child does not derive pleasure (such as losing at a baseball game). In consideration of previously identified elements and Vygotsky's contribution, perhaps the elements that best describe play in play therapy would be activity in which the child is free from adult direction, actively engaged, experiencing a flow with little self-consciousness, and released from literal grounding to reality.

Types of Play

Again, just as there is no consensus on the definition and properties of play, there are a multitude of identified types of play. David Elkind (2007), a leading child psychologist, identified four types of play, including mastery play, innovative play, kinship play, and therapeutic play. Mastery play is denoted by exploration and repetition. The child is goal oriented and working toward competence of a given skill. Only after a child has mastered skills is there the opportunity to expand and elaborate on them. Piaget claimed that play could only occur after a skill had been mastered (Kohlberg & Fein, 1987). The mastery of language and motor skills leads to innovative play, which is an expansion of both nonverbal and verbal types of play. Kinship play occurs with the interaction of more than one child, usually through self-initiated games. Therapeutic play helps a child deal with stress, impulsivity, or trauma, among others, by offering an outlet for the child to express troublesome reactions to events. Elkind cited that all children use play therapeutically as a way of dealing with stress.

Smith (2010) attempted to summarize six types of play that are commonly recognized in the literature: social contingency, sensorimotor, object, language, physical activity, and fantasy. Social contingency play is play that is based on the participant's interaction with another person. Sensorimotor play is primarily confined to infancy and involves activities with objects based on the sensory properties of the object. Children usually initiate object play following the sensorimotor period by engaging in activities with objects. Language play consists of playing with words and verbalization of concepts. Physical activity play includes play that involves gross motor skills. Fantasy or pretend play is play that uses objects, actions, or verbalizations and is released from the boundaries of realism, allowing for symbolic expression. The modality of play therapy allows for each and every type of play identified by both Elkind and Smith, especially play therapy that allows for child self-direction.

Play Development

Developmental theories on play typically measure play behaviors up to 4 years of age, due to children's mastery of play structure to process and communicate by this age. Although the majority of play therapy clients will exceed 4 years old, comprehension of developmental sequence of play allows the play therapist to track the child client's history and mastery of play as a developmental marker. The seminal author on children's play as developmentally linked was Jean Piaget (1962). To understand play in Piaget's cognitive theory, one must master the two basic concepts he purported: assimilation and accommodation. Assimilation is taking new stimuli from the real world and fitting it into the child's already established pattern of thinking, making it fit. Accommodation is the changing of the structure, in this case the child's way of thinking, based on something new in the environment. Piaget identified play as dominated by assimilation in which the child "... is able to dismantle established instrumental behavioral sequences and reassemble them in new ways" (Kohlberg & Fein, 1987, p. 396). Expanding this understanding of play to play therapy, it is easy to see how processes of assimilation and accommodation work together for change. In play therapy, the child uses the process of assimilation to completely control her world, making everything outside the playroom fit into her way of thinking in the playroom. As the child experiences mastery, safety, and empathy from the therapist, processes of accommodation start to occur where the child changes structural patterns that can be practiced in the playroom and then initiated in the real world, thereby changing self to meet the demands of the environment.

Upon understanding assimilation and accommodation, Piaget then moves into the explanation of the four stages of play development. Piaget described the first type of play to take place in infancy as sensorimotor play, also identified as practice play. This was the contributory basis for Elkind's (2007) discussion of mastery play described earlier in which the child strives for mastery of basic motor skills. Between the first and second year of life, symbolic play emerges in which the child initiates pretend play. Symbolic play allows the child to develop early pretend gestures of using a cup that has nothing in it, moving to short storylines of feeding a doll with a bottle or pretend food. The period of symbolic play is marked by solitary play. During the second and third years of development, sociodramatic play emerges in which the child engages others or the pretense of others as part of play. It is during this period that the child can pretend to be someone else and role playing becomes part of play. Following the age of 6 years old, the child engages in games that are affected by internal and external rules, and this play often supersedes symbolic play (Smith, 2010). Each stage is accompanied by increasing acquisition and use of language.

Hirsh-Pasek and Golinkoff (2003) characterized play development differently but still similarly aligned with Piaget. Babies begin to play as early as 3 to 6 months old when they learn to grasp objects. Between 6 and 9 months, infants begin intense object exploration, usually involving only one object at a time and only using the object for its intended use. The second year of life brings three major changes to play: an increase in the use of multiple objects at the same time, the use of objects in appropriate ways, and the ability to pretend things are real (symbolism). Progress toward symbolism allows the learning of language, reading, and problem solving. Pretend play dramatically increases in the fourth year as children become directors of elaborate play scenes that can be focused and lengthy. Hirsh-Pasek and Golinkoff (2003) concluded, "...pretend play is practice for children in freeing themselves from what is right in front of their eyes. Pretend play allows children to consider answers outside the box. Pretend play allows our children to consider alternative worlds" (p. 219).

A final notable developmental theory of play involves progression of play between children, categories of social participation observed by Mildred Parten in 1932 and described by Smith (2010). The social participation developmental theory addresses a child's movement toward social interaction in a play environment. In the first stage, the child is *unoccupied* and not engaged in any activity. In the second stage, the child is described as an *onlooker* and just watches others but does not join in. During the third stage, *solitary*, the child plays alone, away from others. *Parallel* play takes place in the fourth stage in which the child plays near others with the same materials but does not interact. At the fifth stage, the child is *associative* by interacting with others at an activity and doing similar things. And finally, the child engages in *cooperative* play where the child interacts with others in a complementary way. The significance of the social participation developmental theory can be seen in its application to the social interaction of child clients. Children who have emotional or behavioral difficulties can be found anywhere along the developmental continuum of social participation, indicating possible challenges to peer relationships. However, Smith (2010) cautioned that solitary play behavior may not necessarily be an indicator of immature behavior due to some children's preference to play alone.

Vygotsky and Three Functions of Play

The two major influential developmental theorists contributing to current understanding of play were Jean Piaget and Leo Vygotsky. Piaget (1896–1980) worked for most of his life as head of the Jean-Jacques Rousseau Institute at the University of Geneva. In the progressive environment of Geneva, his ideas were allowed exploration and exposure. Due to his environment, his lengthy lifespan, and his meticulous approach to observation of children, Piaget's work became most widely known and most widely accepted in the mid-twentieth century. His emphasis on the cognitive development of children limited discussion of child's play as a purely cognitive feature and was readily embraced by educational experts and institutions. As Piaget's ideas flourished, Vygotsky (1896–1934) was performing similarly meticulous research with children but in a much different environment. In the suppressive Russian political environment of the 1920s, Vygotsky was extremely productive in his research and theoretical contemplation through his many writings. However, a year after Vygotsky's death at the age of 38 to tuberculosis, Stalin outlawed developmental psychology and most of Vygotsky's work went underground, delaying translation and dissemination of his work for a great number of years. In the late 1960s, English translations of Vygotsky's publications began to emerge and appeared to offer an alternative to Piaget's highly concentrated cognitive work. For play therapists, Vygotsky's work is especially energizing because it offers a view of play as an affective process in addition to a cognitive process. He claimed that play was the leading source of development in the preschool years.

Speaking to cognitive processes, Vygotsky described play as liberating children from the constraints of reality and allowing them to move into the world of ideas, necessary for cognitive development. Affectively, Vygotsky recognized that play is invented by a child when the child can no longer make reality fit with desires or tendencies, usually about the age of 3 years. He proposed that, "...why a child plays must always be interpreted as the imaginary, illusory realization of unrealizable desires" (pp. 7–8). Vygotsky recognized three functions of play, including the creation of the child's zone of proximal development, helping the child separate thought and action, and finally the facilitating of self-regulation (Hirsh-Pasek & Golinkoff, 2003). Vygotsky characterized the concept of the "zone of proximal development" as a dynamic that occurs in play in which the child acts above his average age, able to reach a higher level of development without the restriction of reality. The second function of play occurs through the ability of the child to be liberated from external constraints through his activity in an imaginary situation, thereby allowing a separation of thought and action. Self-regulation occurs through two processes: the practice of subordination to rules and the narration of private speech. Vygotsky (1966) claimed that one paradox of play is that the child "learns to follow the line of greatest resistance, for by subordinating themselves to rules children renounce what they want since subjection to rule and renunciation of spontaneous impulsive action constitute the path to maximum pleasure in play" (pp. 13–14). Private speech was a unique concept in Vygotsky's theory, which he noted as a child's way of working out what they want to do and how they should proceed. Based on the need for private speech, Hirsh-Pasek and Golinkoff (2003) recommended environments where children can verbalize as they play. A final contributing concept of Vygotsky's was the observation that as children grow older, play is converted to internal processes moving to internal speech and abstract thought. Whereas Piaget claimed that egocentric speech disappeared in deference to concrete thought, Vygotsky believed that private speech and play still occurred but within internal thoughts and imagination of the older child and adult.

Vygotsky's contribution to understanding play is perhaps even more influential than that of Piaget in the practice of play therapy. There are multiple implications for play therapy based on his work. The first is the recognition that play is not necessarily born of a need for fun but appears to be born as a reaction to distress caused by the child's inability to meet a growing set of internal needs with resources from the real world. In terms of play therapy, this first implication provides a rationale for why play therapy is critical to children under stress from the environment. For troubled children, normal development dictates growing desires, but reality offers fewer sources of help, as parental or other adult figures cease to provide support, thereby increasing the need for play. Practically speaking, one implication of Vygotsky's work is that play therapy is most effective following the age of 3 when the child is using play to work through environmental stressors. Play therapy can still be useful for children under 3 but for different reasons such as relationship building and attachment. The zone of proximal development again provides a rationale for the benefit of play therapy where children can experience their capabilities beyond everyday life, bringing about an increase in confidence and self-direction. And finally, the issue of verbalization becomes a focal point in play therapy. For nondirective forms of play therapy, verbalization is seen as unnecessary for therapeutic work. However, according to Vygotsky, verbalization might be a marker for understanding the child as a child narrates her play. For younger children, this can give significant insight into the inner workings of a child's processes. Experienced play therapists have certainly observed play-by-play commentary by a child in play that seems to have no interactive quality. Some play therapists interpret this behavior as unattached or disconnected. In reality, such verbalization demonstrates the ongoing narrative taking place within the child, the child making sense of the world. For older children, the concept of private speech indicates that children are still formulating a narrative of which the play therapist may not be privy. In this case, play therapists are limited by, but attuned to, the child's open verbalizations and play behaviors as a method of understanding the child's inner world.

Rise and Development of Play Therapy

In the context of a lengthy history of ambivalence toward child's play, acknowledgment of childhood as a separate phase of life from adulthood, study of developmental and play processes related to children, and growing interest in psychology and human motivation and distress, theories of play therapy have emerged. Throughout the 20th century, the medical and psychology communities attempted to address the peculiarities of children using the modality of play. As true for most psychological interventions, the beginnings of play therapy trace back to Sigmund Freud (1909/1955) who never directly worked with children but described the case of "Little Hans," a child who had developed a phobia, refusing to leave the house due to his fear of being bitten by a horse. S. Freud directed Hans' father to observe and report Hans' play behavior to Freud, who then analyzed the boy through correspondence. S. Freud concluded that the case was further confirmation of his theory regarding sexual stages of development. Psychoanalysts subsequently provided analysis to children using the modality of play. Hermine Hug-Hellmuth (1921) is regarded as the first child psychoanalyst, using play as a means of analysis. She was a prolific writer and published multiple descriptions of her work with children, citing the importance of play in conducting psychoanalysis yet not providing a structural framework for therapy. Melanie Klein (1975/1932) and Anna Freud (1946), both of Vienna, were credited with the expansion of play therapy through their exploration, writings, and presentations on play as a method for psychoanalysis. Long before the publications of Piaget or Vygotsky, Klein (1975/1932) recognized the value of play in therapy when she wrote "in child-analysis we are able to get back to experiences and fixations which, in the analysis of adults can often only be reconstructed, whereas the child shows them to us as immediate representations" (p. 9). Klein believed that play was the child form of free association and interpreted everything done in play as having an underlying symbolic function. She also suggested that children have the insight necessary to recognize the meaning of their behaviors if pointed out by the therapist. A. Freud (1946) differed from Klein in that she did not believe that interpretations of child's play were valuable without the transference relationship necessary for analysis. She proposed that children needed a preparatory period for analysis in which the therapist establishes the transference relationship. A. Freud (1946) wrote, "…I took great pains to establish in the child a strong attachment to myself, and to bring it into a relationship of real dependence on me" (p. 31). Despite differences in approach, both analysts practiced a nondirective approach to play therapy in which they allowed free play with available toys. Hence, psychoanalytical play therapy offered the first organized approach to play therapy, providing a theoretical rationale and description of practice. Psychoanalytic play therapy was the primary form of play therapy in the early 20th century until the introduction of child-centered play therapy (CCPT) in the 1940s.

As a response to the unstructured play methods of Klein and Freud, a new strand of play therapy emerged in the 1930s that embraced a structured approach to play, including the goal-oriented practice of eliciting play reenactments for catharsis. Structured play therapy still held psychoanalytic beliefs regarding children but believed that goals were more readily achieved through structure imposed by the therapist. In David Levy's (1938) *Release Therapy*, he worked specifically with traumatized children by providing toys that he believed would facilitate trauma-related play allowing for resolution through catharsis. Gove Hambridge (1955) took release therapy one step further, calling his method structured play therapy, by directing children to play out stressful events from their lives, and then allowing free play.

The third, and arguably most influential, wave of play therapy was the introduction of play therapy as an expansion of Carl Rogers' (1942) person-centered approach to counseling. Rogers (1902–1987) is cited as being the most influential counselor and psychotherapist in American history (Kirschenbaum, 2004). Virginia Axline (1947), who was a student and colleague of Rogers, fully applied the philosophy and concepts of person-centered theory to her work in counseling children. Axline utilized person-centered theory in a developmentally responsive manner in her work with children by providing an environment conducive to their natural way of communicating. This environment consisted of a playroom of specific toys that allowed children to express their inner selves through play. The development of the relationship within the context of the playroom provided children a safe environment in which to express themselves verbally and nonverbally. Axline was especially influential for several reasons. First, she was the first play therapist to undertake extensive investigation of her therapy methods through research, thus providing evidence of its efficacy. Second, she provided a structure to the theory and delivery of play therapy in her publication, *Play Therapy* (Axline, 1947). Third, and probably most likely the basis of popularity of the approach, was the publication of her book, *Dibs: In Search of Self* (Axline, 1964). *Dibs* is widely known in the play therapy profession as essential play therapy reading in which Axline presented a case of a boy, described as autistic by today's criteria, over the course of a year in play therapy. While presenting the mechanics and rationale of play therapy, Axline involves the reader in an emotional tale of a child's triumph. Axline labeled her approach to play therapy as nondirective, highlighting the person-centered therapist conditions of unconditional positive regard, empathic understanding, and congruence. Through continued presentation of the person-centered, nondirective approach in the works of Guerney (2001) and Landreth (2002), this approach to play therapy is now referred to as child-centered play therapy (CCPT). Chapters 3, 4, and 5 in this book elaborate extensively on the theory and practice of CCPT.

Although CCPT emerged as a defined approach to play therapy, relationally based play therapy has contributed significantly to its definition and practice. Clark Moustakas (1959) presented essential conditions for relationship play therapy, including respect for the uniqueness of the child, focus on the present living experience, therapist empathy for and unqualified acceptance of the child, and freedom of expression for the child. Haim Ginott (1959) also contributed to the relational focus in play therapy by suggesting permissiveness in the therapist/child relationship allowing for all verbal and symbolic expression of feelings.

In the latter part of the 20th century, play therapy modalities were supported by various theoretical approaches to psychology. Child therapists working within the frameworks of Adlerian, Jungian, Gestalt, psychodynamic, cognitive-behavioral, and attachment theories defined the play therapy modality according to adopted theoretical principles. These approaches are addressed in detail in Chapter 3 of this book. The growth of play therapy indicates that there is professional acceptance of play as a prominent means of communication in therapeutic healing.

Conclusion and Implications for Play Therapy

This chapter attempted to cover a substantial amount of information regarding play, including the history of play, properties and types of play, purpose of play, developmental theories regarding play, and historical use of play in therapy. Although broad, when consolidated, this play information has global implications for the practice of play therapy. In reviewing information on play, questions arise for the advanced play therapist regarding the role of play in play therapy. Here are a few that came to mind. I do not attempt to answer these questions; I only offer them as points of discussion.

1. If fun is a required element that defines play, can what most children do in play therapy be considered play?
2. Are children actually free in play therapy? Based on Vygotsky's view, children are always restricted by implicit rules of play. How confined are they by these internal rules, and how much freedom do they experience?
3. Is play always voluntary and non-goal oriented? If this is true, is the scene that is played out by a child with disturbing and negative affect voluntary and without an internal goal? As a play therapist, I question the child's voluntary and non-goal-directed nature of reenacting traumatic scenes that appear painful, yet the child

appears compelled to play it out until the end. Again, is this play or something else?

4. In modern American culture, has free play disappeared to the extent that play therapy is needed by more children as an environment that is not afforded them in any other setting? Is play therapy needed for the progression of normal development?
5. What is the role of the therapist in the facilitation of play? Based on historical perspectives, do therapists work in the adult guidance role or in the nondirective role of providing a facilitative environment? How is the answer to this question related to a therapist's view of humankind?

Although questions abound, the advanced play therapist knows the value of ambiguity in thought and the richness of discussion for these areas. But there do appear to be some definitive implications for the purposes of play in therapy based on accrued information in this chapter. I developed a list of functions served by play in play therapy resulting from a review of the history and theories of play. Play in play therapy is used for

1. *Fun:* The use of play in play therapy provides the opportunity for fun, either for the child or for the therapist and child. Although it is recognized that play is not always fun for the child, especially in therapy, it can often be fun. The allowance of fun in a therapeutic environment lowers a child's resistance to the therapeutic relationship, and offers an experience that is often missing from the life of a child who is experiencing several environmental conflicts.
2. *Symbolic expression:* Play in play therapy allows for the symbolic expression of thoughts and feelings. As eloquently presented by both Piaget and Vygotsky, children use symbols for the acquisition of language and expression of emotion and cognition. The symbolic expression of play in therapy invites the play therapist into the child's world. The child is no longer confined by reality and can pretend, creating scenes for the expression of emotion or building of coping skills.
3. *Catharsis:* Play in play therapy allows a child to work through those issues of greatest consequence to the child. Nondirected play provides an environment in which the child chooses direction of effort.
4. *Social development:* Play not only allows for the expression of the child's world, but also promotes communication between child and therapist—or in the case of group play therapy, between peers. The building and maintenance of a nurturing relationship facilitated through play strengthens a child's social motivation and skills.

5. *Mastery:* In play therapy, play is used by the child to control her world. She has the power to be anything and the capability to do anything. She is not limited by real-world restraints. The child uses play in play therapy to develop a sense of control and competence over the environment.
6. *Release of energy:* Although the use of play to release energy may not seem like a therapeutic endeavor, children are likely to use play therapy as a place of free expression for unused or confining energy. Children who spend the day attempting to "keep it together" in structured environments often need a safe place for energy release, which, once expended, allows for focused therapeutic work.

References

Axline, V. (1947). *Play Therapy*. New York: Ballantine.

Axline, V. (1964). *Dibs: In search of self*. Boston: Houghton Mifflin.

Brown, S. (2009). *Play: How it shapes the brain, opens the imagination, and invigorates the soul*. New York: Penguin.

Chudacoff, H. (2007). *Children at play: An American history*. New York: New York University Press.

Elkind, D. (2007). *The power of play: Learning what comes naturally*. Philadelphia: Da Capo Lifelong Books.

Freud, A. (1946). *The psycho-analytical treatment of children*. New York: International Universities Press.

Freud, S. (1909/1955). *The case of "Little Hans" and the "Rat Man."* London: Hogarth Press.

Garvey, C. (1977). *Play*. Cambridge, MA: Harvard University Press.

Ginott, H. (1959). The theory and practice of therapeutic intervention in child treatment. *Journal of Consulting Psychology, 23*, 160–166.

Guerney, L. (2001). Child-centered play therapy. *International Journal of Play Therapy, 10*(2), 13–31.

Hambridge, G. (1955). Structured play therapy. *American Journal of Orthopsychiatry, 25*, 601–617.

Hirsh-Pasek, K., & Golinkoff, R. (2003). *Einstein never used flash cards: How our children really learn-and why they need to play more and memorize less*. New York: Rodale.

Hug-Hellmuth, H. (1921). On the technique of child analysis. *International Journal of Psychoanalysis, 2*, 287–305.

Hughes, F. (2010). *Children, play, and development* (4th ed.). Thousand Oaks, CA: Sage.

Kirschenbaum, H. (2004). Carl Rogers's life and work: An assessment on the 100th anniversary of his birth. *Journal of Counseling and Development, 82*, 116–124.

Klein, M. (1932/1975). *The psychoanalysis of children*. London: Hogarth Press.

Kohlberg, L., & Fein, G. (1987). Play and constructive work as contributors to development. In L. Kohlberg's *Child psychology and childhood education: A cognitive-developmental view.* White Plains, NY: Longman, 392–440.

Landreth, G. (2002). *Play therapy: The art of the relationship.* New York: Routledge.

Levy, D. (1938). Release therapy in young children. *Psychiatry, 1,* 387–389.

Moustakas, C. (1959). *Psychotherapy with children: The living relationship.* New York: Harper & Row.

Piaget, J. (1962). *Play, dreams and imitation in childhood.* New York: W.W. Norton & Co.

Rogers, C. (1942). *Counseling and psychotherapy.* Boston: Houghton Mifflin Company.

Rousseau, J. (2007). *Emile, or On education.* Sioux Falls, SD: NuVision Publications, LLC. (Original work published in 1762.)

Smith, P. (2010). *Children and play.* West Sussex, UK: Wiley-Blackwell.

Vygotsky, L. (1966). Play and its role in the mental development of the child. *Voprosy Psikhologii, 12,* 6–18.

CHAPTER 2
A Primer on Child Development

For play therapy, play is the modality therapists use to develop a relationship with a uniquely individual child. Three components are of concern: play, child, and relationship. Chapter 1 discussed the role of play in children's lives, culture, and therapy. Chapter 3 discusses the therapeutic nature of the relationship between child and play therapist. This chapter presents a brief summary of various developmental models that help inform the play therapist regarding the uniqueness of a child in comparison with other children. There are several complications in the presentation of stage models for child development, including their ability to accurately convey development on the individual level, the misinterpretation by readers that children who fall outside the group model are labeled as pathological, and the inference that children are in a race to achieve higher levels from their current states. The purpose of this chapter is to present contextual information regarding "average" child development based on statistically aggregated groups of children in current Western culture. Although many developmental theorists conducted cross-cultural research and applied their models to multiple societies, most of the models cited in this chapter represent a decidedly individualized approach to human growth, not necessarily accepted by other cultures or even all cultures within Western society. The developmental information presented here provides a framework from which to understand the individual child participating in play therapy. This information does not provide dictates on practice or goals for therapy.

Misunderstanding Developmental Models

Development Applied to All

When developmental models are offered in the form of stages, ages, and descriptions, there is a tendency by the counselor to apply the model to all children. Obviously, the structure of the models themselves implies that the models are applicable to all. However, there should be restraint on the part of the play therapist to generalize to every child, in every context. The uniqueness of the child and the child's environment is the play therapist's first concern. Developmental models are just one tool to inform conceptualization of such uniqueness. In all models, there are inherent inadequacies in their ability to explain the development of all children, whether development is focused on cognitive, personality, emotional, or behavioral processes. Burman (2008) wrote, "The normal child, the ideal type, distilled from the comparative scores of age-graded populations, is therefore a fiction or myth. No individual or real child lies at its basis" (p. 22).

Pathological Inference of Using Average Descriptors for Development

Because developmental models seem to provide a roadmap for what can be expected from average children, it is sometimes assumed that children who are not on the same road must be deviant. As previously stated, developmental models cannot account for the growth of all children. There are children who operate on their own individual paths that are different from average, but not clinically pathological. These children take development at their own pace, applying their own meanings to experiences that are uniquely different from those of other children. As a play therapist, I might ask, "Because this child is wearing a cape and flies around the room at 12 years of age, is this a clinical problem?" "Because this 8-year-old child spends the entire session sucking on a baby's bottle, is this a diagnosable disorder?" Maybe not. Although these behaviors do not look as if they are developmentally age appropriate, they may be indicative of the child's individual developmental path that leads the child to a place of full functioning at a later time in life.

I am a director of a mental health clinic in a university setting that serves approximately 70 children per week. When we conducted an evaluation of our clinic's services using reasonably valid and reliable measures, results indicated that approximately 45% to 50% of our child clients were not reported by their parents as demonstrating clinical levels of problematic behavior (Ray, 2008). Although parents, schools, or some other entity has referred the child for services because of environmental or behavioral concerns, the child is not exhibiting behavior that would be considered a clinical mental health problem. These types of referrals might signify that a child is experiencing "glitches" in development for which a child or parent may need additional therapeutic support. However, they do not seem to indicate a need to pathologize the child.

Race to the Top

The stage structure of developmental models also contributes to the misunderstanding of movement from stage to stage. One interpretation that appears to be pervasive is that higher is better. Attribution of higher value to higher stages undermines the base of developmental models, which purports the value of each and every stage. Burman (2008) warned, "Development thus becomes an obstacle race, a set of hoops to jump through, with cultural kudos accorded to the most advanced, and the real or imagined penalties of professional intervention or stigmatisation if progress is delayed" (p. 79). Developmental theorists emphasize the significance of each stage, including the implications of meanings acquired in each stage that are unique to the individual. Each stage is of value to each child. From the mental health perspective, there is no race to the top because higher levels do not necessarily indicate better functioning, sense of belonging, or positive emotional state.

A comprehensive method to understanding development is the direct observation of individual and groups of children. In my experience, I have found that play therapists are limited in their perspectives on development because their experiences are limited to children who are referred for therapy. This often skews professional perception into pathologizing children who are functioning in an average way but are identified by perfectionistic or disturbed caretakers as problematic or normalizing children who operate in a maladjusted manner as compared to peers. Teachers, school counselors, and other mainstream school personnel are at a particular advantage in recognizing developmental patterns. They are surrounded by children with whom they interact on a daily basis. In a group of 20 school children, approximately 5 may be following noticeably different developmental paths, 1 is likely to be on a disturbing path, and 15 will probably present as similar in concentrated developmental tasks and phases. The actual experience of observing and interacting with children consistently becomes the preferred evaluation tool for discerning between normal, divergent, and problematic development.

History and Structure of Development Models

The developmental view traces back to Plato and his cited levels of consciousness. Each level builds on the previous one. Plato described four stages of mind and how they relate to development (Ivey, 2000), beginning with imagining (*eikasia*), which describes sensorimotor operation and magical thinking. The second level is belief (*pistis*), which is concrete knowledge based on what is visible. The third level is thinking (*dianoia*), marking the beginning demonstration of abstract reasoning. The fourth and final state of mind is knowledge (*episteme*), which emphasizes the examination of premises and assumptions. Because each state of mind can be matched to a cognitive function, Plato can be said to have been the first cognitive developmentalist.

Centuries later, Jean Piaget (1932) detailed the specifics of cognitive development in children with his book, *The Moral Judgment of the Child.* Piaget's stages included sensorimotor, preoperational, concrete operations, and formal operations, structuring a child's cognitions from experiential feeling to abstract thinking. Loevinger (1976) cited Piaget's influence on developmental theory as being critical not only because of his cognitive model, but also due to his espousal of structuralism in stages. Piaget opened the door to the many developmental models that have been created since his time. A few influential developmental models include Sigmund Freud's (1949) phases of instinctual life, Erikson's (1963) stages of psychosocial maturation, Kohlberg's (1981) moral development, Super's (1963) career development, Fowler's (1981) faith development, Gilligan's (1982) female development, Loevinger's (1976) ego development, Gesell's (see Ilg, Ames, & Baker, 1981) maturational development, and Greenspan's (1997) emotional development, just to name a few. Each model focuses on a different aspect of human development. The one common denominator among all the aforementioned models is the belief in personality formation through development, a lifelong process.

There are three types of developmental models as cited by Young-Eisendrath (1988). The first includes the chronological age models, which focus attention on biological and sociobiological factors that change with aging, such as current brain development theories. The second model type is life-phase models that intermingle biological, sociocultural, and interpersonal influences in typifying the general responses of groups of people passing through periods of life, such as Erikson's (1963) model. Finally, the third model is the structural model that patterns individual adaptation to maturational and sociocultural changes, such as the models of Kohlberg (1981) and Loevinger (1976).

A key concept that is instrumental in developmental models is the idea of stages. As Hayes and Aubrey (1988) have stated,

> Human growth is viewed as orderly, following a sequence of stages or milestones in the life cycle. These stages are laid out in an invariant sequence that is hierarchical and becomes more complex as the process of development unfolds. Each stage is qualitatively distinct from the other stages, forming a structured whole. It is not simply a means of responding to the demands of the environment at a given

> moment in time; rather, it is a means of both perceiving and making sense of the environment. (p. 4)

Furthermore, Young-Eisendrath (1988) specified that stages are a frame of reference for meaning making, neither entirely dependent nor entirely free from chronology, dependent on the achievement of earlier ones, mental operations, habitual assumptions, and assumed to be universal patterns of development. Stages are the structural basis for developmental theory and, hence, are imperative in the understanding of development. Both Hayes and Aubrey (1988) and Young-Eisendrath (1988) present development with a level of definitive clarity that was cautioned against earlier in this chapter. Although developmentalists may feel strongly that they have captured the essence of growth and movement in human development, there is little doubt that such a universal task is limited by historical and current approaches to research and theory. The significance of stage structure is the conceptual understanding that stages become increasingly complex over the lifespan impacted by the individual's own meaning-making perspective and demands of the environment.

Ivey (2000) claimed that development is cyclical by noting that earlier stages of development do not disappear with childhood, but continue as active processes within humans as new developmental tasks and stages confront them. According to this assumption, humans are engaged in the constant process of redefining themselves and their environments. Loevinger (1976) delved into much more detail, explaining that personality develops by acquiring successive freedoms, initially from personal impulses, followed by conventions and social pressures. Again, the point is made that personality develops through a relationship between the person and the environment, a concept easily embraced by person-centered theory discussed in the next chapter.

In addressing the importance of development in its relationship to play, Vygotsky (1966) wrote the following:

> It seems that every advance from one age stage to another is connected with an abrupt change in motives and incentives to act. What is of the greatest interest to the infant has almost ceased to interest the toddler. This maturing of new needs and new motives for action is, of course, the dominant factor, especially as it is impossible to ignore the fact that a child satisfies certain needs and incentives in play, and without understanding the special character of these incentives we cannot imagine the uniqueness of that type of activity which we call play. (p. 7)

From this statement, play therapists can deduce how play can be used to understand a child's level and stage of development.

Developmental Models Applicable to Play Therapy

There are many, many developmental models that a play therapist might find useful for conceptualization and practice. And I found it particularly difficult to narrow the presentation of models to only a few. However, for the purposes of integrating developmental knowledge into play therapy, there seemed to be a need to confine explanation to a limited number of relevant models. The goal of this section on models is to present a brief description of each model, specifically concepts impacting play therapy, that will inform the play therapist's practice and possibly initiate a further desire for study in development.

Maturational Stage Theories

Maturational stage theories are structured with the acknowledgment that a person will go through each stage simply by living long enough to reach each developmental phase. They are chronologically based, indicating that movement into each stage is reliant on the age of a person, and not on the perceptual field or cognitive ability of the person. Maturational theories are marked by the assumption that positive resolution of each stage depends on the previous one.

Erikson's Psychosocial Identity Theory Erik Erikson's model (see Erikson, 1963) is perhaps the most popular of all models regarding development. Countless numbers of mental health professionals memorize the stages at some point during graduate training. They are quickly forgotten once the test is passed and there seems to be little relevancy to play therapy practice. Yet, Erikson provided a model that appears to cross generational lines, seemingly as applicable today as it was 50 years ago. Erikson defined eight stages across the lifespan, four occurring prior to adolescence. In each stage, there is a specific psychosocial crisis that must be mastered by the person. Each step is predicated on the resolution of the crisis in the previous stage. As each stage is encountered and crisis is resolved, new meaning is assigned to all the lower stages, as well as future stages. Additionally, unresolved tasks lead to future unresolved tasks and set a trajectory of cumulative failure. Hence, the earlier there is task failure, the more likely the child is to present clinically due to accumulated task failures. Erikson noted that a person emerges with a psychosocial strength from each stage, born of the struggle that took place during that stage. For each stage of development, a child's play is likely to reflect the corresponding psychosocial crisis. The following subsections address the four stages that occur in childhood prior to adolescence.

Trust versus mistrust (birth to age 2 years). In this first stage of life, an infant learns whether the environment can be trusted, mostly through the maternal relationship. If basic needs are met and the child experiences nurturing, trust is developed. The resulting psychosocial strength is hope. When the infant emerges successfully from this stage, there is a sense of anticipatory hope for the future and new developmental tasks. Failure in this stage is marked by a general mistrust in the environment, possibly manifested in a withdrawal from relationships and society at later stages. There is a clear connection between Erikson's description of trust and Bowlby's (1982) explanation of attachment, characterized by an intimate emotional connection between infant and caregiver. Because this stage occurs early in infancy, it is rare that a play therapist will encounter a child during this task of life. Unfortunately, play therapists will interact with a child who has established mistrust and a lack of hope long after the stage has passed and the child is now struggling with new tasks of development.

Autonomy versus shame and doubt (ages 2 to 3 years). The concrete task of this stage is toilet training. As a result of gaining self-control over the body and impulses, the toddler establishes a sense of separateness from caregiver(s). If this need for separateness is met with overt parental control or with shaming responses for failures in toilet training or other autonomous ventures, a sense of shame and self-doubt will emerge. Parents who are overly controlling or critical during this stage may provide an environment in which the child grows to feel dependent or rebellious. Successful completion of this stage results in the child's strength of will, developing a sense of assertiveness. As a play therapist, I have found questions about toilet training to be the most advantageous in understanding the child and the parent/child relationship. Parents typically remember the period of toilet training with great detail accompanied by emotional expression. When I ask the question, "Tell me a little about potty training. How did that go?", I receive various but revealing answers:

Mom 1: (with great pride). "She was perfect. She never had an accident." This answer might indicate a need for perfectionism by the child or parent.

Mom 2: (with anger). "It was awful. He would pee right beside the toilet just to make me mad. He's always been like that." This answer might indicate a cyclical problem in the relationship in which the parent interprets the child's developmentally appropriate behaviors as rejecting or punitive and, hence, rejects or punishes the child.

Dad 1: (with apathy). "I don't know. He took care of himself. It was never a problem." This answer might indicate that the parent and child have a lack of connection and the child may perceive a need to approach all tasks on his own.

Initiative versus guilt (ages 3 to 6 years). In this stage, the child initiates action for the sake of the activity itself. They often mimic the adult world, taking on roles of caretakers or others. Children who have successfully maneuvered the previous two stages approach this stage with energy to try new things without limiting fear. There is little need to accomplish at this stage, only a need to try. If desires are thwarted or failure is imposed, a child will establish a sense of guilt. The psychosocial strength that emerges from this stage is a sense of purpose. It is at this stage that play therapists are likely to encounter children. Typical play behaviors are fantasy and experientially driven, with children trying new roles and behaviors throughout their play.

An additional consideration in this stage is the current culture of achievement that is pervasive across childhood and adulthood. In initiative versus guilt, the child's goal is to simply initiate new activities to check for the boundaries of desires and abilities. The child has little need to be proficient at activities in this stage. However, modern culture stresses the importance of doing and achieving, being productive, and performing as the best. This emphasis is evinced through the practice of enrolling children in organized sports and activities with a concentration on competition. Examples include 5-year-old girls who are enrolled in gymnastics five times a week or 4-year-old boys who are required to attend soccer practice four times a week. Although children may indicate a desire to participate in activities at this level, each practice is a reminder that they have not achieved mastery and must continue to work toward perfection. In addition, organized practice in one area limits the child's ability to initiate new and different activities for the purpose of exploration, not achievement. In other words, the practice of limiting a child's activity to a mastery task for multiple hours each week is developmentally inappropriate and disallows natural movement toward sense of purpose. Free play provides the child with the ability to be and do anything on a symbolic level and is a more appropriate match for this age group.

Industry versus inferiority (ages 6 to 12 years). In industry versus inferiority, a child has progressed from a need to try different activities to a need to master certain activities. At this stage, children explore their desires in correlation with their abilities, seeking to match the two. They become very attuned to activities in which they are competent compared to activities in which they show no aptitude. The psychosocial strength emerging from this stage is a sense of competence. An example of the qualitative difference between initiative versus guilt and industry versus inferiority is the experiment of asking a group of kindergartners who can sing and the answer is all of them (initiative); but when asking a group of fifth graders who can sing, only a few of the accomplished singers will be identified by the child and the whole group (industry).

Play therapists work with children in the stage of industry versus inferiority on a consistent basis. Although counselors may be tempted to remind children that they can be good at anything, it is children at this stage who find this answer unsatisfying and disingenuous. They have learned that some people are good at some things while others are not. They are seeking an area of competency, and the therapist's role can be helpful in this journey by providing an environment in which the child can experiment with mastery. Play therapists can also work with parents to support their children in their quest of mastery by not concentrating on things where they are failing and seek activities of mastery.

In one example from practice, I conducted a parent consultation with two biological parents of a 9-year-old boy. The parents had three children, all of which they named with a name that started with the letter "A" so that they would make As in school. My client was the youngest of the children. The older two children had achieved highly in school, with one on the honor roll in high school and one at an elite private university. My client had a diagnosed learning disability and struggled in school. He was passing but only barely. The parents brought him to play therapy because he was not achieving in school and seemed to be depressed. When I asked the parents to talk about his strengths, they paused for what seemed a long period of time, challenged by the question. They then told the story of this child in which he had been asked to present a scripture for a public Bible reading at church. His reading was so poor that he was quite nervous about the presentation. Three weeks before the scheduled reading, the client memorized the scripture, which was lengthy, and created a skit to act out each part of the reading. I pointed out to the parents that although he was not achieving in grades at school, he had instinctually placed his energy in an activity in which he felt confident and competent. My experience is that this dynamic often takes place with children but the competency area goes unnoticed because adults are focused on only certain achievement tasks. A play therapist can be a valuable support for the child and parent when seeking awareness regarding a child's motivation and achievement of competency areas.

Gesell's Maturational Development Model Through intensive and extensive observation of children, Arnold Gesell developed a set of normal behaviors assigned to stages and patterns of development (see Ilg, Ames, & Baker, 1981). He identified a cyclical pattern of development in which a child matures between periods of equilibrium followed by periods of disequilibrium. In the cycle, a stage of equilibrium in which the child has relatively little difficulty within self or with the outer world is followed by a breaking-up period in which the child is disturbed, troubled, and at odds with self and environment. Equilibrium is reestablished after breaking up

Table 2.1 Gesell Developmental Cycle

Age in Years			Stage	Description
2	5	10	Smooth, consolidated	Equilibrium, little difficulty within self or with environment
2½	5½–6	11	Breaking up	Disturbed, troubled, at odds with self and environment
3	6½	12	Rounded, balanced	State of equilibrium, little difficulty with self or outside world
3½	7	13	Inwardized	Drawing in of outer world to be digested, marked sensitivity, excessive withdrawal
4	8	14	Vigorous, expansive	Outgoing behavior, possibly dangerous
4½	9	15	Inwardized-outwardized, troubled neurotic	Marked by worry, less outgoing, little is known about this stage
5	10	16	Smooth, consolidated	Equilibrium, little difficulty with self or outside world

Source: Adapted from Ilg, F., Ames, L., & Baker, S. (1981). *Child behavior: The classic child care manual from the Gesell Institute of Human Development.* New York: HarperPerennial.

and then an inwardizing stage emerges in which the child takes in the outside world as an observer. Inwardizing is characterized by a child's sensitivity and touchiness, in addition to excessive withdrawal and pessimism. After taking in and digesting the outside world during inwardizing, the child moves to an expansiveness stage in which behavior is outgoing, energetic, and possibly dangerous. Expansiveness leads to a neurotic stage that is indicated by a child's excessive worrying and a lack of outgoing behavior. To round out the cycle, equilibrium is again reestablished. Table 2.1 presents each stage of the cycle with short descriptions.

The Gesell model also offers more specific descriptions of each age group as follows:

- *2 years old.* The 2-year-old is in a state of equilibrium in which she experiences confidence in motor skills, the use of language effectively, less need to be demanding, and tolerance of frustration. Two-year-olds also tend to be loving and affectionate.
- *2½ years old.* Most of what the child does is in direct contrast to what is desired by parents. Children at this age are rigid, inflexible, domineering, and demanding. These characteristics are accompanied by extreme emotion and an inability to choose between alternatives for any length of time.

- *3 years old.* Three is back into equilibrium and likes to be cooperative. Motor skills improve, as does vocabulary. People are important, and sharing to be social may ensue.
- *3½ years old.* The child experiences a period of insecurity, disequilibrium, and incoordination. Along with motor and verbal problems, 3½-year-olds have challenges in relationships. They frequently cry, whine, and question caretakers regarding their relationships, demanding exclusive attention.
- *4 years old.* The key words for the 4-year-old are "out of bounds" (Ilg, Ames, & Baker, 1981, p. 32). In motor skills, the 4-year-olds hit, kick, and break things. They are loud and can throw fits of rage. Relationally, they are defiant and can be shocking in their use of language. They are highly imaginative with no limits.
- *4½ years old.* The 4½-year-old is working on separating what is real from what is not real. They appreciate discussion and desire details. It is often a period of rapid growth in intelligence or motor skills.
- *5 years old.* Children are reliable, stable, calm, friendly and not too demanding. They are again in a state of equilibrium. Relationships with parents are especially important.
- *5½ to 6 years old.* Children are violently emotional, rigid, demanding, and negative. They have energy and look for new experiences. They may engage in thievery and lying to get what they want.
- *7 years old.* Seven-year-olds are typically calm and withdrawn. They are moody and like to be alone. They may feel that the world is against them. They stay busy with touching, feeling, and exploring the outside world.
- *8 years old.* Eight-year-olds go out to meet the world. They have excessive energy and stay busy, starting new activities constantly. They desire two-way relationships but may be self-critical and sensitive.
- *9 years old.* Nine is a quieter age in which the child operates independently, is self-contained and self-sufficient. Friends have now become a primary source of interest. They worry and engage in excessive complaining.
- *10 years old.* Ten is an equilibrium age in which children are flexible and accepting. They want to do good and tend to obey authority. It is described as "one of the very nicest ages of all" (Ilg, Ames, & Baker, 1981, p. 45).
- *11 years old.* Children may be moody and self-absorbed. They like to challenge rules and argue but often have trouble making decisions. They are increasingly able to see multiple perspectives (Wood, 2007).

- *12 years old.* Twelve-year-olds are capable of self-awareness, insight, and empathy. They are enthusiastic and appear to feel secure. The adult personality begins to emerge and friends are the focus for approval (Wood, 2007).

The attempt of the Gesell model to describe each age results in an ability to apply the model to every child. However, the cycle of development can be embraced by play therapists for its effectiveness in describing how children do not progress in a naturally positivistic manner from one stage to the next but they cycle through stages of challenges and smoothness. Each stage allows the complexity of the next to be grasped. Children inwardize to allow time for synthesis of outside experiences and information. They expand to actively interact with the world and determine personal boundaries and abilities. They relax into equilibrium to have downtime from turmoil. From an individual perspective, it is understood that each stage is relative to the personality of the child. Hence, especially challenging children will not suddenly become angels at the age of 10 but they may exhibit less problematic behaviors and characteristics in equilibrium stages. The same holds true for especially calm children. They will not suddenly turn into uncontrollable hyperactive children at the age of 6 but they may exhibit uncharacteristic negative energy at the breaking-up stages. The play therapist can use this model to better understand how maturation can be unpleasant for even the average child and parent, and also lend hope to the parent that each stage evolves into the next. There is no homeostasis, and the current difficult child will be heading for changes soon.

Sexual Development Perhaps one of the most detrimental gaps in the development literature is the lack of research on childhood sexuality. Sexuality appears to follow a developmental trajectory in a structural way similar to cognitive, ego, and identity development. However, due to adult anxiety related to the acknowledgment of childhood sexuality and ethical implications of conducting sexuality research with children, this area of development is relatively unknown (Weis, 1998). This is especially concerning for play therapy, an environment in which children often express themselves sexually. Play therapists struggle with the discernment of concerning sexual behaviors versus normal developmental patterns of sex play. One model that has been presented is Schepp's (1986) presentation of sexual issues within life stages:

- *Infancy (ages 0 to 3 years).* Infants enjoy the discovery of genitals and develop sensual feelings through touching. The sex role identification process begins.
- *Childhood (ages 3 to 10 years).* Children experience self-pleasuring and possible sex play with others. There is an interest in reproduction

and sexual vocabulary is expanded. Children at this age observe adult sexual behaviors, including sex roles. They become attuned to sexuality issues addressed in the media and among peers.

- *Puberty (ages 10 to 14 years).* At this stage, children have a need to understand the physical changes they are experiencing. They have a curiosity about intercourse and masturbation, with specific concerns about menstruation and ejaculation. They are developing a body image that is connected to global self-worth.

Although this description of stages is not enough to guide a play therapist regarding sex play, it does confirm that children are sexual beings who integrate sexuality into their overall development. Sex play can be expected in play therapy as part of normal development and should be embraced with the same acceptance as maturational and cognitive play.

Cognitive and Ego Developmental Theories

The premise of cognitive and ego developmental theories is the interaction between person and environment. The child is born with natural abilities used to interact with the environment. Interaction influences the child's perception of the environment and motivates the quality and quantity of future interactions leading to a constant interplay between child and world. One main difference between maturational and cognitive/ego theories is that movement on the cognitive/ego continuum can cease or pause at any time during development. This basic assumption for these theories indicates that each child will be moving at an individual rate and may halt progression at any given stage.

Piaget's Cognitive Theory Jean Piaget (see Piaget, 1932/1935) is responsible for modern developmental psychology. Although his theory goes in and out of favor with current approaches to development, basic tenets of cognitive development remain consistent. The world of play therapy often cites Piaget's theory as cognitive rationale for the intervention, emphasizing his explanation of symbolic communication (Landreth, 2002). Cognitive development theory suggests that children actively construct reality out of experiences with the environment and, hence, must be able to interact with the environment in a hands-on way to learn. Children think qualitatively differently from adults, unable to think, reason, and judge in the same way adults do (Elkind, 2007). Progression through cognitive stages represents a movement toward a more adult-like content and structure of thinking. As each stage is achieved, regression is not possible and most children will reach the formal operations stage allowing for abstraction.

- *Sensorimotor operations (birth to age 2 years).* The primary goal of the sensorimotor period is to establish object permanence, the knowledge that objects exist even when the infant can no longer see them. With no ability to abstract the meaning of items, the ability to physically manipulate objects through touch, taste, and feeling informs the infant of the world. The word "objects" extends to primary caretakers, connecting the sensorimotor stage to Erikson's trust stage and Bowlby's (1982) attachment theory. The establishment of primary objects of affection as permanent nurturing figures leads to the development of trust and attachment. However, it should be noted that even if children do not establish object permanence with another human, they will more than likely move to the next stage of cognitive development because concrete object permanence has been established through mere innate intelligence. Because of the early onset of this stage, play therapists will usually only interact with children who have completed and passed through this stage of development.

- *Preoperational operations (ages 2 to 6 years).* As explained by Elkind (2007), children at this stage can now mentally represent objects through symbols, specifically through the acquisition of language. They form concepts of classes of objects. They attach meaning to symbols and vehemently defend those symbols. The attachment to symbols explains the child's emphasis on being identified by the correct name, or not sharing toys that belong to the me symbol. The attachment to symbols also explains the child's preferred communication modality of play. Each symbol has meaning and allows the child to express thoughts and emotions, whereas a limited vocabulary of words does not allow full expression. It is this particular stage that has been cited by play therapists as the rationale for providing a therapeutic environment that allows expression through concrete symbols with meaning attributed by the child. Magical thinking is a characteristic of this stage in that children attribute causality to events, often misinterpreting their roles in events. If two events happen together, one must cause the other.

In one of my supervision cases, Sophie, a 7-year-old girl, was participating in a divorce education group with her school counselor. Her parents divorced due to the father's realization that he was homosexual and his desire to end his heterosexual marriage. He was involved in a new relationship with another man. Sophie had participated in two rounds of divorce education and showed signs of withdrawal and depression. When I asked the school counselor if it were possible that Sophie blamed herself for the divorce, she vehemently responded that there was no way Sophie could possibly think that way because the divorce group concentrated on dispelling this myth for the children. I asked the school counselor to experiment and ask Sophie why her parents divorced. When asked, Sophie related an event where she and her sister were arguing loudly and started fighting. Her father came into her room to yell at them and separate them. This occurred the night before he left the home. Sophie was sure that this fight had caused her parents' separation and if she could just be "good," her father would return home. The school counselor was shocked about Sophie's interpretation after receiving so much information on divorce and the child's role. Sophie is an example that although education is important to children, it does not substitute for the child's own experience and magical interpretation of the world.

- *Concrete operations (ages 6/7 to 11/12 years).* Children shift from the manipulation of things to the manipulation of symbols. They acquire mental images that allow for the manipulation of ideas. They can now visualize the meaning of numbers and words without physical manipulation. At this stage, children learn rules that make cooperative play possible. They also embrace rules with a heightened need for logic. At concrete operations, logic is king and generalizable to all situations. If a person has done something good, that person is a good person. If an adult has broken a rule, that adult is a bad person. Elkind (2007) described the characteristic of cognitive conceit, which accompanies this stage: "When children catch their parents in an error, they assume that if the parent did not know that simple fact, then the parent doesn't know anything" (p. 129). The positive aspect of cognitive conceit is that it is a marker of desired independence from the parent.

  When just reviewing Piaget's cognitive development, a play therapist might ask if play therapy is appropriate for children in concrete operations. There is an obvious connection between the preoperational stage, symbolic reliance for communication, and play therapy. But when logic and concrete understanding are primary, how does symbolic expression in play therapy work? In concrete operations, children are acquiring a new skill of thinking about images and meaning. They are still very much learning through doing. In addition, concrete operations is marked by a focus on peers and relational expression. Play therapy allows the child to move in and out of mental imaging by providing concrete materials to make sense of the world, a most important task for the child in concrete operations. The relationship between child and play therapist can also serve as a place to explore relationship rules and independence from adults. Finally, children in concrete operations may now become potential participants in effective group play therapy.

- *Formal operations (ages 11/12 years to adulthood).* Formal operations is characterized by the onset of abstract reasoning, the ability to think about thinking, to conceptualize. A higher level of reasoning brings an awareness and understanding of complex emotions. Complicated emotions related to relational patterns such as guilt and resentment are now experienced. Early adolescence signifies the emergence of the imaginary audience observed by Elkind (2007). Because children have a new complex cognitive ability, they are able to think about other people's thinking. However, they make an error by assuming that other people are thinking about their same concerns, such as appearance, feelings, and thoughts. This is the imaginary audience. Another magical construct of early adolescence is the personal fable in which the child feels that she is unique and unlike others; hence, the thought is that nothing bad will happen to her, leading to a feeling of invulnerability and resulting in possible engagement in risky activity. It should be noted that abstract thinking is not only an ability but a developed skill. Children do not wake up one day with the ability and motivation to critically conceptualize events. Providing an environment where abstract skills can develop is a worthy goal for both teachers and therapists.

Loevinger's Ego Development At the core of Jane Loevinger's (1976) developmental theory is the concept of the ego, the internal structure that organizes and gives meaning to experiences of a person. Ego development encompasses the holistic growth of the person, including feeling, thoughts, and behavior. Loevinger's theory appears to subsume aspects of other well-known theories in social and moral development. Kirshner (1988) conceptualized Loevinger's stages as movement from needs and immediate gratification to immersion in the acceptance of others to awareness of complex individual differences and separateness. Early stages describe typical childhood development but they also describe adults who may function at any given stage. Loevinger was hesitant to assign any age suggestions to the described stages and cautioned against expectations that persons would develop at a given rate. However, subsequent developmentalists have assigned ages that seem to fit typical developmental rates of infancy and childhood. The earliest stages of infancy will not be addressed in this description. Cited age ranges for each stage should be reviewed with caution due to the significant variability of individual growth in Loevinger's model.

- *Impulsive (ages 3 to 5 years).* Children in early childhood are in the impulsive stage of development. They are ruled by physical and emotional impulsivity. They are egocentric and focused on their own immediate needs, with little regard for the needs of others.
- *Self-protective (ages 6 to 10 years).* Children learn to control their impulses in this stage and realize the function of rules. They are particularly opportunistic and view the world as a place where they must get their needs met before others. Their behavior is structured to gain rewards and avoid punishment. Children in this stage, comprising the majority of play therapy clients, are susceptible and amenable to behavioral techniques that offer a reward for good behavior. This stage should be considered in the context of Piaget's coinciding preoperational and operational stages, whereas the logic of behaviorism is understood and responded to by children, but expression is still grounded in symbolism. The self-protective stage is often perceived negatively by adult caretakers due to children's preoccupation with doing what they have to in order to get what they want, an externalized motivator. However, this stage marks the child's entrance into the realities of rule following and rule breaking. They are learning consequences of actions in their experiences with the outer world, which will later (in the next stage) inform their sense of belonging in the world.
- *Conformist (ages 10 to 15 years).* In this stage, children begin to see individual welfare as related to the group. This stage is characterized by conformity to the identified group and a strict adherence to group rules. There is a preoccupation with external appearances that indicate group belonging. Children tend to think concretely with little toleration for ambiguity. Decisions are made based on what is good for the group. There are several implications of this stage for the practice of working with children. First, group play therapy becomes a preferred option at this stage because children are more susceptible to change based on group acceptance. Second, behaviorism ceases to be effective, especially if the sense of group belonging outweighs the child's need for an external reward, a common occurrence in the conformist stage. Third, there is little sensitivity to the acceptance of differences. Counselor impact on multicultural appreciation is limited. Finally, children are relationally based in this stage and seek out relationships in which they feel a sense of comfort. Children who enter this stage but do not have a sense of belonging in an identified group will exhibit emotional and social difficulties. As in the case of the self-protective stage, mental health professionals who value individualism and appreciation for diversity often view the conformist stage in

an unfavorable light. Yet, the search for belonging and meaning in the context of a group brings about emotional growth, development of cooperative social skills, and acknowledgment of personal impact on others. This prepares children for the next stage, in which they feel socially confident and stable enough to explore individual experience apart from the group.

- *Self-aware (ages 15 years to adult), conscientious (adult), individualistic (adult), autonomous (adult), and integrated (adult).* Although most play therapists will not work with children in the upper levels of development, it would be important to note that the majority of U.S. adults are classified in the self-aware stage, just one step beyond older childhood. In the self-aware stage, adolescents or adults are just becoming aware of individual differences that do not meet the standards of the group. As stages progress, an individualized structure within the context of a broader group emerges in which a person balances the needs of self in the context of the needs of the group. Experiences and cognitions become more complex as the individual attempts to take multiple perspectives and acts with respect toward those perspectives. Again, it should be noted that life becomes more complex in upper levels of development, not necessarily more fulfilling or adjusted.

Greenspan's Emotional Development Greenspan (1993, 1997) held great regard for the developmental theories of Erikson and Piaget but discovered that the emotional life of children was somewhat ignored in historical conceptualizations of development. He sought to observe and categorize areas of emotional development that coincided with the physical and cognitive changes taking place in children. He identified four areas (that he labeled as milestones) through which all children needed to maneuver for emotional growth: self-regulation, relationships, reality and fantasy, and communication (Greenspan, 1993). For each age period, a child would need to master specific capacities within the milestone area. If at any point a child skips these abilities, therapeutic care is indicated to direct a return to mastery of that area.

- *First 5 years (ages 0 to 5 years).* In the milestone of self-regulation, the child is able to be calm and regulated, control impulses, and be attentive and focused. Regarding relationships, the child relates warmly to parents, peers individually and in a group, and new adults, such as teachers. For the milestone of reality and fantasy, the child participates in and enjoys fantasy play, appreciates reality, and can distinguish make-believe from reality. In communication, the child shows wants, desires, and intentions with gestures, as well as intuitively responds to others' gestures. In addition, the child is able to organize words and ideas to communicate two or more ideas at a time.

- *World is my oyster (ages 5 to 7 years).* For self-regulation, the child is able to carry out self-care and self-regulatory functions, including calming down, focusing, dressing, washing, among other tasks, with minimal support. In relationships, the child enjoys and feels secure in parental relationship, able to take interest in parents, peers, and "me." They are able to play parents against one another to get what they want. They can form relationships with peers and play independently from parents, and can assert their wills with peers. Children at this stage can also survive not getting their own way with parents and peers. For the milestone of reality and fantasy, the child will try to get expectations met but learns to deal with the frustration and disappointments of reality. In emotional thinking, the child lets fears, shyness, worries, and conflicts coexist with great expectations. They begin to understand the reason for reality limits.
- *World is other kids (ages 8 to 10 years).* At this stage, children establish self-regulation through the ability to concentrate for longer periods of time, even on harder tasks. They carry out most self-care without support. In relationships, children participate fully in peer groups and are aware of their roles in groups. They are mostly concerned and involved with friends. They maintain nurturing relationships with parents who they use for guidance in maneuvering peer relationships. They compete and can also be close to siblings. For the milestone of reality and fantasy, children continue to be able to enjoy fantasy as well as follow rules. In communication and emotional thinking, children organize ideas, including those dealing with emotions, into communication. They prioritize emotions and group them into categories. They can experience competition without avoidance or overreacting to it. They can also experience disappointment without withdrawing or becoming aggressive.
- *World inside me (ages 11 to 12 years).* Children at this stage have developed a new "internal yardstick" (Greenspan, 1993, p. 306) that allows them to define self by ongoing characteristics instead of peer group perceptions. They have a growing internal sense of right and wrong, separate from the group. For the self-regulation milestone, they are able to concentrate long enough for homework on their own and carry out self-care. In relationships, they enjoy one or a few intimate friends and are less dependent

on position in the group. They take interest in parents or other adults as role models but they secretly enjoy power struggles with parents as a way of establishing independence. In communication and emotional thinking, children are able to observe and evaluate personal communication, understand and empathize with others, and hold in mind and communicate two competing feelings. For the reality and fantasy milestone, children enjoy daydreams and reflecting upon them. They are able to use rules flexibly by understanding context.

Greenspan offered a theory that incorporates what can be expected from a child regarding physical maturation, cognitive patterns, social and communicative interactions, and emotional understanding. The result is a developmental theory that integrates aspects of all other theories to help provide a more holistic view of the child. In addition, Greenspan provided a listing of capacities that are needed for positive mental health development.

Racial/Cultural Identity Development As multicultural sensitivity increased, various models of developmental stages related to diverse multicultural populations emerged. In an attempt to represent the global experience of marginalized groups, Sue and Sue (2003) created the racial/cultural identity development (R/CID) model to describe individual growth patterns of cultural identity. R/CID is based on the idea that racial/cultural identity is not stagnant but is created over time by the individual in collaboration with the environment, specifically an oppressive environment. No ages have been assigned to the R/CID but it seems noteworthy that children from marginalized groups engage in an ongoing attempt to integrate cultural identity with all other developmental foci. There are five identified stages outlined in the R/CID:

- *Conformity.* In this stage, the individual views the majority culture as superior, accepting the values of the dominant culture with little questioning. Persons at this stage engage in self-deprecating thoughts and may distance themselves from others of the same minority cultural group. For children maneuvering through other obstacles of development, the self-deprecating characteristic of the conformity stage can augment an already treacherous path of self-concept development.

  I supervised a case involving a 6-year-old African-American boy who had been severely abused by his mother. He was removed from the home and temporarily placed with a Caucasian foster family. In his play sessions, he would first choose to play with the black baby doll that he proceeded to hit and then bury in the sand. He would then follow up this play by gently picking up the white baby doll, holding her, then feeding her. He would gently place her in the blankets when he was done. In this case, confusion regarding race and individual crisis appeared to dovetail into a burgeoning concept of self, with the deleterious consequences of a destructive self view of the child's race and elevated perception of the dominant culture.

- *Dissonance.* The individual encounters conflict between the values of the dominant culture and view of self. This stage is characterized by the questioning of previous perceptions and ideas as they are juxtaposed against current experience. The person may become suspicious of others from the dominant culture.
- *Resistance and immersion.* In this stage, the person identifies solely with the minority group, rejecting all association with the dominant culture. This stage is characterized by heightened emotions of anger and shame, and there is an increasing appreciation for self.
- *Introspection.* There is an emergence of self in this stage based on the need to develop independently from the group. Persons in this stage seek to differentiate personal views from group views.
- *Integrative awareness.* The person in this stage develops an inner sense of security and autonomy. There is a developing appreciation of the person's culture, as well as the dominant culture. This stage may also include a commitment to social action to eliminate oppression.

Brain Development

In recent years, the exploration of brain development has become a key focus of medical research, extending interest between brain processes and child development. Most of this literature involves the acquisition of language and intellectual pursuits but play therapists have demonstrated a decidedly curious nature as to how this information might relate to the profession of helping children emotionally. Hirsh-Pasek and Golinkoff (2003) refer to the educational focus on brain development as "hype" and dispel myths that adults are responsible for "molding the intelligence and capabilities" (p. 18) of children, or that scientific research "provides us with a manual for building better brains" (p. 19). They explain that in the early months and years of life, the child's brain synapses, the connectors for communication within the brain, become sturdier and more resilient each time they fire, affecting the permanent circuitry of the brain. However, findings indicate that the brain produces new synapses, strengthens old ones, and eliminates unused ones throughout the developmental process. The consistent finding among brain researchers is that the brain grows and changes over the lifespan.

Specific to the work of play therapists, Sprenger (2008) described two types of learning that affect brain development. The first is experience expectant, in which the assumption is that circumstances within the brain will be present for the child to learn. "Neural networks in the brain are expecting to form from specific stimuli that will be present" (p. 16). The brain is naturally set up to grow. The second way of learning, experience dependent, occurs when the brain is exposed to certain types of experiences based on the environment. Based on experience, the brain will change, demonstrating a level of plasticity. This type of learning is provided by home, school, and other environments. Although the emotional brain system that encompasses personality, temperament, and emotional reactions is established in the first 24 months of life, regulation of emotions through the frontal lobe of the brain occurs much later. Sprenger concluded that according to brain research, emotional development continues throughout childhood and adulthood.

Implications for Practice

Upon first review of this chapter, a play therapist may decide that the breadth and depth of the information are limited in applicability to practice. After all, this chapter was an attempt to bring together a diversity of theories concentrating on various components of human growth and development. However, my intent is that the advanced play therapist will learn to integrate historical and current theories of development with the conceptualization of each unique child. Here are a few suggested ways in which to use this chapter:

1. Prior to conducting a child intake for therapy, review the ages addressed in this chapter and their corresponding stages (see Table 2.2). Develop a picture of a typical child of this age. For example, a 4-year-old initiates action for the sake of action (Erikson), displays vigorous energy (Gesell), shows interest in self sexual pleasure (Sexual Development), communicates through symbols and engages in magical thinking (Piaget), acts impulsively with little regard to others (Loevinger), engages in fantasy play and acquisition of language (Greenspan), and if aware of his cultural/racial environment, accepts the dominant culture's value system (Sue & Sue).
2. Use this picture to help educate parents regarding their expectations.
3. Use this picture as an assessment comparing the uniqueness of the child within the context of normal group descriptions of development.

Table 2.2 Developmental Theory Chart

Psychosocial Identity (Erikson)	Maturational (Gesell)	Sexual (Schepp)	Cognitive (Piaget)	Ego (Loevinger)	Emotional (Greenspan)	Ages (Approximate)	Racial Cultural Identity (Sue and Sue)
Trust/Mistrust	Smooth, consolidated	Infancy	Sensorimotor	Symbiotic	First 5 years	Birth to 2	***This column not matched to ages.***
	Breaking up (2½)					2½	
Autonomy/Shame	Rounded, balanced	Childhood	Preoperational	Impulsive		3½	Conformity
	Inwardized					3	
Initiative/Guilt	Vigorous, expansive					4	Dissonance
	Inwardized-outwardized					4½	
	Smooth, consolidated			Self-protective	World is my oyster	5	Resistance and immersion
	Breaking up					5½	
	Rounded, balanced					6	Introspection
						6½	

Continued

Table 2.2 (*Continued*) Developmental Theory Chart

Psychosocial Identity (Erikson)	Maturational (Gesell)	Sexual (Schepp)	Cognitive (Piaget)	Ego (Loevinger)	Emotional (Greenspan)	Ages (Approximate)	Racial Cultural Identity (Sue and Sue)
Industry/Inferiority	Inwardized		Concrete			7	Integrative awareness
	Vigorous, expansive				World is other kids	8	
	Inwardized-outwardized					9	
	Smooth, consolidated	Puberty		Conformist		10	
	Breaking up		Formal		World inside me	11	
	Rounded, balanced					12	

Note: Ages are approximate correlational ages and do not represent a definitive match to each stage.

4. In initial parent consultations, review major developmental milestones with parents. Specifically, a play therapist should have knowledge of the child's birth, early disposition, walking, talking, potty training, and language acquisition.
5. Once you have begun a relationship with the child, assess the child's characteristics on the continuum of development. What characteristics is the child demonstrating, and how do they match chronologically to the various theories of development? This process is reversed from the process suggested in Item 1 above and may place the child in various stages for each theory.
6. During play sessions, note the link between child's play and expected developmental stage. How do they match, and how do they differ?
7. Use developmental markers to help determine progress in play therapy. Note changes in cognitive operations, emotional expression, and behavior.

References

Bowlby, J. (1982). *Attachment and loss: Attachment* (Vol. 1). New York: Perseus.

Burman, E. (2008). *Deconstructing developmental psychology* (2nd ed.). London: Routledge.

Elkind, D. (2007). *The hurried child: Growing up too fast too soon* (3rd ed.). Cambridge, MA: Perseus.

Erikson, E. (1963). *Childhood and society*. New York: Norton.

Fowler, J. (1981). *Stages of faith: The psychology of human development and the quest for meaning.* San Francisco: Harper & Row.

Freud, S. (1949). *An outline of psychoanalysis*. New York: Norton.

Gilligan, C. (1982). *In a different voice: Psychological theory and women's development.* Cambridge, MA: Harvard University Press.

Greenspan, S. (1993). *Playground politics: Understanding the emotional life of your school-age child.* Reading, MA: Addison-Wesley.

Greenspan, S. (1997). *The growth of the mind: And the endangered origins of intelligence.* Reading, MA: Perseus.

Hayes, R., & Aubrey, R. (1988). *New directions for counseling and human development.* Denver, CO: Love Publishing Company.

Hirsh-Pasek, K., & Golinkoff, R. (2003). *Einstein never used flash cards: How our children really learn and why they need to play more and memorize less.* Emmaus, PA: Rodale.

Ilg, F., Ames, L., & Baker, S. (1981). *Child behavior: The classic child care manual from the Gesell Institute of Human Development.* New York: HarperPerennial.

Ivey, A. (2000). *Developmental therapy: Theory into practice.* Sunapee, NH: Author.

Kirshner, L. (1988). Implications of Loevinger's theory of ego development for time-limited psychotherapy. *Psychotherapy, 25,* 220–226.

Kohlberg, L. (1981). *The philosophy of moral development: Moral stages and the idea of justice.* San Francisco: Harper & Row.

Landreth, G. (2002). *Play therapy: The art of the relationship.* New York: Routledge.

Loevinger, J. (1976). *Ego development.* San Francisco: Jossey-Bass Publishers.

Piaget, J. (1932/1965). *The moral judgment of the child.* New York: Free Press.

Ray, D. (2008). Impact of play therapy on parent-child relationship stress at a mental health training setting. *British Journal of Guidance & Counselling, 36,* 165–187.

Schepp, K. (1986). *Sexuality counseling: A training program.* Muncie, IN: Accelerated Development.

Sprenger, M. (2008). *The developing brain: Birth to age eight.* Thousand Oaks, CA: Corwin Press.

Sue, D., & Sue, D. (2003). *Counseling the culturally diverse: Theory and practice* (4th ed.). New York: Wiley.

Super, D.E. (1963). A theory of vocational development. *American Psychologist, 8,* 185–190.

Vygotsky, L. (1966). Play and its role in the mental development of the child. *Voprosy Psikhologii, 12,* 6–18.

Weis, D. (1998). Interpersonal heterosexual behaviors. In P. Koch & D. Weis (Eds.), *Sexuality in America: Understanding our sexual values and behavior* (pp. 91–105). New York: Continuum.

Wood, C. (2007). *Yardsticks: Children in the classroom ages 4–14* (3rd ed.). Turners Falls, MA: Northeast Foundation for Children.

Young-Eisendrath, P. (1988). Making use of human development theories in counseling. In R. Hayes & R. Aubrey (Eds.), *New directions for counseling and human development* (pp. 66–84). Denver, CO: Love Publishing Company.

CHAPTER 3

A Philosophy of Working with Children

The Child-Centered Way

It would be easy to skip this chapter because it focuses on the "how," and not the "what" of therapy. Psychotherapy training today tends to focus on the mechanics, explicitly laying out what the therapist is doing in therapy. New therapists are especially attracted to techniques that will provide a directional map for their role in counseling. And yet, this chapter will explore how play therapy works by discussing the elements necessary to facilitate effective change. These elements are not words or techniques, but much less tangible and measurable dynamics that work together to effect change for the child and play therapist. A second reason this chapter will likely be scanned or passed over as trivial is that I will provide a lengthy explanation of the person-centered theory of development and change. Because the Carl Rogers approach is a mainstay subject in most entry-level counseling and therapy programs, many readers may assume that information in this chapter is unnecessarily repetitive of their previous learnings. For those of you who have made it thus far in the chapter, I would like to encourage you to read further, all the way to the end. My goal is to provide a new awareness of the fit between work with children and person-centered theory.

In my experience, new, and even some experienced, play therapists demonstrate difficulty in explaining the process of change that takes place in play therapy. Hence, parents and other decision makers lose confidence in the process when understanding is limited. In addition, play therapists can hardly facilitate growth when they do not grasp the dynamics involved in effective counseling. In one supervised parent consultation, I observed a play therapist explaining play therapy like this:

> We do play therapy here. In play therapy, I sit and observe your child while he plays, which is the language of children. Whatever your child does, I reflect what your child is saying or doing. Your child will learn to express himself in lots of different ways.

As I listened to this explanation, I cringed at the play therapist's lack of knowledge of her therapist role, the child's role, and the role of the relationship. I also anticipated the parent's response, which was as predicted: "So, you just sit there while my child plays. How is that going to help?" The therapist stumbled through an inaccurate response, explaining that the child would feel better after he fully expressed himself. One testament to the desperation of parents upon entry into therapy is that these parents returned to enter their child into therapy. Fortunately, I was able to work with the play therapist on the theoretical underpinnings of play therapy so that she could better communicate with parents and also increase her effectiveness in the delivery of play therapy.

Operating from a clear theoretical rationale in working with clients provides counselors with "…an explanation of how each person was innately endowed and developed throughout one's lifetime so far: how one became who one is today" (Fall, Holden, & Marquis, 2010, p. 2). In addition, comprehensive theory offers an explanation of problems faced by people and a description of dynamics or conditions for change. These benefits of theory also apply to working with children. An inclusive theory provides an explanation of child development, thereby rendering it particularly useful in working with children during their development. When Rogers introduced the 19 propositions in his 1951 work, *Client-Centered Therapy*, he provided a framework for human development (encompassing child development), as well as a hypothesis for the human response to life problems and how change occurs. A play therapist's knowledge of the following 19 propositions and their application to play therapy is essential to effective practice (Rogers, 1951, pp. 481–533):

Prop 1. Every individual exists in a continually changing world of experience of which he or she is the center.

Prop 2. The organism reacts to the field as it is experienced and perceived. This perceptual field is, for the individual, "reality."

Prop 3. The organism reacts as an organized whole to this phenomenal field.

Prop 4. The organism has one basic tendency and striving—to actualize, maintain, and enhance the experiencing organism.

Prop 5. Behavior is basically the goal-directed attempt of the organism to satisfy its needs as experienced, in the field as perceived.

Prop 6. Emotion accompanies and in general facilitates such goal-directed behavior, the kind of emotion being related to the seeking versus the consummatory aspects of the behavior, and the intensity of the emotion being related to the perceived significance of the behavior for the maintenance and enhancement of the organism.

Prop 7. The best vantage point for understanding behavior is from the internal frame of reference of the individual.

Prop 8. A portion of the total perceptual field gradually becomes differentiated as the self.

Prop 9. As a result of interaction with the environment, and particularly as a result of evaluational interaction with others, the structure of self is formed—an organized, fluid, but consistent conceptual pattern of perceptions of characteristics and relationships of the "I" or the "me," together with values attached to these concepts.

Prop 10. The values attached to experiences, and the values that are a part of the self-structure, in some instances are values experienced directly by the organism, and in some instances are values introjected or taken over from others, but perceived in distorted fashion, as though they had been experienced directly.

Prop 11. As experiences occur in the life of the individual, they are (a) symbolized, perceived, and organized into some relationship to the self, or (b) ignored because there is no perceived relationship to the self-structure, or (c) denied symbolization or given a distorted symbolization because the experience is inconsistent with the structure of the self.

Prop 12. Most of the ways of behaving that are adopted by the organism are those that are consistent with the concept of self.

Prop 13. Behavior may, in some instances, be brought about by organismic experiences and needs that have not been symbolized. Such behavior may be inconsistent with the structure of the self, but in such instances the behavior is not "owned" by the individual.

Prop 14. Psychological maladjustment exists when the organism denies to awareness significant sensory and visceral experiences, which consequently are not symbolized and organized into the gestalt of the self-structure. When this situation exists, there is a basis for potential psychological tension.

Prop 15. Psychological adjustment exists when the concept of the self is such that all sensory and visceral experiences of the organism are, or may be, assimilated on a symbolic level into a consistent relationship with the concept of self.

Prop 16. Any experience that is inconsistent with the organization or structure of self may be perceived as a threat, and the more of these perceptions there are, the more rigidly the self-structure is organized to maintain itself.

Prop 17. Under certain conditions, involving primarily complete absence of any threat to the self-structure, experiences that are inconsistent with it may be perceived and examined, and the structure of self revised to assimilate and include such experiences.

Prop 18. When the individual perceives all his sensory and visceral experiences and accepts them into one consistent and integrated system, then he is necessarily more understanding of others and more accepting of others as separate individuals.

Prop 19. As the individual perceives and accepts into his self-structure more of his organic experiences, he finds that he is replacing his present value system—based so largely on introjections that have been distortedly symbolized with a continuing organismic valuing process.

At the base of personality development, the belief in the phenomenological character of the organism is essential. Props 1 and 2 emphasize that each person is the center of the perceived experiential field and that perception of experience is reality for that person. Both Props 3 and 4 highlight the human response as organic and holistic but also forward moving and striving for enhancement of the organism. Props 5, 6, and 7 delineate the roles of behavior and emotion by describing behavior as an attempt to maintain the organism with accompanying emotion dependent on the perceived need for behavior. Yet, the only way to understand behavior is to understand the phenomenological world of the person. Props 8 through 13 describe the development of the self-structure that is separate from the phenomenological field yet highly influenced by it. The self is developed through perceived interactions with significant others in development. If a person perceives that love is given by others only under certain conditions, the self will formulate a sense of values based on these conditions and actively measure self-worth based on these conditions (termed "conditions of worth"). Subsequent experiences are then perceived in the context of the developed self and may or may not contribute to functionality based on the perception of the experience and its relationship to the self construct. Hence, behavior is directly consistent with the view of self, whether or not it is within the awareness of the person. Props 14, 15, and 16 address the development of maladjustment or adjustment based on the person's inability or ability to integrate experiences into the construct of self. Those experiences that are not integrated can be perceived as threats to self. Finally, Props 17, 18, and 19 propose a path to which the person, when given a nonthreatening environment, can examine experiences in a nonjudgmental way, integrate them into a self-structure that is respectful of the intrinsic direction of the organism, and hence enhance relationships with others. The final three propositions indicate the facilitative nature of the therapeutic environment, although the same process can occur outside of therapy.

Rogers' theory of personality development and behavior has been described as elegant (Wilkins, 2010), which is defined as "pleasingly ingenious and simple" by the *New Oxford American Dictionary*. Rogers' ability to observe, research, and explain the human condition is impressive, but how can this theory be applied specifically to children? Child development is explained through the development of the self-structure, the perceptions of conditions of worth, and the behavior and emotions that accompany the construct of self. Consider the following scenario:

Ethan and Michael are brothers, ages 5 and 7 years. Michael has stolen a toy car from Ethan's room because Ethan broke one of his earlier that day. Ethan demands to have the car back. Michael denies having it. Ethan asks loudly and then starts to scream. Michael screams back and calls Ethan "a stupid idiot." Ethan punches Michael and a fight ensues. Mom quickly breaks up the fight by putting herself between the boys. She yells, "Stop fighting. You are brothers and you shouldn't be fighting." They quickly try to resume arguing by yelling their sides of the story to Mom. Mom, who has had a tough day, begins to cry and says, "You are brothers and you love each other. Tell each other right now." Both boys are angry and refuse to say anything. Mom says, "Michael, tell your brother right now that you are sorry and you love him." Michael, seeing that Mom is upset, complies. Mom then says, "Ethan, you tell your brother you're sorry and tell him you love him." Ethan refuses. Mom then moves to anger and says, "Tell your brother you love him or no video games this week." In an angry voice, Ethan mumbles, "I'm sorry. I love you."

This scenario occurs across the world every day and might seem to be a benign example of person-centered theory of development; but upon closer inspection, the dynamics are at work. Both boys are experiencing an organismic reaction to feeling wronged; they are both angry. They act out behaviorally on this sense of self being intruded upon. When Mom enters the picture, both boys are in touch with their organismic valuing process by fully expressing their anger toward one another. They are quickly told that this expression is unacceptable. In addition, they each perceive two different conditions of worth as expressed by Mom. Michael is compliant when he realizes that his mother is emotionally upset. He perceives that his expression of anger will lead to his mother's unhappiness and so he complies with her request, thereby solidifying his perceived condition of worth that "Mom will love me more and be happy if I do not express my anger." Operating from a different construct of self, Ethan perceives that he cannot get what he wants if he expresses anger, and hence is willing to deny his expression if he can achieve another purpose. He accepts his Mom's introjected value that he can get tangible things that he wants when he does not express anger. Neither boy is given the opportunity to express anger appropriately so that it is integrated into the self in a way that leads to expression of the organismic valuing process and enhances relationships. Although this is one small incident that will more than likely not lead to maladjustment, continual similar interactions between significant others may interfere with the development of self by denying the experience of the organism.

In the following paragraphs I will present two cases of child development in the context of the 19 propositions that will hopefully exemplify the use of the theory in everyday conceptualization of practice.

Elizabeth

Elizabeth was born as the second child to both of her biological parents. Her parents maintained a lengthy but unhappy marriage. Both parents worked extensively outside the home. Elizabeth's older sister was a gregarious and sweet child but was strongly willful and struggled with temper tantrums and demandingness. When Elizabeth's parents were at home (which was not often), they fought vehemently with her sister and each other regarding her sister's behaviors. Elizabeth perceived that because her parents were often angry with her sister due to her behavior, they loved her sister less, and hence they would love her less if she exhibited such behavior. In response, from the earliest age, Elizabeth was a smiley, happy child and caused no behavioral problems. If she made any mistakes or had an accident, she would quickly try to cover it up so that her parents would not find out. From the time she entered school, she performed above expectations and attempted to achieve any possible external rewards provided by the school. Elizabeth's achievements were lauded by her parents and used to compare her with her sister. Due to her sister's resentment, her relationship with her sister deteriorated and Elizabeth's sense of isolation grew. By the time Elizabeth was 9 years old, she was regularly overeating and had developed a weight problem. In addition, she habitually bit her nails until they bled and pulled out chunks of her hair. However, none of these behaviors were noticed by her parents due to her success in school and other activities.

Theoretical Explanation

In understanding Elizabeth through the 19 propositions, Elizabeth's first understanding of her being was perceived through observation of her parents' interaction with her sister, a perception born of being the center of her experiences (Prop 1) and vicarious experience (Prop 10). She quickly perceived that love was given conditionally based on her ability to act in a more pleasing manner with her parents (Prop 9). However, her attempt to be pleasing manifested itself as an attempt to be perfect, which was met with achieving the love she desired yet her reality of being human and imperfect could not meet the conditions set forth (Prop 14), causing her great amounts of anxiety. Her focus on achievement and success were behaviors chosen to support her view of self (Prop 12). Her overeating, nail biting, and trichotillmania behaviors were attempts to reduce the threat inherent in her incongruent feelings (Prop 13) that were denied to awareness.

George

George was born to a drug-addicted mother and did not know his father. As an infant, he was left alone or with strangers. He was routinely ignored and often experienced lengthy periods of hunger, dirtiness, and not being touched. When he was 4 years old, he was permanently removed from his mother by social services. He was placed in a foster home with two parents who were loving, nurturing, and kind. George threw significant temper tantrums when he did not get his way. During these tantrums, he would often hurt himself or one of his foster parents. At the age of 5, he began threatening to kill himself, even hiding knives in his room. His foster parents were confused about the deterioration of his behavior when they had been fairly consistent with nurturing and nonaggressive discipline.

Theoretical Rationale

Understanding George through the 19 propositions is more challenging because of his age and reliance on his behavior as his primary mode of communication, but here is one such explanation. George learned early in infancy that his organismic desires were not aligned with his environment. His basic physiological needs went unmet and, because the organism is holistic, the result was a full experience both physiological and psychological of being unimportant, unworthy (Prop 3). Yet, as a person, he maintained a striving to survive, to develop a sense of self (Prop 4). In his perceptual world, the self was developed out of a context of an unreliable relationship in which he was unworthy (Props 8 and 9). The only self that could survive in his world was one that demanded to get his needs met, through whatever means necessary. The more he needed or wanted something, the angrier (Prop 5) or more behaviorally outrageous (Prop 6) he would need to become to get this need or want met. When George was provided an environment that was different, in that his basic needs could be met without extreme behaviors, he could not allow himself to be vulnerable to this experience (Prop 14). The more nurturance his foster parents provided, the more he acted out in a consistent way with his sense of self, not allowing integration of the new experience (Prop 16). The challenging aspect of working with George from the perspective of the 19 propositions is how to provide him with a nonthreatening environment in which he can start to explore the maladjusted sense of self to move to a fully functioning sense of self.

In the cases of Elizabeth and George, development is conceptualized through the 19 propositions up to the final three: Props 17, 18, and 19. Both George and Elizabeth are dealing with incongruence between themselves and their environments. In the case of Elizabeth, her incongruence is self-focused, only seeing herself as worthy if she is high-achieving but intrinsically knowing that she cannot continue to achieve at such a high rate to maintain her parents' love. In George's case, he developed a rigid sense of self that must demand needs in order to survive but, when faced with a completely different environment, he experiences incongruence between his self-structure and his new nurturing environment. In his case, the threat of removal of parent is so great that clinging to the rigid sense of self with greater emotion and destructive behavior is a safer choice, although out of his awareness as a choice. Child-centered play therapy (CCPT) operates under Prop 17 by providing an environment in which all threats, as perceived by the therapist, are removed and hopefully experienced by the child. And under Props 18 and 19, the child will be able to behaviorally act out the feelings and thoughts of incongruence between self and the ideal self or environment, through play, within a relationship where the child is positively regarded. In this exploration of self and congruence, the child will begin to accept the acts of others (such as George's acceptance of his foster parents' nurturance) and will integrate the natural organism of self into awareness to develop full functioning (such as Elizabeth's acceptance of worth minus achievements).

Necessary and Sufficient Conditions for Change

The 19 propositions provide a roadmap for conceptualization of child development and accompanying constructs, behaviors, and emotions. The practice of CCPT is particularly concerned with Prop 17, which hypothesizes that the removal of any threat to self-structure will allow a person to explore experiences that are consistent or inconsistent with self so that they can be assimilated into an integrated revised self. The removal of threats is the basis for the key person-centered concept of nondirectivity provided by the therapist to acknowledge the client's right to autonomy and belief in the client's constructive nature (Wilkins, 2010). Nondirectivity is not defined as a set of passive behaviors but as an attitude that promotes the client's self-sufficiency by not guiding the client's goals or therapeutic content. For Prop 17, Rogers (1951) specifically uses the words, "Under certain conditions," (p. 532) which are precursors for the removal of threat to the self-structure and define the nondirective nature of therapy. According to Rogers (1957), certain conditions were necessary to work toward constructive personality change, which he defined as follows:

> [C]hange in the personality structure of the individual, at both surface and deeper levels, in a direction which clinicians would agree means greater integration, less internal conflict, more energy utilizable for effective living; change in behavior away from behaviors generally regarded as immature and toward behaviors regarded as mature. (p. 95)

These words as a goal for therapy still ring true today for CCPT. Rogers (1957) identified the conditions in his introduction of the six necessary and sufficient conditions for therapeutic change. They are as follows:

1. Two persons are in psychological contact.
2. The first, whom we shall term the client, is in a state of incongruence, being vulnerable or anxious.
3. The second person, whom we shall term the therapist, is congruent or integrated in the relationship.
4. The therapist experiences unconditional positive regard for the client.
5. The therapist experiences an empathic understanding of the client's internal frame of reference and endeavors to communicate this experience to the client.
6. The communication to the client of the therapist's empathic understanding and unconditional positive regard is to a minimal degree achieved. (p. 96)

Wilkins (2010) points out two misassumptions of person-centered theory related to the six necessary and sufficient conditions. The first, and most widespread, misassumption is that there are only three conditions, typically identified as empathy, congruence, and unconditional positive regard, also commonly referred to as the core conditions. Rogers, and subsequent person-centered theorists, were very clear that all six conditions must be present in order for change to occur. Second, change will occur in the presence of the six conditions regardless of theoretical orientation. Although required, the conditions are not specific to the work of person-centered therapists. In the introduction of conditions, Rogers presented a grouping of meta-conditions that were cross-theoretical in nature and could be applied to any therapy approach. If conditions are met and the style of the therapist does not conflict with them, effective outcome will be the same.

The conditions seem clearly presented when addressing counseling with adults. Applying the conditions to work with children needs further exploration. In the first condition, the therapist and child must be in psychological contact—or in simpler terms, in a relationship. In this relationship, both the therapist and child must be in each other's awareness, allowing the other to enter the perceptual field. For children with significant attachment issues or other social challenges, this type of relationship cannot be assumed due to the child's reactive behavior that disallows the entry of others into the perceptual field. The very first condition of being in contact, so often assumed with adults who do not experience dissociative or mental impairments, may be a greater challenge in working with children. In addition, the therapist's assessment of contact may be limited with children due to any child's tendency to avoid eye contact, verbalization, and inclination to enter into intense play at the exclusion of the therapist. Accurate assessment of contact may be enhanced by the therapist's ability to be fully attuned to nonverbal child gestures, child facial expressions, and interactions occurring between therapist and child.

Second, the child must be in a state of incongruence, which may be demonstrated through anxiety or vulnerability. Assessment of this condition is especially tricky for the play therapist. Children are most often identified by adults as needing help; some might be significant others and some just observers of the child. The identification of the child as needing help is usually determined by observing the behaviors of the child and interpreting these behaviors as expressions of problematic emotions. The identification of the need for therapy is the most significant difference between working with adults and children. Most adults who seek therapy become aware of incongruence, probably manifested as not getting what they want from life or experiencing barriers to their functioning. Alternately, most children brought to therapy are not consciously aware that they are in need of help, and some actually do not need help but are misassessed by adults. However, the condition still exists that the client, the child, must be in a state of incongruence. Fortunately, this condition can be assessed generally through the child's exhibition of problematic behaviors. Relying on Rogers' original explanation of development, behavior is directly related to the structure of self. Problem behaviors typically demonstrate a child's incongruence between self and introjected values, or incongruence between the child's self-structure and environment. Problem behaviors serve as indicators of a state of incongruence for most children, but certainly not all. As in any therapy, there will be children who act in inappropriate ways compared to societal standards but who do not feel any sense of conflict about these behaviors because the behaviors in question work toward getting needs met. In these cases, the second condition is not met and change is unlikely to occur. The great benefit of working with children can be seen in Rogers' use of the term "vulnerability," which is an indicator of incongruence. Because of age (or lack thereof), the vast majority of children experience a sense of vulnerability in relationships because they are still relatively new to relational encounters. Consequently, even if children do not recognize anxiety or problem behaviors, they are often susceptible to the benefits of a healthy relationship, thereby meeting the second condition of change.

The next three conditions address the person of the therapist, including the therapist's experience and communication of congruence, unconditional positive regard, and empathic understanding. These three phrases are weakly explored in the therapy world and have become a list of memorized terms that hold relatively little meaning for many therapists. Because of their importance in the effectiveness of the play therapy relationship and because their use in play therapy is often misunderstood, I will devote all of Chapter 4 to exploring these concepts as characteristics of an effective play therapist. Speaking to the process of therapeutic change, the therapist is required not only to communicate, but also to experience a sense of genuineness, a sense of acceptance or unconditional positive regard for the child, and a sense of empathic understanding of the child.

The final condition is one over which the therapist has very little control. Not only does the therapist have to experience and actively attempt to communicate empathy and unconditional positive regard, but the client must perceive these conditions. Some would argue that the client's ability to receive empathy and unconditional positive regard from the therapist is often limited by the therapist's experience and expression of these conditions. However, there are certainly children who will not experience these conditions despite concerted efforts on the part of the therapist. This is the reality of any therapy: Sometimes the child is not ready and the conditions cannot be experienced. Hence, change does not occur. The good news is that most often in CCPT when the play therapist is able to provide empathic understanding and acceptance, these conditions are experienced by the child as activators of change.

In essence, this is how CCPT works. Because therapists understand that in an environment of threat, a child cannot integrate emotions and behaviors into a forward-moving, holistic, organismic self-structure that enhances view of self and relationships with others, CCPT offers an environment that provides the six conditions to facilitate change within a child. Change within the self-structure will be manifested into forward-moving behaviors and emotions that are consistent and enhancing for the new structure. Returning to the initial scenario of this chapter, a play therapist's explanation of therapy might be retooled to read something like this:

> As you have described, your child is exhibiting behaviors that cause him problems, as well as problems in school and home functioning. I believe that those behaviors are a way of telling us that he is confused or does not understand how to get his needs met in his environment according to how he sees himself now. In play therapy, I will actively present him an environment where he will be able to express himself through the child's language of play and explore how to change his view of self to fit what is best for him and his environment outside of therapy. I will facilitate this change by providing an environment that opens up new ways of seeing himself and allows experimenting with new behaviors within appropriate limits so that he is able to get his needs met. My hope is that he will emerge from this experience with a new sense of self that improves his life through better decision making about his choices.

A thorough exploration of the theory behind CCPT would not be complete without paying considerable attention to Virginia Axline (1947). As a student and later a colleague of Carl Rogers, she is acknowledged as the founder of modern-day CCPT, referred to as *nondirective play therapy* by her. Her contribution to play therapy was to operationalize the philosophy of person-centered theory, so aptly described for adults, into a coherent working method for children. She first introduced the nondirective philosophy as such:

> By playing out these feelings (tension, frustration, insecurity, aggression, fear, bewilderment, confusion) he brings them to the surface, gets them out in the open, faces them, learns to control them, or abandons them. When he has achieved emotional relaxation, he begins to realize the power within himself to be an individual in his own right, to think for himself, to make his own decisions, to become psychologically more mature, and by so doing to realize selfhood. (Axline, 1947, p. 16)

The relationship between Axline's description of play therapy and Rogers' 19 propositions is clearly observed. The feelings of incongruence are explored in the absence of threat so that the actualizing tendency is released to develop an organismically enhancing self-structure.

Axline (1947) offered guidelines to enact the philosophy and therapeutic conditions described by Rogers. These guidelines helped define the nature of CCPT, the role of the therapist, and continue to guide practice today. They are referred to as the eight basic principles and are paraphrased as follows:

1. The therapist develops a warm, friendly relationship with the child as soon as possible.
2. The therapist accepts the child exactly as is, not wishing the child were different in some way.
3. The therapist establishes a feeling of permissiveness in the relationship so that the child can fully express thoughts and feelings.
4. The therapist is attuned to the child's feelings and reflects those back to the child to help gain insight into behavior.
5. The therapist respects the child's ability to solve problems, leaving the responsibility to make choices to the child.
6. The therapist does not direct the child's behavior or conversation. The therapist follows the child.
7. The therapist does not attempt to rush therapy, recognizing the gradual nature of the therapeutic process.
8. The therapist sets only those limits that anchor the child to reality or make the child aware of responsibilities in the relationship. (Axline, 1947, pp. 73–74)

These principles highlight the provision of an environment that will allow the child a place to express and explore current versions of the self-structure without interruption by or threat from the therapist. The institution of these principles as the guide for CCPT led to facilitative skills presented by Landreth (2002) and further detailed in Chapter 5 of this book.

Summary of Person-Centered Philosophy That Guides CCPT

The person-centered philosophy that serves as the basis for CCPT is marked by its trust in the innate tendency present in all individuals for growth-enhancing self-structure, emotions, and behaviors. Another primary concept is the belief in the individual as a person who experiences the world in a uniquely conceptualized way and who is fully capable of enacting change in self and in relationship to environment. Person-centered theory is tempered by the acceptance that when an individual is placed under certain environmental structures or perceives the environment in an incongruent manner with self, behaviors and emotions will contradict movement toward self-enhancement and healthy relationships with others. These person-centered tenets are formalized in such a way as to encourage the therapist to act in a way that is consistent with these beliefs through the use of the self of the therapist and structuring of the environment. When the therapist provides an environment that is nonthreatening and sends a message of empowerment to the client, the client will emerge with a structure that is self-enhancing as well as positively influential on relationships. These beliefs hold true whether a client is 4 years old or 40 years old. The child is as capable as the adult of determining the direction for therapeutic change, and the effective CCPT therapist provides self and environment to facilitate the child's active and innate processes for enhancement.

Other Theoretical Approaches in Play Therapy

The field of therapy, counseling others toward greater health, is characterized by various perspectives of human development and elements of change. Play therapy is a modality approached from a range of diverse theoretical orientations. By far, CCPT is recognized as the most popular approach to play therapy in the United States (Lambert et al., 2005) and enjoys a strong international reputation (see West, 1996; Wilson, Kendrick, & Ryan, 1992). Due to its long-standing history of literature and research, CCPT offers evidence of effectiveness as well as clear guidelines for practice. Perhaps what provides CCPT with its strongest support is the use of the necessary and sufficient conditions that were proposed by Rogers to be the effective agents of change for all therapy. Although many approaches to play therapy have emerged over time, they are heavily influenced by the CCPT approach. The next few paragraphs will simplistically describe basic concepts in play therapy approaches that are identified as influential methods of working with children. My descriptions are by no means exhaustive and only serve to provide the reader with the knowledge that other approaches to play therapy are available. Advanced play therapists are knowledgeable about most approaches of consequence to play therapy and have made an informed choice about adopting such an approach. Readers are encouraged to further review these approaches with rigor, noting that a thorough analysis of these approaches is beyond the scope of this book.

Cognitive-Behavioral Play Therapy

Although identified as the second most cited play therapy approach among play therapists (Lambert et al., 2005), cognitive-behavioral play therapy (CBPT) is perhaps the least explicated in play therapy literature. The popularity of the approach appears to be born from overwhelming support of cognitive-behavioral therapy with adults. There have been innumerable attempts to marry cognitive-behavioral techniques with play techniques but little guidance exists on how to structure such interventions. In addition, because there are multiple cognitive-behavioral approaches, conceptualization of child clients becomes challenging, leading to a less than unified methodology. The most consistent contributor to the integration of cognitive-behavioral techniques and a play therapy modality is Susan Knell (1993), who conceptualizes children from Aaron Beck's (1976) cognitive therapy framework.

Beck and Weishaar (2008) described personality as shaped by an interaction between innate characteristics and environment, emphasizing the role of information processing in human responses and adaptation. Each person is susceptible to cognitive vulnerabilities that lead to psychological maladjustment. Psychological distress can be caused by any number of innate, biological, developmental, and environmental factors but cognitive distortions are the most evident features of maladjustment. However, Knell (2009) points out that there is no personality theory underlying cognitive-behavioral play therapy due to a focus on psychopathology.

CBPT as conceptualized by Knell (2009) is brief, structured, directive, and problem oriented within the context of a trusting relationship between child and therapist. CBPT is considered developmentally sensitive due to its use of play materials and activities. Features of CBPT include establishment of goals, selection of play activities, education, and use of praise and interpretations (Knell, 2009). An expected outcome of therapy is that children will modify their irrational ideas, thus leading to less psychopathology.

Compared to other approaches in play therapy, CBPT is most diametrically opposed to the philosophy and practice of CCPT. There are so many points of variance that I will narrow down to just two for the sake of brevity. The first philosophical difference that leads to an entirely different approach is the CCPT belief in the self-actualizing tendency innate in all human beings. CBPT focuses on the individual as predisposed to cognitive vulnerabilities that lead to psychological distress (Beck & Weishaar, 2008). It becomes the therapist's role to educate the child about what is rational or irrational. The child is incapable of knowing what is good for her, and relies on the therapist's guidance to move toward psychological health, as demonstrated through behavior. CCPT would see a direct educational role of the therapist as interference in the child's process, disrupting the child's own internal movement toward health. A CCPT therapist would ask, "How can the therapist really know in what the child needs to be educated or directed to move toward fuller psychological functioning? After all, many children who exhibit psychological distress actually hold information for change but do not utilize it." Second, the emphasis on problem over person is a major delineating feature between CCPT and CBPT. The philosophy of CCPT goes to great lengths to emphasize the child as a person who needs to be fully understood and accepted in order to explore change. The cognitive-behavioral approach sees each child as a problem or set of problems that need to be solved, thereby discounting the personhood of the child.

Adlerian Play Therapy

When play therapists were surveyed, participants noted Adlerian play therapy as the third most identified theory in use (Lambert et al., 2005). Similar to Rogers, Adler believed in the concepts of phenomenology, an individual's perception of experience was reality for that person; and holism, the view that mind and body work together for a unified personality (Fall, Holden, & Marquis, 2010). The central motivation for development in each person is to move from a natural state of inferiority to superiority, causing an individual to develop a lifestyle that organizes experiences. Behavior is a manifestation of this lifestyle and a response to immediate environmental demands (Mosak & Maniacci, 2008). One unique component of Adlerian theory is the concept of social interest, which Fall et al. (2010) defined as "the motivation to strive for superiority in a way that contributes constructively to others and to society" (p. 106). The development of social interest serves as a marker of mental health.

Terry Kottman is noted as the founder of Adlerian play therapy. Although the Adlerian theoretical approach to counseling adults was widely known and Adlerian philosophy had influenced child guidance centers and theories of child development for almost a century (Mosak & Maniacci, 2008), Kottman (2003) was the first to formalize Adlerian principles into a comprehensive methodology for play therapy. Kottman (2009, p. 244) offered seven goals of Adlerian play therapy, including helping the client (a) gain an awareness of and insight into lifestyle, (b) alter faulty self-defeating apperceptions and move from private logic to common sense, (c) move toward positive goals of behavior, (d) replace negative strategies for belonging and gaining significance with positive strategies, (e) increase his or her social interest, (f) learn new ways of coping with feelings of inferiority, and (g) optimize creativity and begin to use his or her assets to develop self-enhancing decisions about attitudes, feelings, and behaviors.

Adlerian and CCPT approaches share many similar views of children, including the acknowledgment of their phenomelogical worlds and acceptance that their behaviors are an outcome of how they perceive themselves in their worlds. The main distinguishing feature separating the Adlerian approach from CCPT is the role of directivity of therapist, influenced theoretically by the belief in the self-actualizing tendency hypothesized by Rogers. Holding the belief that children sustain a striving to self-enhancement leads the CCPT therapist to provide conditions to awaken and avoid disruption of this tendency. The Adlerian belief that children hold mistaken beliefs of inferiority and the absence of a belief in the self-actualizing tendency requires the Adlerian play therapist to sometimes directly guide the thinking and play of children to help develop insight and replace destructive behaviors with coping behaviors.

Gestalt Play Therapy

Gestalt therapy was founded by Fritz Perls (although he objected to being solely identified as its founder) and is based on the philosophical concepts of holism and field theory (Yontef & Jacobs, 2005). The Gestalt understanding of holism asserts that humans are inherently self-regulating and growth oriented, and field theory emphasizes that humans cannot be understood without understanding the context in which they live. All behavior is regulated by the process of organismic self-regulation in which the child experiences needs, causing discomfort, leading the child to take action to satisfy this need by interacting with the environment (Blom, 2006). The satisfaction of the need leads to a state of homeostasis. Interaction of the child with the environment is called contact and is the core of experience that develops the self, a key concept in Gestalt theory (Carroll, 2009). Violet Oaklander (1988) is noted as the founder of Gestalt play therapy and the most prolific author on its use.

In Gestalt play therapy, the child needs help to restore healthy self-regulation, become aware of internal and external experiences, and be able to use the environment to get needs met (Carroll, 2009). Blom (2006) clearly stated, "The aim of gestalt play therapy with children is to make them aware of their own process" (p. 51). With awareness, the child perceives a diversity of choices to enable behavioral change for need satisfaction. As with Adlerian play therapy, Gestalt play therapy and CCPT share commonalities such as the holistic view of humans as forward-moving beings who are fully capable of making organismically enhancing decisions when operating from awareness. The fundamental difference between CCPT and Gestalt play therapy is the approach to therapy. From the Gestalt perspective, it is the therapist's duty to use multiple methods to "bring out" awareness in a child. Regarding her work with children, Oaklander (1988) wrote:

> So it is up to me to provide the means by which we will open doors and windows to their inner worlds. I need to provide methods for children to express their feelings, to get what they are keeping guarded inside out into the open, so that together we can deal with this material. (pp. 192–193)

Whereas, in CCPT, there is trust in the child that awareness will be a given outcome of meeting the six conditions for change. The use of the word "awareness" is also questionable between Gestalt play therapy and CCPT. The Gestalt approach seems to emphasize the need for the child's expression of awareness, often verbally, of the child's world. CCPT holds that the child's awareness is an organic process that is experienced holistically and may not be cognitively understood or verbally expressed by the child.

Jungian Play Therapy

Play therapy, as did all modern therapy, began as a psychoanalytic technique but psychoanalytic play therapy has not retained its popularity among the modality. Interestingly, a Jungian analytical framework emerged as a leading approach to play therapy. Jungian play therapy is the foremost current approach focused on the unconscious processes that occur within the child during the therapeutic process. From a Jungian perspective, Douglas explained that personality rests upon the psyche, which is made up of conscious and unconscious components that are tied to the collective unconscious, "underlying patterns of images, thoughts, behaviors, and experiences" (Douglas, 2008, pp. 103–104). In healthy people, Allan (1998) clarified that there is a fluid yet regulated connection between the conscious and unconscious. Jungian theory involves the understanding of several concepts related to the unconscious, both personal and collective, that have a direct impact on the orientation and behavior of the person.

John Allan (1988) is perhaps the most credited figure in the presentation and organization of Jungian play therapy. His seminal work on play therapy, *Inscapes of the Child's World: Jungian Counseling in Schools and Clinics*, laid the framework for conducting Jungian play therapy, demonstrating its effectiveness in both school and private settings. Allan (1997) pointed out that the goal of Jungian play therapy is the activation of the individuation process, which he defined as "helping the child to develop his or her unique identity, to overcome or come to terms with his or her losses or traumas while accepting and adapting to the healthy demands of family, school, and society at large" (p. 105). Green (2009) described the therapist role as an analytic one in which he utilizes directive techniques such as drawings, drama, or sand play to benefit the exploration of symbols in art interpretation and analysis of transference. These processes allow children to acknowledge unconscious components, integrate into conscious components, and activate the self-healing mechanism available to them.

The most obvious difference between CCPT and Jungian play therapy is the focus on the collective and personal unconscious, which is integral to the Jungian philosophy. The belief in the role of the child's unconscious processes encourages the Jungian play therapist to directly act upon the child by presenting activities, questioning, and interpreting the child's symbols. CCPT has little concern regarding the need to reveal unconscious processes. Rogers did not deny the presence of the unconscious but did not observe that it was a necessary part of facilitating therapeutic change. Similarities between the two approaches are noticeable in that both CCPT and Jungian play therapy recognize the importance of the child's process as primary to therapeutic change, and hence both are accepting toward more emotional and aggressive expressions.

I have listed a simplistic view of only four of many approaches to play therapy and again I would highly encourage the reader to review the original resources referenced. However, by all accounts, these appear to be the most popular current approaches. O'Connor and Braverman (2009) also listed psychoanalytic, filial, theraplay, ecosystemic, and prescriptive play therapy as major theoretical models of play therapy. However, filial and theraplay are primarily described as parent interventions utilizing play techniques. Psychoanalytic, ecosystemic, and prescriptive approaches benefit from structured frameworks but are not seemingly as utilized as the four reviewed for this chapter. Remarkably, the theoretical approaches to play therapy appear to be somewhat divergent from the general counseling field. CCPT is, by far, the most identified play therapy approach, with the other approaches falling far behind. However, the recognition of Adlerian, Gestalt, and Jungian approaches as heavily influential in the field of play therapy seems counterintuitive to the experienced counselor who has observed the rise of the cognitive-behavioral movement. Although CBPT is recognized as a second most popular approach, it has not emerged with supportive literature or exploration to the same degree as the others reviewed. I would hypothesize that the growth of certain theoretical approaches strongly correlates with the theory's leading author/teacher. Over the past three decades, CCPT has been heavily explored and researched by Garry Landreth in the southwestern United States and Louise Guerney in the northeastern United States. Adlerian play therapy has emerged in the past two decades by the prolific work of Terry Kottman, who remains committed to its growth as a primary modality for child mental health. Violet Oaklander and John Allan committed their long careers to Gestalt play therapy and Jungian play therapy, respectively. These five leaders in play therapy have traveled and lectured extensively to help improve understanding and training in play therapy, which appears to have impacted the growth of their approaches.

References

Allan, J. (1997). Jungian play psychotherapy. In K. O'Connor & L. Braverman (Eds.), *Play therapy: A comparative presentation* (2nd ed., 100–130). New York: Wiley.

Allan, J. (1998). *Inscapes of the child's world: Jungian counseling in schools and clinics.* Dallas, TX: Spring Publication.

Axline, V. (1947). *Play therapy*. New York: Ballantine.

Beck, A. (1976). *Cognitive therapy and the emotional disorders*. New York: Meridian.

Beck, A., & Weishaar, M. (2008). Cognitive therapy. In R. Corsini & D. Wedding (Eds.), *Current psychotherapies* (8th ed., 263–294). Belmont, CA: Thomson.

Blom, R. (2006). *The handbook of gestalt play therapy: Practical guidelines for child therapists*. London: Jessica Kingsley.

Carroll, F. (2009). Gestalt play therapy. In K. O'Connor & L. Braverman (Eds.), *Play therapy theory and practice: Comparing theories and techniques* (2nd ed., 283–314). Hoboken, NJ: Wiley.

Douglas, C. (2008). Analytical psychotherapy. In R. Corsini and D. Wedding (Eds.), *Current psychotherapies* (8th ed., 113–147). Belmont, CA: Thomson.

Fall, K., Holden, J., & Marquis, A. (2010). *Theoretical models of counseling and psychotherapy* (2nd ed.). New York: Routledge.

Green, E. (2009). Jungian analytical play therapy. In K. O'Connor & L. Braverman (Eds.), *Play therapy theory and practice: Comparing theories and techniques* (2nd ed., 83–121). Hoboken, NJ: Wiley.

Kottman, T. (2003). *Partners in play: An Adlerian approach to play therapy* (2nd ed.). Alexandria, VA: American Counseling Association.

Kottman, T. (2009). Adlerian play therapy. In K. O'Connor & L. Braverman (Eds.), *Play therapy theory and practice: Comparing theories and techniques* (2nd ed., 237–282). Hoboken, NJ: Wiley.

Knell, S. (1993). *Cognitive-behavioral play therapy*. Northvale, NJ: Jason Aronson.

Knell, S. (2009). Cognitive-behavioral play therapy. In K. O'Connor & L. Braverman (Eds.), *Play therapy theory and practice: Comparing theories and techniques* (2nd ed., 203–236). Hoboken, NJ: Wiley.

Lambert, S., LeBlanc, M., Mullen, J., Ray, D., Baggerly, J., White, J., & Kaplan, D. (2005). Learning more about those who play in session: The national play therapy in counseling practices project. *Journal of Counseling & Development, 85*, 42–46.

Landreth, G. (2002). *Play therapy: The art of the relationship*. New York: Routledge.

Mosak, H., & Maniacci, M. (2008). Adlerian psychotherapy. In R. Corsini and D. Wedding (Eds.), *Current psychotherapies* (8th ed., 67–112). Belmont, CA: Thomson.

Oaklander, V. (1988). *Windows to our children*. Highland, NY: The Gestalt Journal Press.

O'Connor, K., & Braverman, L. (Eds.). (2009). *Play therapy theory and practice: Comparing theories and techniques* (2nd ed.). Hoboken, NJ: Wiley.

Rogers, C. (1951). *Client-centered therapy: Its current practice, implications and theory*. Boston: Houghton Mifflin.

Rogers, C. (1957). The necessary and sufficient conditions of therapeutic personality change. *Journal of Consulting Psychology, 21*(2), 95–103.

West, J. (1996). *Child centred play therapy* (2nd ed.). London: Hodder Arnold.

Wilkins, P. (2010). *Person-centred therapy: 100 key points*. London: Routledge.

Wilson, K., Kendrick, P., & Ryan, V. (1992). *Play therapy: A nondirective approach for children and adolescents*. London: Bailliere Tindall.

Yontef, G., & Jacobs, L. (2005). Gestalt therapy. In R. Corsini & D. Wedding (Eds.), *Current psychotherapies* (7th ed., 299–336). Belmont, CA: Brooks/Cole.

CHAPTER 4

The Person, Knowledge, and Skills of the Play Therapist

The practice of play therapy requires many different resources, including a space, some furniture, and a variety of toys. However, no resource in the play therapy room is more essential than the play therapist. The play therapist is the central provider of the environment to the child, as well as to parents and other caretakers. And it is the play therapist who facilitates therapy through the use of knowledge, skills, and the very person of the therapist. Although child-centered play therapy (CCPT) relies on the relationship between therapist and child as the key therapeutic factor for change, it is the play therapist who initiates that relationship and manages an environment to nurture that relationship.

Therapist Conditions

As reviewed in Chapter 3, the six conditions necessary and sufficient for change include (a) two persons are in psychological contact, (b) the first person (client) is in a state of incongruence, (c) the second person (therapist) is congruent in the relationship, (d) the therapist experiences unconditional positive regard for the client, (e) the therapist experiences an empathic understanding of the client's internal frame of reference and attempts to communicate this experience to the client, and (f) communication to the client of the therapist's empathic understanding and unconditional positive regard is, to a minimal degree, achieved (Rogers, 1957). Conditions 3, 4, and 5 are typically considered therapist-provided core conditions, more accurately referred to as attitudes (Bozarth, 1998) and traditionally labeled as congruence, unconditional positive regard or acceptance, and empathy, respectively. The purpose of the attitudinal therapist conditions is to provide an environment that promotes the actualizing tendency accessible within all persons, including children.

The three therapist attitudes are intimately related to each other and work together to provide an environment conducive to change. Bozarth (1998) conceptualized the relationship between congruence, empathy, and unconditional positive regard in the following pattern. Congruence or genuineness is a state of readiness within the therapist that allows the therapist to experience the client through empathic understanding and experience unconditional positive regard for the client. Empathic understanding is the action state of the therapist in which the client's world is accepted as he or she is experiencing it, allowing the client to experience unconditional positive regard. Finally, unconditional positive regard is the primary change agent in which the client's needs for positive regard and positive self-regard are met, resulting in congruence between experience and self-concept and promotion of the actualizing tendency. Each condition is predicated upon the other and therefore requires the therapist to experience and exhibit all three. Wilkins (2010) warned that favoring one condition over another is a mistake and suggested that the three conditions be conceptualized as a "super-condition" (p. 44), of which congruence, unconditional positive regard, and empathic understanding are components.

Empathic Understanding

Rogers (1975) revisited his many writings on empathy and attempted to provide a process definition that encompassed the full meaning of the word "empathy."

> It means entering the private perceptual world of the other and becoming thoroughly at home in it. It involves being sensitive, moment to moment, to the changing felt meanings which flow in this other person, to the fear or rage or tenderness or confusion or whatever, that he/she is experiencing. It means temporarily living in his/her life, moving about in it delicately without making judgments, sensing meaning of which he/she is scarcely aware, but not trying to uncover feelings of which the person is totally unaware, since this would be too threatening.... It means frequently checking with him/her as to the accuracy of your sensings, and being guided by the responses you receive. You are a confident companion to the person in his/her inner world. By pointing to the possible meanings in the flow of his/her experiencing you help the person to focus on this useful type of referent, to experience the meanings more fully, and to move forward in the experiencing. (Rogers, 1975, p. 4)

Empathic understanding involves entering the client's world as if it were your own without losing a sense of self as the therapist. The idea of pure empathy, entrance into the client's world, can be threatening to many play therapists due to the nature of the pain involved in the client's world.

One of my clients, referred to me because of behavioral issues in school, was a 7-year-old boy who had been left abruptly by his father at a local children's home. His mother had been out of his life since early childhood due to drug addiction. His father remarried a woman who was unhappy being a mother and insisted on my client being given away. The father signed away legal custody to the state and disappeared from the child's life 2 months prior to the initiation of play therapy. Our sessions were held in a classroom within the school where I had set up a play area. Outside the play area were other items such as a computer, projector, teacher desk, and phone. In our second session (and repeatedly for several sessions), my client left the play area to use the phone. As I set limits, he continued to look through the desk for a phone book. He found one. I set limits regarding the use of the phone and returning to the play area. The client seemed to be in another world, unable to even hear my limit setting. He worked himself into a frantic state as he quickly went page to page looking for his father's name in the phone book. He was a poor reader and speller, and could not figure out how to use the phone book but he was certain that his father's name was in it. I dropped all limit-setting statements and moved close to the client. I reflected his need to find his father. He responded, "I have to call him. He's looking for me. I know he wants me. He just doesn't know where I am." I reflected, "You know he just really wants you and you really want him. You have to find him." The client looked at me, handed me the phone book and the phone, and said, "Can you please help? Can you please find him?" Finding my own feelings of empathy (panicked, frantic, confused) to be completely overwhelming, I responded with a congruent statement "You really need to find him but I don't know where he is and I don't know how to find him." As we continued the session, I moved in and out of the client's world, expressing the empathy I was feeling, mixed with the reality of setting limits. He continued to be frantic and started to dial numbers on the phone, trying his hardest to remember what his father's phone number used to be. The empathy involved in this session was extremely painful for me. Being open to taking on his feelings of complete and utter powerlessness and confusion as a 7-year-old in this situation was difficult but necessary in order to understand the kind of pain he was in on a daily basis. Experiencing his level of pain helped me be in full contact with him and move around in his world, helping to unleash his actualizing tendency that would allow him to survive, possibly thrive, through his circumstances. A secondary benefit of experiencing empathy with clients is the ability to advocate for them with other caretakers. For example, as I consulted with the teacher in this client's situation, I was able to express the client's state of being on most days. I said to his teacher, "He seems to be extremely concerned with finding his dad and consumed with the feeling that his dad really wants him, unable to accept that this is not the case. It makes sense to me that he has difficulty concentrating on his school work or following rules because he spends a lot of energy on his confusion about his situation." Although most mental health professionals would find this to be common sense, the teacher was surprised to hear that the client even thought about his dad because he had never said anything in class. My ability to express the client's world to the teacher helped her be more understanding (possibly empathic) to his behavioral problems.

Empathy is a key concept of person-centered theory that was enthusiastically embraced by the mental health community. Both Wilkins (2010) and Bozarth (2001a) suggested that empathy is the most taught, researched, and written about condition of the six conditions. Bozarth further traces the trajectory stemming from Rogers' initial presentation of empathy and his emphasis on the need to express empathy to clients. As interpreted by others, verbal reflections of feeling and content became the focus of expression of empathy. Thereby, empathy was operationalized as a set of responses from therapist to client, missing the essential feature that the client is the expert on the client's feelings, not the therapist. The operational definition of empathy as demonstrated solely through verbal reflection places authority back with the therapist, something to be avoided in CCPT. Reflection is an encouraged skill in CCPT as a method of entering the child's world but it is not the sole source of expressing empathy. Bozarth (2001a) presented several crucial points about reflection and its relationship to empathy that are helpful in the practice of CCPT. They include

1. Reflection is a way for a therapist to become empathic by checking and communicating understanding to the client.
2. Reflection is primarily for the therapist, not the client, because it helps the therapist move into the world of the client.
3. Reflection is not empathy, only a way to become more empathic.
4. Empathy is not reflection. Empathy is a process of entering the client's world, but reflection is only a technique that might help in that process.
5. Other modes of empathy have not been explored in person-centered literature but are valuable ways to express empathy to clients.

A final point of empathic understanding is its intertwined nature with the concept of unconditional positive regard. Empathy may be considered a vehicle for the expression of unconditional positive regard (Bozarth, 2001b). When a therapist enters the world of the client, there is an underlying message that the client's world is a valuable world, one in which the therapist has the utmost respect for the client's experience and abilities. The attitude of empathic understanding expresses the therapist's unconditional positive regard for the client.

Unconditional Positive Regard

Rogers (1957) described unconditional positive regard as experiencing a warm acceptance of all aspects of the client's experience. Unconditional positive regard is also frequently referred to as acceptance. Axline (1947) described unconditional positive regard in the second of her eight basic principles of CCPT by encouraging the therapist to accept the child exactly as is, not wishing the child were different in some way. If the therapist anticipates that the child will change, such an attitude will send a message of unacceptance or, referring back to Rogers' 19 propositions, the establishment of a condition of worth. Hence, unconditional positive regard serves as the curative factor, a natural antidote to the conditionality described in Rogers' theory of pathology (Bozarth, 1998). The child's acceptance of the unconditional positive regard offered by the therapist leads the child to connect with the actualizing tendency.

In my experience, unconditional positive regard has been my biggest struggle as a therapist in working with children. Growing up with a felt sense of considerable conditions of worth, I have struggled with positive self-regard my whole life. This lack of self-acceptance is the focus of my own therapy over my lifetime, and has impact on my practice. A lack of self-acceptance inhibits my ability to provide acceptance for my clients. For example, if I feel that I am lacking in my ability to be extraverted and generally likable, then I am more likely to want the children I work with to experience something better than me in their relationships and this might become my focus in therapy, whether or not it is their focus.

In addition, the external requirements from society, schools, and parents place tremendous pressures on children to change, thereby pressuring the therapist to elicit such change. If only the child would stop hitting others, the school would not send him to alternative school. If only the child would stop tantruming, the parent would not be so critical of the child. If only the child would exhibit proper social skills, the child would have more friends. The list goes on and on. For every "if only," the intention is derived from a place of benevolence among therapists. However, the active attempt to change children negates the presence and activation of the self-actualizing tendency. Direction of the therapy session presupposes the therapist's expertise and authority over the child by sending the message that the therapist knows best.

I have most often experienced this scenario in working with schools. Teachers typically refer children for behavioral problems exhibited during school. Often, teachers request that play therapists address some aspect of this behavior, such as getting the child to pay more attention, sit still, stop disrupting class, or many other problems. By the time of referral, the child has probably participated in behavioral plans, lectures and discussions with authority figures, and possibly punishment, with no evident change in behavior. In play therapy, a child may express innumerable variations of play behaviors or verbalizations that seem unrelated to the teacher's concerns. One example may be a child who is referred for yelling and cursing at the teacher. When provided a CCPT play session, the child attempts to destroy the playroom while the therapist provides empathic statements and sets limits. The therapist hypothesizes that the child only feels in control or a sense of mastery when exerting power-oriented behaviors. Through the therapist's acceptance of the child's feelings and reasonable limits on behavior, the child begins to experience empowerment derived intrinsically from a sense of self-regard. Concurrently, the child's yelling and cursing behaviors at the teacher have ceased to be necessary for expression. Instead of the child being told or directed as to how to handle his anger or control issues, the therapist's expression of unconditional positive regard through the allowance and acceptance of the child's direction in play therapy releases the actualizing tendency, leading the child to healthier behavior. Healthy behavior is not anticipated in CCPT but it is acknowledged by play therapists as a natural outcome to the provision and acceptance of the conditions.

Wilkins (2010) noted that unconditional positive regard presents personal challenges to the therapist, including that it is within human nature to carry some level of prejudice and fear that precludes the experience of unconditional positive regard. Unconditional positive regard is not a required part of being a child-centered play therapist; however, it is a requirement for change. Hence, to the extent that play therapists can experience and communicate unconditional positive regard, change is more likely to occur. Effective play therapists are often attuned to their level of unconditional positive regard as it applies to each client. It would not be expected for a play therapist to always experience acceptance for all clients, and a play therapist will occasionally need to refer specific clients with whom they are struggling. If a play therapist is experiencing a lack of unconditional positive regard toward clients in general, this might be an indication of a need for the therapist to work on self-regard.

A final point regarding the expression of unconditional positive regard is the apparent misunderstanding that unconditional positive regard may be expressed as being overly positive to or for the client. Referring back to the previous example of the 7-year-old boy who was experiencing intense pain over his father, I might have responded with an explanation that his father is gone but he will be okay because he is smart and capable, or I might have distracted him by asking him to play a board game to make him feel better. Both of these responses would be attempts to rescue the client from pain, which is a therapist need but not a client need. Such attempts at rescuing clients reveal a failure to offer unconditional positive regard (Wilkins, 2010) and need to be further explored by the therapist.

Congruence

Cited as the third condition for change, Rogers (1957) described congruence of therapist, also labeled genuineness, as the ability to feel free to be self within the therapeutic relationship, able to experience congruence between experience and awareness of self. And in later writings, Rogers acknowledged congruence as the most important of the three core conditions, representing the full expression of therapist presence with client (Bozarth, 1998). Wilkins (2010) proposed that therapists must be congruent in the relationship before and if their empathy and unconditional positive regard are to be perceived by clients as trustworthy.

Congruence is often lightly referred to as encouraging the therapist to "just be yourself." However, congruence involves a combination of the therapist's self-awareness, acceptance of such awareness, and appropriate expression of awareness to the client. Cornelius-White (2007) presented a five-dimensional model of congruence that addresses the multiple facets of its relationship to the therapist and to therapy. The first dimension, *genuineness*, is simply described as being real, free from pretense. This realness is predicated on the therapist's experience of empathy and unconditional positive regard. The second dimension, *symbolization*, marks the therapist's ability to experience consistency between self and experience, allowing experiences to be available to awareness and accurately symbolizing such experiences within the self-structure. *Authenticity*, the third dimension, is described as a consistency between experience, self, and communicativeness. This dimension works beyond the symbolization dimension by expressing felt therapist congruence within the relationship. The fourth dimension, *organismic integration*, extends the concept of personal congruence to a systemic view in which the organism recognizes its relationship and interdependence with the broader world. The therapist recognizes the need to expand congruence for the purposes of becoming facilitative to the world at large, an actionable dimension of congruence. The fifth dimension, labeled as *Dimension 0* or *flow*, is distinctive because it describes more of a process than a concept. Flow is characterized by the therapist's ability to be in the moment, feeling a lack of self-consciousness and exhibiting a unity of being and doing. Cornelius-White (2007) further suggested that the dimensions may not be experienced exclusively or simultaneously but they can be used to explain each other, deepening understanding of the term "congruence."

Once the play therapist experiences a sense of congruence within the relationship related to the ability to be authentic, the question still arises regarding the expression of such congruence. This is especially questionable in working with children who might interpret the therapist's expression of congruence in an egocentric way, lacking the developmental ability to follow the logic of the therapist. For example, a child breaks a limit in the playroom and throws sand up in the air, unintentionally getting it in the therapist's eyes. The therapist instinctively yells out, "Ouch, that hurt," with a tone of anger. In an effort to be congruent, the therapist might attempt to recover by explaining, "When the sand hit my eye, I was hurt and angry. But sometimes accidents happen in here." Although the therapist has expressed himself genuinely and without blame, the child might interpret that the therapist is angry with her. The fear of the therapist's anger is not verbally expressed but inhibits the child's play for the duration of the session and into the next few sessions. Therapists might have different reactions to this scenario. Whereas some therapists would say that the therapist harmed the relationship by expressing self so genuinely, others might feel that the genuineness was most appropriate for the long run of the relationship.

Wilkins (2010) suggested that congruence takes precedence over other conditions only if the therapist has feelings other than empathy for the experience of the client. As in the above scenario, there are times when the therapist experiences a feeling or thought that interferes with his or her ability to be in the world of the client. Haugh (2001) recommended the following criteria in determining when congruent responses are appropriate: (1) when the therapist's feelings are interrupting provision of conditions, (2) when such feelings are persistent, (3) when not expressing congruence would result in the therapist being inauthentic in the relationship, (4) or when it is appropriate as assessed by the preceding points. However, encouraging therapists to be congruent is not permission to contradict, express an opinion about the client, or self-disclose therapist material (Wilkins, 2010).

Congruence is a little explored concept in the CCPT literature. Landreth (2002) addressed operational expression of empathy and unconditional positive regard but congruence is only alluded to through the explanation of therapist self-acceptance, postulating that self-acceptance leads to the therapist's ability to be genuine in the playroom. For Landreth, there appears to be an assumption that when the therapist is self-accepting, congruence in the play relationship will be the natural outcome, a logical conclusion based on person-centered theory. Ryan and Courtney (2009) contributed to the literature through a critique of the United States approach to congruence versus the United Kingdom approach. They concluded that leading CCPT experts in the United States do not emphasize the theory and practice of congruence to the same extent as in the United Kingdom.

Recognizing that congruence has only been minimally addressed in U.S. literature on CCPT, I would argue that the training and supervision of play therapists heavily addresses the practice of congruence. In my experience as a play therapy supervisor, facilitating congruence in the therapist is the main focus of supervision following the therapist's acquisition of basic skills. CCPT therapists are especially concerned with their abilities to be genuine in their relationships with children and wrestle with how to communicate this genuineness for the benefit of the client. I would further hypothesize that the most significant barrier to the genuineness of the therapist appears to be the therapist's lack of belief in the curative factor of unconditional positive regard. New and experienced play therapists sometimes fail to accept unconditional positive regard as the base for freeing the child's actualizing tendency, and hence struggle in their genuine expression of nondirectivity.

Although congruence is not a skill, it appears to be an advanced practice concept that is difficult for new play therapists. Congruence is intimately correlated with the therapist's self-awareness and sense of self. A lack of self-regard leads some play therapists to cover up feelings of inadequacy, replacing these feelings with a façade of competence. As already addressed, this lack of self-regard inevitably interferes with the expression of empathy and unconditional positive regard. Wilkins (2010) expressed that congruence is about "trusting yourself and being enough at ease with yourself to allow the free-flowing of your experience while you concentrate on the lived experience of another" (p. 219).

The three therapist conditions necessary for client change involve deep and substantial awareness, as well as response to such awareness from the therapist. They require the whole of the therapist as a person. CCPT calls for the therapist to "be" someone, not just "do" something. It can be a daunting task for the play therapist and suggests the need for support in this endeavor. Perhaps the greatest tool for training CCPT therapists is participation in personal counseling. And the greatest tool for long-term professional practice is also personal counseling. Counseling provides a setting for the play therapist to explore feelings about unconditional positive regard without judgment, increased self-awareness, and self-acceptance. Counseling also provides the opportunity for the therapist to experience the conditions as a client on a personal level to reveal the power of the process, encouraging continuation in facilitation of the therapeutic process. Wilkins (2010) warned that therapist burnout includes a decreased ability to be congruent due to the increasing need of the therapist to protect parts of the self-structure under stress, leading to a problem-focus in therapy because it is less demanding of the therapist's personal resources. The advanced play therapist will value the support of personal therapy over a lifetime of professional practice.

Knowledge and Skills

The most important assets of the play therapist are the integration and expression of the therapist conditions of empathy, unconditional positive regard, and congruence. However, play therapists are in need of specific knowledge and skills, including certain learning experiences that will help in the expression of the conditions.

Knowledge

In my experience, play therapists appear to lack basic knowledge that informs the practice of working with children through play. Some experienced play therapists demonstrate limited knowledge of child development or the process of play itself. It seems that they may have read and memorized Piaget or Erikson's stages of development many years ago and have since felt no sense of urgency to remember their initial knowledge or read current scholarly literature regarding children and development. Occasionally, as I attend play therapy conferences, I will observe that presenters will cite one to two sources that may or may not provide a conceptual framework for the presentation's newest method or technique. There are feeble attempts to list quotes that lend tangential support but not a theoretical or research framework that substantiates practice. Although I sound critical, it is my observation that many experienced play therapists are not grounded in scholarly knowledge as a guide for practice. This is a concerning trend that must be corrected by advanced play therapists who actively pursue knowledge to consistently improve effectiveness.

Table 4.1 is a compilation of knowledge concepts that inform effective play therapy practice. The list is extensive and may be overwhelming when first read. However, CCPT involves a convergence of various areas of expertise, from general knowledge of children and counseling to specific knowledge of presenting problems. CCPT requires a broad knowledge base that is beyond the scope of most adult therapeutic practice. This list is not meant to be exclusive and the play therapist can benefit from further knowledge in many different areas.

1. Child development is the base knowledge for CCPT practice. Play therapists need to have an understanding of the physical, emotional, cognitive, moral, sexual, social, and identity trajectories of normal childhood. Knowledge of average experiences of development help guide the play therapist in understanding a child client's current situation and informs parent consultation.
2. If a therapist chooses the modality of play, there needs to be an extensive understanding of the history of play development and the current role of play, especially within the context of the developmental phases of childhood.

Table 4.1 Knowledge Concepts Necessary for Effective Play Therapy Practice

Child Development Theories	**History and Role of Play in Child Development**
Current and historical theories of counseling and psychotherapy	Philosophy and theory supporting the play therapist's practice orientation
Medical Knowledge Relevant to Children	**Criteria for Diagnostic Categories**
Role and current use of psychopharmacological drugs for children and adults Current educational methods used in local schools Current scholarly research on issues affecting children and child mental health interventions	Origin, symptoms, prognosis, history, and current research on typical presenting problems encountered by play therapist Parenting methods popular in current culture Knowledge to critically analyze literature and research

3. Play therapy is a modality, not a theory. Play therapy can be practiced from a variety of theoretical belief systems. The play therapist should have knowledge regarding current and historical theories of counseling and psychotherapy to help guide understanding and practice with clients.
4. For the therapist to operate consistently and with reasonable rationale, the therapist should hold extensive knowledge of philosophy and theory supporting the play therapist's practice orientation. Such knowledge includes readily accessible definitions and rationale for play therapy practice based on sound theory.
5. General medical knowledge relevant to children is necessary for understanding the physical development of child clients. Medical knowledge might include brain development, genetic influences, and symptoms, treatment, and prognoses for common childhood medical problems.
6. Regardless of theoretical orientation, play therapists benefit from familiarity with diagnostic criteria. Even if play therapists choose to avoid assigning diagnosis by working in certain settings, children will often enter play therapy with an already labeled diagnosis. Knowledge of diagnostic criteria helps the play therapist to communicate to other professionals, as well as provide information regarding client behaviors.
7. Psychopharmacological medications are prescribed at an alarming rate for many children. Due to the significant side effects and possible benefits of medication, play therapists need to be aware of current medications and their relationship to specific diagnoses.

In addition, play therapists need to be aware not only of the child's medications, but also medications of the parents to monitor their ability to care for the child under certain medications.

8. Although it is impossible for play therapists to be fully knowledgeable of all presenting problems, they should attempt to familiarize themselves with the origin, symptoms, prognosis, history, and current research on typical presenting problems encountered by the play therapist.
9. Working with children necessitates an understanding of school processes and practices as the child probably spends more time in school than in the home. Play therapists should keep abreast of current educational methods used in local schools for education, discipline, and development.
10. Because information is readily available to parents, they are consistently bombarded with new and questionable parenting techniques. Play therapists need to keep updated on parenting methods popular in current culture to enhance relationships with parents and parent consultations.
11. Although it is difficult for practitioners practicing outside the academic setting, play therapists should attempt to remain current in scholarly research on issues affecting children and child mental health interventions. Conferences and professional organizations are good sources of information to keep play therapists up to date.
12. To effectively utilize the literature, play therapists should retain knowledge on how to critically analyze research, discerning between when research findings are relevant to practice and when they appear unsound.

Skills

When a play therapist encompasses the core conditions and possesses extensive knowledge regarding a rationale for practice, it is then time for the acquisition of skills to communicate the person and knowledge of the play therapist for the benefit of the client. Of the concepts referred to in this chapter, skills are of least concern because the therapist can be successful in CCPT through the provision of conditions and practice based in sound knowledge. However, skills are provided to aid the CCPT therapist in building confidence through operational expression of conditions and knowledge.

Response categories. Chapter 5 provides an extensive list of responses basic to the practice of play therapy. These include categorization of responses that are effective in expressing the therapist-provided conditions necessary and sufficient for change. Responses are categorized as tracking behavior, reflections of content and feelings, facilitating decision making, facilitating creativity, esteem building, facilitating relationship, and limit setting. These responses are defined with specificity that provides exemplary statements for each category. Responses represent a skill set that helps the play therapist concretely express the conditions for change.

Silence. Silence is a particularly essential skill for play therapists. Silence may be considered an easy concept but I have found that the therapist's ability to feel comfortable with silence is a learned skill. There are times when a child in play therapy exhibits a need for silence provided by therapist. This need may be manifested through the child's silence, the child's intensity in play, or a verbalization by the child requesting silence. At these times, play therapists can provide a reverent response of silence in which the therapist and child can still be in full contact but on the child's terms. Many times, I have experienced a child's need for silence, especially children who experience chaos on a regular basis. The silence response can be as effective, or sometimes more effective, as poignant verbal reflections. Comfortable silence sends the ultimate message of acceptance from the therapist to the child: "You don't have to do anything in here but just be and I'll be right here with you."

Focus and mindfulness. The ability to release background noise and thoughts so that pure contact can take place is a skill of focus or mindfulness that benefits play therapy practice. Because play therapy may include physical movement and a lack of verbal contact, therapists will often become distracted and disconnected from the child. When a therapist can live in the present moment and be fully open to experience, it can provide the environment for the full empathic experiencing of the client. Therapists benefit from preparing for therapy through focusing, mindfulness, or meditation. A simple breathing technique can often energize a play therapist to make contact and open self to the coming relational experience.

Organization. Because play therapy involves so many different components, organizational skills are a must for effective practice. Working with children involves the scheduling of child sessions, parent consultation sessions, school consultations, and possibly contact with other caretakers. In addition, the play therapist must have the playroom in order by offering materials within the same structure for each session. And finally, as in all therapy, play therapists are required to maintain current records regarding the client that include informed consents, releases of information for outside contacts, treatment plans, session summaries, assessments, and final treatment summaries.

Conceptualization. The play therapist's ability to integrate knowledge of play, child development, and counseling with the individualized unique person and context of the client results in a holistic conceptualization of the client. Assimilating all this information into a coherent explanation and understanding of the client helps the play therapist to approach the relationship in a consistent and theoretically supported manner. New play therapists are challenged with putting all the puzzle pieces together for a complete picture. Yet, advanced play therapists often become complacent and do not take the time to thoroughly think about the client, relying on previous experiences of success. Conceptualization helps focus the play therapist in understanding the unique state of the current client in context. Such focus leads to more deliberate responses in the playroom and consultations with parents.

Experiences That Promote Conditions, Knowledge, and Skills

Therapists can be provided the opportunities to develop empathy, unconditional positive regard, genuineness, knowledge, and skills through training, supervision, and consultation. The following is a list of recommended experiences and/or credentials that will help initiate or inspire therapist development:

1. Personal therapy with a person-centered or humanistically inclined therapist
2. A series of didactic courses addressing child development, counseling theory, and play therapy
3. A series of didactic courses addressing the medical model, including diagnosis, physical development, symptom relief, and psychopharmacology
4. Observation of play therapy sessions facilitated by experienced play therapists
5. Video recordings of play therapy sessions
6. A series of clinical courses requiring the facilitation of play therapy sessions with clients from diverse backgrounds and with diverse presenting problems
7. Live supervision of play therapy sessions with immediate feedback, as well as subsequent review of session video recordings with a supervisor
8. A master's degree in the mental health profession
9. Ongoing personal reviews of video-recorded sessions
10. Ongoing organized consultation with play therapist colleagues
11. Participation in continuing education opportunities
12. Membership in mental health professional organizations
13. Consistent reading of materials related to person-centered theory and CCPT
14. Review of current scholarly literature related to child mental health and interventions

References

Axline, V. (1947). *Play therapy*. New York: Ballantine.

Bozarth, J. (1998). *Person-centered therapy: A revolutionary paradigm*. Ross-on-Wye: PCCS Books.

Bozarth, J. (2001a). Beyond reflection: Emergent modes of empathy. In S. Haugh and T. Merry (Eds.), *Empathy. Rogers' therapeutic conditions: Evolution, theory and practice* (Vol. 2, 131–143). Ross-on-Wye: PCCS Books.

Bozarth, J. (2001b). An addendum to beyond reflection: Emergent modes of empathy. In S. Haugh and T. Merry (Eds.), *Empathy. Rogers' therapeutic conditions: Evolution, theory and practice* (Vol. 2, 144–154). Ross-on-Wye: PCCS Books.

Cornelius-White, J. (2007). Congruence: An integrative five-dimension model. *Person-Centered and Experiential Psychotherapies, 6*(4), 229–239.

Haugh, S. (2001). A historical review of the development of the concept of congruence in person-centred theory. In G. Wyatt (Ed.), *Congruence. Rogers' therapeutic conditions: Evolution, theory and practice* (Vol. 1, 1–17). Ross-on-Wye: PCCS Books.

Landreth, G. (2002). *Play therapy: The art of the relationship*. New York: Routledge.

Rogers, C. (1957). The necessary and sufficient conditions of therapeutic personality change. *Journal of Consulting Psychology, 21*(2), 95–103.

Rogers, C. (1975). Empathic: An unappreciated way of being. *The Counseling Psychologist, 5*(2), 2–10.

Ryan, V., & Courtney, A. (2009). Therapists' use of congruence in nondirective play therapy and filial therapy. *International Journal of Play Therapy, 18*(2), 114–128.

Wilkins, P. (2010). *Person-centred therapy: 100 key points*. London: Routledge.

CHAPTER 5
Basics of Play Therapy

The beginning play therapist must first master the basic skills of the process. Basic skills include setting up a playroom, selecting materials, and the use of effective nonverbal and verbal ways of being with the child. This chapter serves as a short review of basic skills for the novice play therapist. For more detailed information on the basics of play therapy, I refer the reader to more detailed descriptions of getting started by Landreth (2002) and Kottman (2003). Before a play therapist can successfully progress to more advanced concepts in play therapy, forming a relationship with the child in which the child is provided an environment of acceptance and understanding is essential. The basics of play therapy provide the skills to provide this type of environment.

The Playroom

Before meeting a child, a play therapist prepares an environment in which the culture of childhood is addressed. This environment is the playroom. Because play is the developmental language of the child, a playroom is designed and filled with materials that help the child speak with clarity. The size of the playroom allows enough space for a child to move freely without becoming overwhelmed with too much space. Landreth (2002) suggests that an ideal playroom be 12 by 15 feet. Although this is an ideal size for playrooms, many therapists are restricted in their settings and compromise space for utility. Play therapy can be effective in different sizes of rooms. Essential features of a playroom include shelves for placing toys above the floor and allowing more room for movement and at least some space for free movement. Optimal features include access to water through a sink, noncarpeted floors, durable wall paint, and a two-way mirror for camera and observation possibilities. Figures 5.1 and 5.2 are two different views of the same playroom, an example of the more ideal type of playroom.

Play Materials

Materials for the playroom include toys, craft materials, paints, easel, puppet theater, sandbox, and child furniture. In selecting toys, the most fundamental criterion is that the toy serves a purpose in the playroom. For each and every toy or play material in the playroom, a therapist should ask the following questions:

1. What therapeutic purpose will this serve for children who use this room?
2. How will this help children express themselves?
3. How will this help me build a relationship with children?

When a therapist chooses purposefully, appropriate selection becomes more clear. I once inherited a playroom that had been set up to include 25 large and small stuffed animals. Because there were so many, they took up quite a bit of play space in the room. I also discovered that there were 25 because that was what had been donated by people in the community. When I asked myself the previously listed questions, I concluded that one or two stuffed animals could serve to comfort a child, allow for expression of physical aggression, or inspire care taking from a child. I could not foresee the need for 25 of them. I studied each stuffed animal to see which ones would be most helpful for expression and settled on two. I donated the rest to charity. This type of careful selection (not collection), as termed by Landreth (2002), helps focus the play therapist on what toys are essential to the process. Materials such as computerized games, board games, puzzles, and books may meet the criteria for one or two of the above questions but they rarely meet the criteria for all three.

When setting up a playroom for the first time, a play therapist might become overwhelmed by the vast number of different toys and materials, especially if space is limited. Kottman (2003) provides categorization of materials in five general areas, including family/nurturing toys, scary toys, aggressive toys, expressive toys, and pretend/fantasy toys. This more global approach to selecting materials might be helpful to a new play therapist. See Table 5.1 for a specific listing of materials suggested by Kottman. For the family/nurturing category, materials provide the child with the opportunity to act in the role of adult or child especially within family contexts, whether it be a meticulous role of sweeping and washing or the nurturing role of feeding and clothing. Scary toys include materials that typically

Figure 5.1 Front view of playroom.

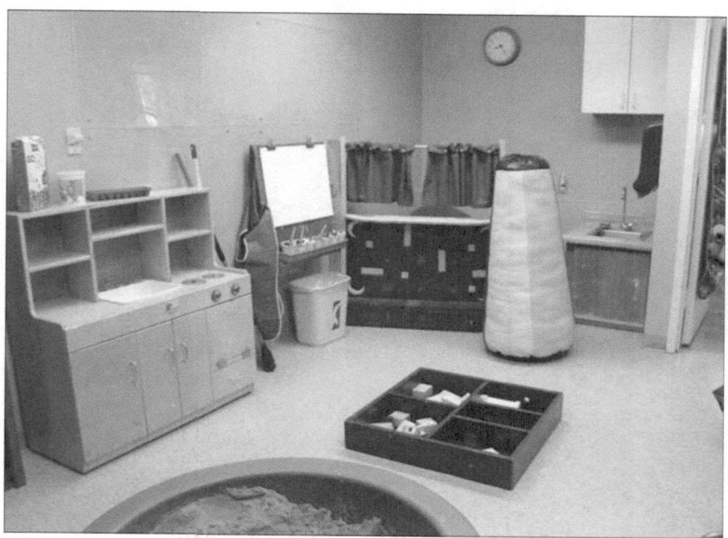

Figure 5.2 Back view of playroom.

Table 5.1 Toy Categories and Toys

Toy Categories	Examples of Toys	
Family/Nurturing	Dollhouse Baby dolls Cradle Animal families People puppets Baby clothes Baby bottles Stuffed toys Child-sized rocking chair Warm, soft blanket	Pots, pans, dishes, silverware Toy cleaning supplies (broom, dustpan, etc.) Several different families of bendable dolls Sand in a sandbox Human-like figures that can be used for family Empty food containers Wooden or plastic kitchen appliances
Scary	Plastic snakes Toy rats Plastic monsters Dinosaurs Insects	Dragons Sharks Alligator Variety of puppets representing dangerous animals
Aggressive	Stand-up punching bag/bop bag Weapons (dart guns, pistols, swords, and knives) Toy soldiers and military vehicles Small pillows for pillow fights	Foam rubber bats Plastic shield Handcuffs
Expressive	Easel and paints Watercolor paints Finger paints Crayons Markers Colored pencils Glue Newsprint Play dough or clay Pencils Scissors Scotch tape Egg cartons	Pipe cleaners Stickers Sequins Beads Needles and thread Socks for puppets Brown lunch bags Yarn Poster board Construction paper Butcher paper Magazines

Table 5.1 (*Continued*) Toy Categories and Toys

Toy Categories	Examples of Toys	
Pretend/Fantasy	Masks	Zoo and farm animals
	Doctor kit	Puppet theater
	Magic wands	Knights and castle
	Blocks and other building materials	Big pillows
	Pieces of fabric	Aliens/outer space creatures
	Human figure puppets	Hats, jewelry, purses, costumes, and other dress-up clothes
	Animal puppets	Cars, trucks, airplanes, and other transportation toys
	Iron/ironing board	Fantasy creature puppets
	Telephones (2)	

Source: From Kottman, T. (2003). *Partners in play: An Adlerian approach to play therapy* (2nd ed.). Alexandria, VA: American Counseling Association.

solicit fear in larger society, such as spiders and snakes. Scary toys help children address their own fears and anxieties. One play therapy client had an initial scared reaction to the large spider in the playroom. She screamed when she saw it and quickly picked it up with her fingertips to throw it in the trash can. She then buried it, covering it with as much paper as possible. Each subsequent week, she would throw the spider away upon her entrance into the playroom and then moved on to other play. Over time, she buried the spider less and then eventually entered the playroom giving no attention to the spider at all. Throughout her play therapy, she exhibited less and less anxious behaviors in her everyday life as reported by her mother.

Inclusion of aggressive toys in a playroom is the subject of much controversy in the play therapy field. The rationale for using aggressive toys is they allow for full expression of anger and issues of power and control. Aggressive toys such as guns and knives are clear replicas of the violence prevalent in society. Because children are members of society, they use these toys to express their internal violence or, more psychologically worded, internal sense of chaos and anger. Allowing aggressive toys in the playroom is the most direct path to allow a child to express aggressive drives. In-depth discussion and analysis of aggression in the playroom will be addressed in Chapter 10.

Expressive toys and materials include arts and crafts materials and allow for expression of creativity. They are used to express both positive and negative emotions in children, and most children who enter a playroom with these materials will use them at some point in their therapy. In a small informal study of our clients, we found that water was the most used material in the playroom among 100 clients. The easel/paints were the second most used materials in the playroom. Both materials are considered expressive and are used creatively by children. Pretend/fantasy toys such as dress-up clothes, puppets, and medical kits allow children to deeply explore the adult world in a safe environment.

Although it is helpful to conceptualize toys categorically in order to design a playroom, it should be noted that effective expressive toys in the playroom are used by children in many different ways. Knives can be used to cut a therapist free for safety, whereas baby bottles can be used to choke a baby doll. A cuddly stuffed bear can be used to suffocate a small cub, whereas a bop bag can be used to hug for an entire session. The successful selection of a toy is confirmed when a play therapist sees that children are using it for varying purposes of expression.

The playroom environment not only provides toys for expression, but also conveys a sense of order and consistency. As children participate in play therapy, they learn to depend on the consistency of the room and the therapist. Placing items in the room should make logical sense, grouping similar categories together. And most importantly, the materials are in the same place in the playroom every time the child enters. This helps send the message to children that this is a place they can truly know and feel safe. They have full mastery over their environment in the playroom so that they can progress to expression and resolution of difficulties in their lives. If toys are strewn carelessly in the playroom and in different places from session to session, the play therapist is reinforcing the child's experience of chaos in the home/external context. As they nervously search through a disorganized playroom to find the toy they need, children learn that they must "fight" to get their needs met, and this environment is just like all the others that have previously failed them.

Nonverbal Skills: A Way of Being

Just as the physical environment is designed as an inviting space for children, the play therapist must convey a way of being that is also inviting to a child. In play therapy, nonverbal skills are equally critical, if not more so, to verbal skills. Because children express themselves in the nonverbal world, play therapists are effective in using the same type of nonverbal expression. The use of nonverbal skills is heavily influenced by the genuineness and personhood of the play therapist. This concept was discussed further in Chapter 4. At the Center for Play Therapy (CPT) at the University of North Texas, certain skills are highlighted for purposes of training new play therapists. Over decades of training and supervising play therapists at CPT, certain skills have emerged as essential to the play therapy process.

When the therapist enters the playroom with a child, great care is taken to provide an environment where the child is in the lead. The therapist sits in a designated chair in the room and does not enter the child's physical space or play without invitation. The therapist maintains an open stance toward the child, leaning forward toward the child and keeping arms and legs positioned to convey a sense of openness to the child. The therapist is attentive and appears interested in the child. The therapist actively works to remain connected to the present moment and avoids preoccupation with other thoughts. Although sometimes difficult with new therapists, a therapist seems comfortable with the child and the situation, remaining relaxed throughout the session.

Tone of voice communicates the therapist's ability to connect with the child on an emotional level. Two considerations emerge when addressing the tone of the therapist's voice. First, the therapist's tone matches the level of affect displayed by the child. Often, new play therapists will present themselves as overly animated to the child. This is generally the way that many adults relate to children. Therapists new to working with children often harbor the idea that their role is to make the child happy and use their tone of voice toward this end. Matching therapist tone to the tone of the child suggests that the therapist has a genuine understanding and acceptance of emotions expressed by the child. Second, the therapist's tone matches the therapist's own words and affect. Matching verbal response with nonverbal response communicates genuineness. The child experiences the therapist more fully as a person. For example, if a child accidentally hits the therapist with a toy, and the therapist experiences a flash of shock or anger but responds, "Sometimes accidents happen in here" with a flat affect, the child will experience the therapist as insincere, which can lead to mistrust in the relationship. A more effective and congruent response might be, "That really hurt, but sometimes accidents happen in here."

Verbal Skills

Child-centered play therapy (CCPT) has benefited from offering distinct categories of verbal responses that guide the play therapist in therapeutic communication. Delivery of therapeutic responses is also key to reaching a child effectively. Two delivery skills are of special note. First, because play therapy recognizes the limited language ability of children, the importance of short therapeutic responses is helpful. Lengthy responses lose the interest of the child quickly, confuse the child, and often convey a lack of understanding on the part of the therapist. Second, the therapist's rate of responses should match the interaction of the child. If the child is quiet and reserved, then the play therapist will slow his responses. If the child is highly interactive and talkative, the play therapist will want to match this level of energy with an increased number of responses. In initial sessions with the child, play therapists often have a quicker rate of response because silence can be uncomfortable for the child in a new situation. In subsequent sessions, the therapist will learn to create a pace that matches the child.

There are nine categories of therapeutic verbal responses. Several of these are presented by Ginott (1961), Axline (1947), and Landreth (2002), and others are from my own experiences in play therapy (Ray, 2004).

1. *Tracking behavior.* Tracking behavior is the most basic of play therapist responses. The therapist tracks behavior when he or she verbally responds to the behavior of the child simply by stating what is seen or observed. Tracking behavior allows the child to know that the therapist is interested and accepting. It also helps the therapist immerse him or herself in the child's world. As a child picks up a dinosaur, the therapist might respond, "You're picking that up." As the child rolls the car across the room, "You're running that all the way over there."
2. *Reflecting content.* Reflecting content in play therapy is identical to reflecting content in adult talk therapy. To reflect content, the play therapist paraphrases the verbal interactions of children. Reflecting content validates children's perceptions of their experience and clarifies children's understanding of themselves (Landreth, 2002). As a child describes the movie that she saw over the weekend, the therapist responds, "You went to see James Bond, and there was a lot of action."

Although tracking behavior and reflecting content are essential to the play therapy process, they are the most basic skills in play therapy. They help build a relationship with a child so that the child can benefit from higher-level skills. The following skills facilitate self-concept, development of self-responsibility, creation of awareness, and the building of the therapeutic relationship:

3. *Reflecting feeling.* Reflecting feeling is the verbal response to emotions expressed by children in play therapy. Reflecting feeling is considered a higher-level skill because children rarely communicate by verbally expressing emotion. However, they are quite emotive. In addition, the reflection of feeling can sometimes be threatening to children and should be presented carefully. Reflecting feeling helps children become aware of emotions, thereby leading to the appropriate acceptance and expression of such emotions. A child says, "This place is stupid and I want to go home." A therapist might respond, "You're angry about being here, and you'd rather be at home."
4. *Facilitating decision making, returning responsibility.* One of the play therapist's goals is to help children experience a sense of their own capability and take responsibility for it. The therapist does not do for children what children can do for themselves (Landreth,

2002). Responses that facilitate decision making or return responsibility help children experience themselves as able and empowered. A child might ask, "What am I supposed to do in here?" Instead of replying with an answer such as, "You can paint or play in the sand," which directs the child and places responsibility on the therapist, a more facilitative response of decision making would be, "In here, it's up to you." Another example might be if a child attempts to open a glue bottle, quickly gives up, and asks, "Can you do it?" The therapist returns responsibility by responding, "That looks like something you can do." Of course, a therapist would only return responsibility if it is determined that the child is capable of the action.

5. *Facilitating creativity, spontaneity.* Helping a child experience his own sense of creativity and freedom is another goal of play therapy. Acceptance and encouragement of creativity send a message to the child that she is unique and special in her own way. Maladjusted children are often trapped in rigid ways of acting and thinking. Experiencing the freedom of expression allows them to develop flexibility in thought and action. For example, a child asks, "What color should the flower be?" A therapist who wishes to encourage creativity might say, "In here, it can be whatever color you want it to be."
6. *Esteem-building, encouraging.* Encouraging children to feel better about themselves is a constant objective for the play therapist. The use of esteem-building statements works to help children experience themselves as capable. As a child proudly finishes a painting, a therapist might respond, "You made that look just how you wanted." After a child spends several minutes trying to make the bullet fit in the gun and succeeds, a therapist might respond, "You did it. You figured it out."

Initially, play therapists may struggle with the difference between praising and esteem-building responses. Esteem-building responses have a deeper therapeutic purpose of helping a child create an intrinsic sense of self rather than relying on praise for external evaluation. A praise response, such as "That's a pretty picture" or "I like the way you did that," encourages the child to perform for the therapist and continue to seek external reinforcement, thereby eroding a sense of self. An esteem-building response, such as, "You're really proud of your picture" or "You made that just the way you wanted," encourages children to develop an internal sense of evaluation leading to an internal sense of responsibility.

7. *Facilitating relationship.* Responses that focus on building the relationship between the therapist and child help the child experience

a positive relationship. Because the therapy relationship serves as a model for all intimate relationships, the therapist should respond to any attempt by the child to address the relationship. Relational responses help the child learn effective communication patterns and express the therapist's care for the child. Relationship responses should always include a reference to the child and reference to self as therapist. A therapist sets a limit with a child that she is not for shooting with the gun. The child responds, "I hate you. I'm going to put you in jail." To facilitate the relationship, the therapist acknowledges the child's direct anger at her by saying, "You're really mad at me that I'm not for shooting. You want to punish me." Another scenario might be a child who cleans up the entire room right before the end of the session and says, "Look, now you don't have to clean." The therapist would respond to this relational gesture by saying, "You wanted to do something to help me."

8. *Reflecting larger meaning.* Reflecting larger meaning is the most advanced of the play therapy verbal skills. Due to the need for supervision in the effective understanding and delivery of reflecting larger meaning responses, I intentionally did not include reflecting larger meaning as a category of verbal skills in the CCPT Treatment Manual (see Appendix at the end of this book). A therapist might reflect the larger meaning by noticing and verbalizing patterns in the child's play ("You always make sure to play with the Mommy doll"). In addition, the category of reflecting larger meaning allows the therapist the opportunity to provide responses related to the child's identified themes ("You like to keep things clean and organized"; see Chapter 7). Reflecting larger meaning provides the child with awareness of the significance of his play and allows him to feel the therapist's broader empathy and understanding for his intentions and motivations. CCPT therapists are hesitant to offer interpretation but reflect the larger meaning by bringing observed and felt experiences to the child's awareness, such as (after being in a therapeutic relationship for a long period), "Sometimes, when you come into the playroom, you really want to be the one in charge." Reflecting larger meaning is difficult to maneuver and the timing is critical. Children may experience reflecting larger meaning responses as evaluative and invasive and cause them to become less engaged in the process.
9. *Limit setting.* Limits are used to set realistic boundaries in the playroom that provide safety and consistency for the child. Limits can be set in simple short directives, or they can develop into complicated battles between therapist and child. The nature of limit setting requires extensive discussion and is addressed in Chapter 6.

The basics of play therapy involve knowing how to set up a playroom and how to use basic skills to provide an environment that is therapeutically helpful to a child. This chapter has provided a brief review of what skills are needed to begin the process of effective play therapy. The CCPT manual provided at the end of this book further clarifies the mechanisms of effective responding in CCPT. At this point, I would like to refer the reader back to points made in Chapters 3 and 4 on the theory supporting CCPT and the person of the play therapist. Through training new counselors in play therapy, I discovered the importance of defining skills and providing concrete examples of ways to express empathic understanding and unconditional positive regard. Developmentally, new play therapists seek definitive actions to guide them in play therapy—hence the skills listed here. However, the path of play therapist development leads to flexibility in delivering the therapist conditions of congruence, empathic understanding, and unconditional positive regard. The skills listed in this chapter are offered as a method of training new play therapists and helping the experienced play therapist with self-review and supervision for novice play therapists. However, it should be the goal of every play therapist to move beyond the concrete skills, progressing to an abstract way of working in which the play therapist provides responses that convey the necessary conditions in a genuine and personal way.

References

Axline, V. (1947). *Play therapy*. New York: Ballantine.

Ginott, H. (1961). *Group psychotherapy with children*. New York: McGraw-Hill.

Kottman, T. (2003). *Partners in play: An Adlerian approach to play therapy* (2nd ed.). Alexandria, VA: American Counseling Association.

Landreth, G. (2002). *Play therapy: The art of the relationship*. New York: Routledge.

Ray, D. (2004). Supervision of basic and advanced skills in play therapy. *Journal of Professional Counseling: Practice, Theory, and Research, 32*(2), 28–41.

CHAPTER 6
Limit Setting

Play therapy requires limit setting so often and with such a certain degree of effectiveness that this particular skill warrants its own chapter. Although published over 40 years ago, Ginott (1965) provided a thorough explanation of balancing beneficial permissiveness with behavioral limit setting that is still relevant today. Ginott directed his words to parents but they are also applicable to play therapists. Permissiveness is the full acceptance of the child as a child. Play therapists not only accept but also embrace children as persons with their own thoughts, feelings, and desires. Hence, all parts of the internal child are accepted and permitted in the playroom. Ginott suggested this should be true of the home also. However, permissiveness does not extend to inappropriate or harmful behaviors. Play therapists need to set limits that will help children feel safe and learn to develop behaviors that will allow expression of self in appropriate ways.

These concepts sound noble but practical application may be tricky for play therapists. Permissiveness related to a child's verbal expression of feelings is typically encouraged in child-centered play therapy (CCPT). A child might say to a therapist, "You are the stupidest grown-up in the world. I hate you. You don't know anything. You just sit there." A permissive environment allows the child to fully express these feelings in the playroom. A therapist might reply, "You are really angry with me. You want to hurt me with your words." This permissive response lets the child know that the therapist fully accepts the child's anger and through this acceptance, the child learns that they can fully trust the therapist to express any feeling. To carry this scenario one step further, the child might throw toys at the therapist while saying, "I hate you." Although the expression of self through words is permitted in the playroom, hurting self or the therapist is not acceptable. In this case, the therapist might reply with a permissive response tied to a limit such as, "You are really angry with me, but I'm not for throwing toys at." This response sends the message that the child's feelings are fully understood and accepted but the damaging action is not acceptable. The fine line between permissiveness and limit setting is a challenging one for most play therapists.

Intentional Limit Setting

In training and supervision, my experience is that new play therapists feel more comfortable if limits are clearly delineated and written as rules for the playroom. Typical questions include, "Is it okay to break a toy?" or "Was it okay to put five containers of water in the sand?" or "Can he paint the bop bag or just the easel; what about the wood on the easel?" These questions are grounded in minutiae and often seem endless because one leads to another, hoping for a final concrete list of all the "don'ts" in the playroom. I often shy away from answering these questions and try to guide the play therapist to think about what is occurring in the playroom for that child. This type of conceptualization leads to more effective limit setting because it is specific to the child and therapist in that moment. The following are questions that will guide the play therapist in deciding what limits need to be set. They progress from clearer distinctions to more murky waters.

1. *Is the child's behavior physically hurting self, therapist or others?* Physical harm is never acceptable in the playroom. The play therapist should not allow a child to hit, kick, scratch, choke, or behave in any such manner. Limits are set in these cases. In addition to the obvious reason that fear of physical harm in the child's or therapist's perception is not conducive to a therapeutic relationship, the allowance of physical aggression sends the message to the child that things are out of control. If a child is allowed to hurt the therapist, the child might possibly conclude that the playroom is chaotic, psychologically unsafe, and cannot be trusted. This perception might lead the child to rely on coping behaviors that the child has previously learned and have been heretofore unhelpful, even harmful.

   A word of caution should be added when answering this first question. There is a distinction between if a child is harming self/therapist and if a therapist perceives that the child might harm self/therapist. A limit is set when harm is imminent, not when it is possible. Keeping in mind that permissiveness is essential to a child learning self-direction, the therapist learns to trust the child, not suspect the child. A child might pick up a toy and aim it as if to throw it at the therapist, and unless proven otherwise, the therapist initially trusts that the child will change direction and throw it to another part of the room. It is only when the child attempts to throw the toy at the therapist that the limit is set. Another more controversial example might be a child's attempt to harm self. In one case example, I worked with a 7-year-old girl who picked up a plastic serrated knife and began to cut her wrist as she looked at me. I knew that the child had threatened to harm herself at home but had never actually followed through. As the child looked at me, I responded, "You're wondering what I think about that." The child then dug the knife into her wrist and pulled it back and forth two times. The child winced and then threw down the knife. I responded, "You didn't like how that felt. It hurt you." In this case, I trusted the child to make a self-enhancing decision and waited to set a limit. The hesitation was beneficial because it resulted in two outcomes. The child was able to experience the consequences of a threatened behavior and realized it did not feel physically good nor did it help the child feel better. Second, I was able to see and encourage the child's ability to act in a self-enhancing way. Notably, the child never attempted the self-harm behavior again, in the playroom or at home.

2. *Will the behavior interfere with the provision of play therapy?* Structural guidelines are followed in the provision of play therapy and were presented in Chapter 5. Play therapy sessions are typically between 30 and 50 minutes, depending on setting and age of the child. And, at the very least, play therapists need to be able to provide play therapy to the child in a playroom. Hence, structural limits are common in play therapy and include setting limits regarding going to the room, going in the room, staying in the room, and leaving the room. Initially, children might not want to leave a parent or waiting room to go to the playroom or go into the room alone with the play therapist for a variety of reasons. I will provide some examples of these situations later in this chapter. Once in the room, children may want to leave to go to the bathroom, find a parent, or run around the building. The need to leave the playroom should be examined by the play therapist for therapeutic value, and then the need for limits can be decided. The structural limits that I have encountered most often with all types of cases are challenges related to leaving the playroom. Children's motivations for not leaving the playroom include being overly involved in their play, establishing power and control, not wanting to leave the therapist, or not wanting to return to their daily routine. Time structure is often difficult for all children, and

persistence in setting structural limits helps them learn how to use their time to their benefit in the most effective way.

In addition to structural limits that are provided to support the continuation of play therapy to the child, another consideration is parents. This is a small point but therapists need to consider how permissive behavior in the playroom may influence the parent's perception of play therapy. A therapist who allows a child to paint her clothes and body and then return to the waiting room may be setting the child up to endure punishment and send the message that play therapy is an out-of-control place. When a play therapist allows such play behavior, there should be a clear understanding with the parent of what is considered permissible by the parent and a clear explanation by the therapist on the therapeutic value of such permissiveness. In the clinic in which I supervise, I encourage the play therapists to set a limit about how a child presents back to the parent in the waiting room. Children are allowed to paint themselves but a limit is set that the paint must be washed off before returning to the waiting room. I have seen too many horrified looks from parents in the waiting room, not only from the parents of the child returning but from other parents who fear the same behavior from their child attending play therapy. As discussed in Chapter 9 on parent consultation, the parent's belief in the play therapy process is essential to their continued participation.

3. *Will the behavior harm the continued use of the playroom for other clients?* The answer to this question is the practical and business side of play therapy. The room and toys in the room are necessary to the therapy of many children. If one child destroys a toy or the playroom, the therapist considers how it will affect subsequent sessions and other children. When therapists allow toys to be destroyed, they consider the ability to replace the toy from a monetary and time perspective with questions such as, "Do I have the money to replace the toy?" and "Can I replace this toy by the time my next client comes in who also relies heavily on this toy?" Room destruction is another consideration. If a play therapist allows a child to throw paint, water, and glue in the sand and every toy on the floor, he would consider whether all of this can be cleaned up before the next client uses the room. Often, a room is in heavy back-to-back use and the therapist only has a few minutes to clean. The decision to set limits on destructive behavior might be influenced by this more practical perspective. In these types of cases, the creative play therapist thinks in terms of how to best serve the client. A therapist might evaluate that the child needs full expression of destruction and decides to set a limit on

ending the session early enough so that there is clean-up time. Or a therapist might decide that mixing the water with the sand appears to allow sufficient expression for the child and sets a limit on glue and paint. This is where limit setting becomes specific to the child.

4. *How will the child's behavior affect the relationship between therapist and child?* The answer to this question is related to the promotion of therapist acceptance of the child. At all times, the effective play therapist works toward acceptance of the child. However, there are some actions of the child that might interfere with this acceptance, going beyond physical harm to the therapist. These "therapist acceptance" limits are very specific to the individual play therapist and will be different for each therapist based on personality. Some examples might be a child smells from urination or bowel movement, a child frequently releases gas, a child paints the therapist, a child spits and uses the spit to clean things in the playroom, or a child picks nose and eats what is found. The list is endless but the main point is that children will often act in ways that make it difficult for the therapist to continue to concentrate fully on the child and be accepting in the moment. In these cases, the therapist sets a limit so that the relationship is enhanced. In a personal example, I once conducted play therapy with a child in a school setting. Because the playroom was one part of a larger classroom filled with the school's discarded items, the child found a metal pipe that fascinated him. He dramatically coughed up a "loogie" (a mix of mucus and saliva) and spit it into one end of the pipe. He then held the pipe up to watch the loogie run down the pipe and back into his mouth. I literally gagged and had to stop myself from throwing up in session. I knew there was no way I could respond authentically and acceptingly so I set a limit. I believe these were my words: "You thought that was fun but the pipe is not for spitting in. You can watch other things roll down the pipe." It was probably not the best example of limit setting, but he willingly followed the limit and I was able to go back to concentrating on him and not on me. As observed through this example, therapist acceptance limits are individual to therapists. There are some therapists who would not have even noticed the pipe behavior and wonder why a limit needed to be set. Because therapist acceptance limits are individual, this marks another reason for therapist self-awareness and how it influences the practice of play therapy.

Play therapists who review these four questions when deciding what limits to set will be able to figure out what limits are essential and/or lead to child self-direction and what limits might be unnecessary and harmful to the therapeutic environment. Although I am not a believer in definitive limits for all play therapy clients, there are a few limits that appear to be close to universal. They include

1. I am not for hurting.
2. You are not for hurting.
3. I am not for touching in private places.
4. In the playroom, you are not for touching in private places.
5. The walls are not for painting, gluing, throwing water on.
6. Sand is not for throwing.
7. The video/two-way mirror is not for playing with.
8. Your clothes are not for taking off.
9. My clothes are not for taking off.
10. The playroom is not for peeing/pooping in.
11. My hair/clothes are not for cutting.
12. Your hair/clothes are not for cutting.
13. Glue/paint is not for drinking.

When to Set Limits

Child counselors do not always agree on when to set limits. Even among CCPT therapists, there are different views on when limit setting is introduced. Cochran, Nordling, and Cochran (2010) suggested that a play therapist initially convey that there might be a need to set a limit. Specifically, they suggested the following introductory statement: "…In here, you may say anything you want, and you may do almost anything you want. If there is something you may not do, I will let you know" (p. 136). The purpose of conveying limits initially is to clarify the reality that there are certain types of behaviors that are prohibited and relieve the child from anxiety related to unclear expectations. However, Axline (1947) suggested only setting limits when it is absolutely necessary. Waiting to set limits sends the message to the children that they are entering a permissive environment in which the therapist trusts children to make self-enhancing decisions. Setting limits only when they are needed also avoids creating a hierarchy in the relationship where the therapist dictates the rules of the playroom. Both of these perspectives suggested by CCPT therapists are consistent with child-centered philosophy because the key concern is the best way to present limits that will build a therapeutic relationship.

I am an advocate of waiting to set limits until they are necessary. In working extensively with aggressive children who operate from a power and control orientation, the presentation of limits prior to problematic behaviors seemingly tends to set an initial negative tone in which the child perceives the therapist as trying to establish control from the beginning of the relationship. For anxious children, setting early limits may be perceived as rules they must follow to please the therapist or gain approval from the therapist. Finally, but most importantly in the child-centered philosophy, the setting of early limits may send the message that proper behavior and following rules is a priority of therapy and the therapist. When outlining the eight basic principles of child-centered play therapy, Axline was careful to list the setting of limits as the eighth principle, highlighting limit setting as necessary but prioritized below all other aspects of the therapist/child relationship. Landreth (2002) suggested that the beginning of the relationship starts with the more permissive phrase: "…this is our playroom. And this is a place where you can play with the toys in a lot of the ways you would like to" (p. 183).

Set the Limit

If following the guidelines of this chapter, a play therapist has made a conscious decision about the need for a limit and has waited until the child demonstrated a problematic behavior before setting the limit. Now the dilemma becomes how to set the limit. Many experts have provided ways to set limits, including using "I" statements, problem solving, or definitive short statements. But perhaps the clearest and most direct communication of limits was coined by Landreth (2002) in his ACT model. Using the philosophy provided by Ginott (1965) in which he stated, "Feelings have to be identified and expressed; acts may have to be limited and redirected" (p. 111), Landreth concretized Ginott's explanation of limit setting. In Landreth's model, *A* is to acknowledge the child's feelings or desires, thereby allowing a child an outlet for expression and sending the message the therapist understands and accepts the child's motivation. *C* is to communicate the limit in a clearly definitive statement. And *T* is to target an alternative, which is to quickly redirect the child so that the child can still express the feeling but in an appropriate way. Here are a few examples:

- Suzanne wants to leave the playroom in the middle of the session because she wants to show the therapist a new game on her handheld video device. The therapist sets the limit: "You are excited to show me your game (acknowledge feeling), but we have 20 more minutes in the playroom (communicate limit); you can show it to me when our playtime is over (target alternative)." Suzanne becomes angry and throws a ball at the therapist's face. The therapist sets the limit, "You're angry with me (acknowledge feeling), but I'm not for throwing things at (communicate limit); you can throw the ball at the Bobo (target alternative)."

- Jonathan is painting at the easel, accidentally spills paint on the floor, laughs, and then purposefully starts to pour paint on the floor. The therapist sets the limit: "You think it's funny to spill the paint on the floor, but the floor is not for paint; you can pour the paint in the sink."
- Katie is playing out a scene in the sandbox where the good animals are trying to keep out the bad animals. Katie begins to throw sand at the animal shelves across the room to keep them out. The therapist sets the limit: "You're trying hard to keep out those bad animals, but the sand is for staying in the sandbox; you can throw the sand into the sandbox."

In each of these examples, ACT is employed to share the therapist's understanding of the child's feelings or intentions, set a clear definitive limit, and provide an alternative to the child's behavior that still meets the child's intentions. Through acknowledgment of feeling, children learn that there are words to express their desires and develop self-awareness of what feelings are tied to behaviors. By communicating the limit, children learn they are in a safe environment where behaviors that are damaging are unacceptable and will be confronted. And through targeting alternatives, the therapist helps children begin to think of new behaviors that are appropriate but still allow expression.

Using ACT is often effective in helping a child move from inappropriate to appropriate ways to get personal needs met. There are a few aspects of limit setting that need to be addressed in order to create the most successful scenario. A calm tone of voice is essential. If children sense fear, hesitancy, or power needs in the limit-setting interaction, it will likely set off an ineffective exchange. The tone of voice is often affected by therapist attitude. If the therapist believes that it is her job to control the child's behavior either from internal or external pressures, tone of voice might reveal this attitude. This is especially true for children who operate from power or control orientations. The child-centered philosophy advocates for children to learn to control or redirect their own behaviors. And ultimately, short of physical restraint, a person—even a child—is in control of personal behavior. Hence, it is always the child's choice to follow or not follow a limit. When a play therapist adopts this philosophy toward limit setting, the process becomes much more effective. Limits are a regular part of being in the playroom and should be communicated casually to the child. Using an analogy from high-school geometry, limits are the "givens" of play therapy. Limits are not the therapist's choices or rules; they simply exist in the playroom and need to be shared with others who are new to the playroom. This attitude toward limit setting allows the therapist to relax, knowing that his job is to communicate the limit for the child, who then makes the personal decision of whether to follow the limit.

The Next Step: Choice Giving

If all three components of the ACT model are presented effectively, most children will follow the limit after one to three repetitions. However, there will be times that ACT is not effective and the therapist needs to move to the next step of limit setting, which involves choice giving. Choice giving aligns with the child-centered philosophy in that the therapist recognizes the child's decision to not follow the limit and is now moving to offer consequences to help the child become aware of natural outcomes to problematic behavior. The therapist offers a choice that includes the communication of a consequence to behavior. Notably, for most behaviors, ACT is presented to a child at least three times, allowing time for the child to process and make a decision. After the third ACT presentation, the therapist might choose to move to choice giving. The following is a scenario in which both ACT and choice giving are used to set and follow through on a limit.

Eric: Picks up the dart gun, points it at therapist, and shoots the dart. He smiles.

Play Therapist: "Eric, you liked shooting me with the gun but I'm not for shooting. You can shoot the Bobo."

Eric: Reloads gun as therapist sets limit. Shoots again as soon as therapist completes limit.

Play Therapist: "You enjoyed shooting me but I'm not for shooting. You can shoot the Bobo or one of the other toys."

Eric: Reloads gun as therapist sets limit and points at therapist but hesitates to shoot.

Play Therapist: "You're thinking about shooting me again but I'm not for shooting. You can shoot the Bobo or one of the other toys."

Eric: Smiles and shoots the gun at the therapist.

Play Therapist: "Eric, I can see that you enjoy shooting me with the gun but I'm not for shooting. If you choose to shoot me, then you choose not to play with the gun."

Eric: Reloads gun and points it around the room. Quickly turns toward therapist and shoots.

Play Therapist: "Eric, when you chose to shoot me, you chose not to play with the gun. You can give me the gun or you can place it on the shelf." (Therapist holds out hand.)

Eric: "I won't do it again."

Play Therapist: "You decided that you won't do it again but when you chose to shoot me, you chose not to play with the gun."

Eric: (in begging voice) "No, really, I won't do it again. I promise. I'm sorry."

Play Therapist: "I can see that you feel bad but when you chose to shoot me, you chose not to play with the gun. You can give it to me or you can place it on the shelf."

Eric: "Come on, please. I won't do it again. Look, I'll just shoot it at the puppets."

Play Therapist: "You thought of a whole new way to use the gun but when you chose to shoot me, you chose not to play with the gun. You can choose to hand it to me or put it on the shelf."

Eric: Throws the gun on the floor and walks to another toy.

Play Therapist: "I see you chose to throw it on the floor." (Therapist casually moves to pick up gun and places it out of the way.)

This scenario is an example of just how tedious the limit-setting process can be with some children. When the goal is to help a child learn to make his own enhancing decisions and not to just stop behavior, patience and persistence are the key elements. In every response, the therapist acknowledges the child's feelings, intentions, and ability to make the decision yet clearly communicates the limit and the consequence of the limit. Once the therapist moved to choice giving and Eric chose a consequence, it was the therapist's role to effectively follow through on the consequence. It is possible that this interaction could take up to 15 or 30 minutes of a play session. I have experienced children who reenact the same scenario with different behaviors for an entire session. For example, the gun would be the first behavior to move to the choice-giving consequence, and then the child might move to throwing a ball at the therapist and the whole process starts over. These cases can be quite frustrating and I have heard therapists question the value of play therapy if these interactions pervade the session time. If children choose to use their playtime engaging in multiple limit-setting interactions, then it becomes obvious that they are choosing to work through what is most problematic for them, making play therapy the environment where the child revisits the need for expression of self and limitation of such expression within a safe relationship.

The Ultimate Limit

Between effective presentation of ACT and choice giving, I would venture to guess that 95% of children will respond in a self-enhancing way and the therapist has no need to progress to other consequences. There remains one last tool in limit setting and it is called the "ultimate limit." I am hesitant to discuss it in this book because it is a last-ditch effort at limit setting and I personally perceive it as a therapist failure when I have utilized it. The ultimate limit is to end the play session prematurely based on the child's choice to not follow limits. The ultimate limit is typically reserved for limit breaking related to harm to self or therapist. A child who breaks limits by throwing sand or paint on the floor does not usually qualify for the ultimate limit. The ultimate limit is presented as a choice (after going through the previously described procedures and the child is still breaking the limit), such as, "If you choose to hit me with the ball, then you choose for our playtime to be over for today."

One of the main reasons why the ultimate limit is sparsely used in CCPT is because it represents a break in the relationship. The therapist will be separating from the child in an abrupt and unplanned way, possibly causing harm in the therapeutic relationship. All efforts and creativity should be utilized to avoid the ultimate limit. In my clinic, a therapist must review all steps that led to the ultimate limit in supervision within a week so that the therapist can engage in problem solving to keep the ultimate limit from being set again. However creative a play therapist might be, there are times when the ultimate limit must be set. When this does occur, the therapist calmly communicates the limit and the consequences of breaking the limit. The following scenario took place after the play therapist had set the limit about the ball four times, and then engaged in choice giving in which Claudia refused to give up the ball.

Play Therapist: "Claudia, if you choose to hit me with the ball, then you choose for our time to be over today."

Claudia: "Yeah, right." (Claudia throws the ball at the therapist's face.)

Play Therapist: "I can see that you chose for our time to be up today." (Therapist stands up and moves to the door to end session.)

Claudia: "I'm not going. I still have more time."

Play Therapist: (opens playroom door). "You'd like to stay but when you chose to hit me with the ball, you chose for our time to be up today."

Claudia: "You can't make me. I'm not leaving."

Play Therapist: "You don't want to leave but when you chose to hit me with the ball, you chose for our time to be up today. You can come back next Tuesday."

Claudia: "Fine!" (Claudia storms out of the room.)

Play Therapist: (as they reach the waiting room) "Claudia, I will see you next Tuesday."

The play therapist would then let the parent know that it is time to take Claudia home and promise to call the parent to explain the situation later that day.

To provide some perspective on how often the ultimate limit should be used, I have facilitated play therapy for approximately 15 years with hundreds of children. I have used the ultimate limit fewer than 10 times. But I did feel that it was necessary for those few times. I have observed the use of the ultimate limit many times in supervision and engage the therapist in creative discussion on how to keep the ultimate limit from being set in the future.

When It All Goes Wrong

Play therapists may execute each component in limit setting to perfection, and yet some children will still escalate inappropriate behavior. This is especially problematic when children are destructive or harmful. Here are a few examples from my experience:

Connor is 7 years old, was severely abused as a young child, and is in play therapy because he is constantly attacking children and teachers at school. In his second play therapy session, without warning, he runs out of the playroom and around the clinic. The play therapist quickly follows, attempting to set the limit of returning to the playroom. Connor uses loud curse words to respond, which I will rephrase in this scenario, "Screw you. You can't catch me. I don't care." He then begins to open counseling room doors throughout the clinic. The therapist follows, unsure of what to do, but continues to use ACT. Connor screams curse words throughout the clinic. By this time, his mother has heard him and sits in the waiting room but does not say anything. After 10 minutes, Connor goes back to the playroom where he throws all the toys on the floor until the end of his session.

Tanika is 5 years old and is in play therapy for aggressive behavior. Her mother is extremely passive. Tanika begins to throw sand at the therapist. The therapist sets a limit. Tanika then moves toward the therapist to kick her. After she kicks the therapist, Tanika runs out of the room. By chance, Tanika runs into another counselor who she promptly kicks several times in the hallway. Tanika runs to the waiting room and begins to kick her mom who says nothing but tries to hold Tanika off. The play therapist reaches the waiting room and Tanika runs toward her to kick her repeatedly. The therapist tries to hold her off and suggests that Mom take Tanika home. Mom says okay and then goes to the bathroom while Tanika is still attempting to kick the therapist. When Mom returns a couple of minutes later, she bribes Tanika with a trip to get ice cream and Tanika leaves with her.

These two scenarios exemplify when limit setting is virtually impossible and the therapist must be creative about how to approach the situation the next time around. It should be noted that in these scenarios, physical restraint was not considered because it is against clinic policy. Just as ending a session early represents a break in the therapeutic relationship, physical restraint complicates and possibly damages the relationship between therapist and child. Physical restraint does not have a place in CCPT. Although therapists should avoid restraining a child, they can protect themselves from being harmed by a child by pushing the child to arm's length when the child is initiating aggression toward the therapist. If a child attempts to harm a bystander, the therapist is encouraged to stand between the child and bystander to offer protection. Fortunately, children are typically smaller than therapists and these methods work to protect the child and others from harm.

What is most helpful in these types of cases is creative solutions for prevention. When a child is acting with such egregious behaviors, there are usually intentions to the behaviors. In the case of Connor, his mother was also in counseling at the same time. He would go back to the playroom and then his mother would go to her session. Although he looked out of control as he ran through the clinic, he appeared to be trying to find out in which room his mother was in counseling. For his next session, Connor and his mother's counselor entered the waiting room at the same time and greeted them both. They then took Connor to show him which room his mother was in and then used the clock to show him what time he and his mother would be out. Connor's mother's counselor ensured that his mother was out of session before Connor so that she would be waiting for him when he was done. In addition to this prevention, which we were not sure would work, I placed two staff members at different points in the clinic to serve as a barrier if Connor ran out of the room again. In his third session, Connor did run out of the room but he ran directly to where his mother's room was, hugged her, and then returned to the playroom.

In Tanika's case, the situation was not quite so easily resolved. She appeared to need to solicit strong reactions from her mother. However, the worse her behavior, the more disengaged her mother became, thereby backfiring on meeting Tanika's needs. In Tanika's case, the play therapist met with the mother prior to Tanika's next scheduled session. She explained that if Tanika ran out of the playroom, it would be the mother's responsibility to restrain Tanika and remove her from the clinic immediately. The play therapist role-played several different scenarios with Tanika's mother that involved removing Tanika from the clinic. The play therapist also developed a sign that she would give Tanika's mother when it was time to act. In the next two sessions, Tanika was again abusive to the therapist and had to be removed by her mother within 20 minutes of arriving at the clinic. With the play therapist's support, the mother was able to remove Tanika; although the scene was unpleasant both times, as

Tanika yelled, screamed, and kicked when her mother finally picked her up to take her out. After the two sessions where Tanika was removed from the clinic, she entered and stayed in the playroom for her entire session length and for the remainder of her therapy. In this case, Tanika received what she needed from her mother when her mother actively engaged with her and set limits when her behavior was out of control. She also learned that the clinic and her mother would be following through on the consequence of ending sessions. Tanika actually enjoyed the play sessions so she learned quickly that if she stopped kicking and running, she could stay in the playroom the full time. And a final word about mom's restraint of Tanika: Although play therapists should not engage in physical restraint, it is a natural part of parenting for parents to sometimes restrain their children. Developmentally, physical restraint is a part of parenting young children (up to 3 years old), and then children learn to restrain themselves upon adult request or self-awareness. When these developmental steps are skipped (as in Tanika's case), parents might have to be taught the need for physical restraint and how to use it sparingly, and only in extreme cases of behavior, and then taught other skills to replace restraint.

Final Words on Limit Setting

As stated early in this chapter, limit setting is often the most difficult part of play therapy, and yet necessary to the therapeutic process. The very nature of limit setting requires confrontation with children and the need to be consistent regarding limits that are set or consequences that are communicated. Approaching limit setting through a deliberative process of considering what limits are needed, when they should be set, and the best way to present them to the child for maximum effectiveness is key to success. In the matter of limit setting, success is not defined through the child's capitulation to rules imparted by the play therapist. Rather, success is defined by the child's thoughtful choice to make a self-enhancing decision that involves the deliberation of consequences and expression of needs.

References

Axline, V. (1947). *Play Therapy*. New York: Ballantine.

Cochran, N., Nordling, W., & Cochran, J. (2010). *Child-centered play therapy: A practical guide to developing therapeutic relationships with children*. Hoboken, NJ: Wiley.

Ginott, H. (1965). *Between parent & child*. New York: Avon.

Landreth, G. (2002). *Play therapy: The art of the relationship*. New York: Brunner-Routledge.

CHAPTER 7
Themes in Play Therapy

Once a play therapist has mastered basic skills and advanced limit-setting skills, a child will respond to the setting of the playroom and the environment provided by the play therapist by engaging in therapeutic play. Therapeutic play is demonstrated through many different types of play behaviors. As described previously, play therapy is effective when a child is allowed to direct play where he needs it to go. Children will naturally lead their play to express personal interpretations of their worlds. Upon expression, children will then move toward understanding and learning to cope with how they perceive their worlds. These types of expressions are identified as themes in play therapy. Going back to our initial description of play as children's language, we can assume that themes expressed in play therapy are the meanings that children assign to that language.

From a child-centered perspective, the identification of play themes could be considered irrelevant and possibly distracting to a play therapist in the ability to work within the present moment with a child. After all, child-centered play therapy (CCPT) emphasizes the healing nature of the relationship between therapist and child and the growth environment established by the therapist. Identification of play themes could be construed as interpretive, placing the therapist's own agenda upon the child. And certainly this is a possible danger if the therapist loses focus of who is in the lead for most effective therapy. Hence, the identification of themes is an advanced skill in play therapy and should not be undertaken until a therapist has solid knowledge of play therapy, extensive self-awareness, and keen interest in following the child's lead. Supervision and/or consultation are crucial when a therapist begins to identify and work within themes in play therapy. Being in contact with another, more experienced therapist allows a play therapist to explore multiple possibilities for themes and to avoid becoming fixated in one direction.

Definition of a Theme

Very little is written about the identification of themes in play therapy. This chapter represents conclusions from my own experiences in facilitating and supervising thousands of play therapy sessions. The first distinction in identifying a theme is to understand the difference between a play behavior and a play theme. A play behavior is one that is acted out by children in the playroom to which a variation of meanings can be attributed. Play behaviors are what the child is actually doing in the room. A boy throws everything off the shelves and across the room. This is usually described as aggressive play. This type of play shows that the child is acting aggressively but it does not explain what meaning the child has attributed to that aggression. The therapist knows that the child is acting out something and even knows that limit setting will be needed, but the therapist does not know the purpose and expression of the action.

In contrast, a play theme is a coherent metaphor from which the child communicates the meaning he or she attributes to experience. The theme informs the therapist of the internal meaning-making system within the child. Going back to the aggressive play, the therapist notices that the boy shows very little emotion while throwing toys and then the child says, "You can't make me pick it all up. I can do whatever I want." The therapist might identify a power/control theme where the child acts aggressively to gather a sense of control over his environment. Alternately, the therapist might notice that the boy is throwing all the toys to one spot, saying in a scared loud voice, "You can't get me again." The therapist might identify a protection theme for this play. Although the play in both scenarios can be labeled as aggressive, the therapist can better understand the child by identifying the meaning behind the larger play behavior.

How to Identify Themes

Identification of themes is often challenging to the play therapist. As children reveal themselves more fully in play therapy, the theme might take on an emergent quality that is revealed layer by layer, session by session. One analogy helpful in the identification of themes is comparing play therapy to adult talk therapy. In counseling an adult, a therapist might notice that in the first session, the adult reveals that she is frustrated with her husband because he does not meet her needs. In a second session, she reveals that her children take advantage of her and do not appreciate her. The therapist may form the impression that this is a client who is narcissistic and avoids personal responsibility. It is in the third session that the client reveals, upon feeling safe within the therapeutic relationship, that she pushes loved ones away because of her fear of being hurt as she has experienced in previous relationships. The third session is where deeper thematic work emerges. Although not typically revealed in verbal communication, this same type of progression occurs in play therapy. As children feel safe within the relationship, they reveal their most intrinsic interpretations of their worlds.

There are three characteristics that are helpful in guiding the play therapist to identify play themes. Two occur within the play session and one occurs external to the session. They are repetition, intensity, and context. Repetition of play behaviors that occur either multiple times in a session or across the length of therapy is an indicator that the child is working on an issue that is important. The repetitive nature of the play behavior demonstrates that the child is determined to express the internal struggle and possibly develop ways of managing that struggle. Examples of repetition include that the child chooses the same lion and cub each time she comes to the playroom. Although the lion and cub are moved around the room, are sometimes in the sand and sometimes in the dollhouse, the therapist comes to expect that the child will pick up these two animals each play session. Another example is that a child might begin to paint, then glob the paint on the paper until there is no form and the paper is tearing. This action occurs for about 5 minutes in every session for 10 sessions. Therapists may note the frequency of repetition and the time length of the play behavior to determine progress or a change in therapy.

A second indicator of thematic work is the level of intensity demonstrated by the child in play. Intensity is marked by the energy and focus applied to play behaviors within the session. Intensity by a child may sometimes be signified by silence or by an increase in emotion. For the self-aware therapist, one way to determine intensity is by how the therapist is feeling. Intense play often has a reverential quality in which the therapist may feel a need to be respectful and quiet in the moment. There might be a hesitancy to interrupt the intensity for fear of disrupting the importance of the child's play. A talkative child who is sharing weekend plans with the therapist may suddenly only focus on going through the medical kit and applying bandages to her arms and giving herself shots. She says no words at all, and the therapist feels that any verbal response would interfere, not facilitate, the child's play. In the playroom, repetition and intensity applied to specific play behaviors can assure the play therapist that a theme is being attended to and expressed.

A play therapist might be aware that thematic play is taking place in the playroom but the next step involves hypothesis testing, which involves knowledge of the child's context. Being informed regarding the child's context—including early development, personality characteristics, and significant life events—helps the play therapist have a context for understanding the child's play. Acquiring background information regarding the child's presenting problem from the child, parents, or significant others also helps the play therapist fully explore possible themes or check out the viability of a theme theorized by the play therapist.

Case Example

In the case of an 8-year-old boy, during sessions, he mostly played with soldiers and acted out war scenes. During this play, he would make bomb sounds but verbalized no words. Midway through each session (Repetition), he cleared out the war scenes from the sandbox and he chose a large spider, a large snake, one large dolphin, and one small dolphin. He verbalized (Intensity) a scene where the large spider and large snake were buried in the sand waiting to come out every 100 years. As the 100 years approached, the identified "Mom" dolphin hid the "baby" dolphin in the sand. While the "baby" dolphin was hidden, the snake came out to wrap around "Mom" so she could not move and the spider came out to "suck out her life." They devoured her and she went back into the sand with them. The "baby" dolphin emerged and cried for his mom. Upon seeing that his mom was no longer there, the boy verbalized flatly, "Oh well, I guess he's on his own." As the play therapist, I knew that thematic work was being done but understanding it completely was dependent on context. The client's mother was suffering through severe depression, exhibited by an acute lack of energy and flat emotional affect. She also was mother to a 1-year-old and a 2-year-old who were high energy, as was the client. She had very little energy to give to my client and struggled to make it through each day. My interpretation was that the spider and snake represented his two younger siblings, the "baby" dolphin represented him, and the "mom" dolphin represented his mother. The purpose of trying to make an accurate interpretation was not to share this with the client or his mother, but rather to understand his deep feelings of abandonment (his theme) by his mother that he attributed to his siblings. The theme, not the actual behaviors, is what I addressed with both him in session and with his mother in parent consultation.

Rationale for Identifying Themes in Play Therapy

The main purpose of identifying themes is that they lead play therapists to a better understanding of the subjective experience of the child. Upon successfully identifying themes, a play therapist can tailor responses to help reveal full acceptance of what the child has attempted to express. Therapists work to find ways to conceptualize their clients so that they develop focused plans of action. Themes allow for greater conceptualization of the child. Conceptualization helps guide a therapist's responses, interaction with parents, determination of progress, and even case notes.

Thematic Responses

Using categorization of basic verbal skills presented in Chapter 5, themes can be addressed in a distinctive way personal to each client to demonstrate our understanding and acceptance. I will integrate the case study above along with basic skill responses to show how responses can be focused to thematic work. During the play behavior described in the case, I might respond to the identified theme of abandonment with the following types of responses:

Reflecting content: (When baby dolphin reappears and is looking around) He came out but his mom is gone.

Reflecting feeling: (When baby dolphin cries, "Where's my mom?") He is scared about where his mom went.

Facilitating decision making/returning responsibility: (When client buries mom dolphin with the snake and spider) You decided she would go away with them.

Facilitating creativity/spontaneity: (As the spider and snake devour mom) You're finding different ways they can take her away.

Esteem building: (After he says, "Oh well, I guess he's on his own") You found a way for him to survive without mom.

Relational: (After the end of play sequence) You wanted me to know how he lost his mom.

Reflecting larger meaning: (After dolphin comes out) Those two always seem to find a way to get mom and then the dolphin is left alone.

Because I was not invited into the play directly, the relational response might not be appropriate. I would only use this particular response if I thought the child intended to share the story with me and wanted me to listen.

All of the sample responses were ways to address the theme of abandonment. They are focused specifically on conveying that, as the therapist, I understand the most significant meaning of what he is sharing is his concern about feeling abandoned by his mother. By directing my responses to this particular theme, I demonstrate an acceptance of this feeling and I do not deny his experience by trying to make him feel better such as saying, "What can he do to find his mom?" or "I'm sure his mom is missing him." These would be responses that address my needs as the therapist and not the needs of the child.

Parent Consultation Using Themes

Parent consultation will be addressed thoroughly in Chapter 10 regarding working with parents. However, identification of themes can aid the play therapist in parent consultation by providing a useful tool in helping parents fully understand their children. Sharing themes with parents allows the parents to attain information about their child without breaking the child's confidentiality. Themes allow parents to see progression in their child's therapy.

In the case example, when I met with the mother, I approached the theme by addressing her issues, then moving on to the client's struggle. Upon entry to the session, I asked his mother how she was doing. She talked about feeling low, struggling with her depression, and not having enough energy to keep up with her younger children. We discussed how she is addressing her depression through her own therapy and seeking a psychiatrist for medication treatment. I gave her a few referrals. I then reflected that it must be difficult to have any energy to spend with my client when the two younger ones take up so much of her time. She agreed and acknowledged that because my client is so difficult, she tries to avoid any kind of confrontation with him, which means she avoids him much of the time. I then shared with her that his play seems to convey that he feels this lack of time and lack of energy that she has for him. I explained that he seems to think she no longer has anything left for him. She cried at this and admitted it was true but she was surprised to hear that he felt that way. She was sure that she had been hiding her feelings from him so that he would not feel rejected. We then discussed possible ways she could spend time alone with him within the restrictions of her younger children and her lack of energy. In subsequent parent consultations, we continued to discuss her depression status and its effects on my client. We monitored her ability to connect and spend time with him and attempted to find simple ways for them to have short spurts of time together.

The use of a play theme to work with this mother was helpful in several ways. First, the play theme allowed me to discuss emotions, not behaviors. I was able to maintain my client's confidentiality but reveal the most important part of his work that involved her. Through my client's play, I was able to see how damaging the drain of his brothers was on his mother. In his play, he was acknowledging how powerless he perceived his mother. I knew I needed to approach her with much empathic understanding, and not just directives on how to help my client. By sticking with theme work, we were able to address both of their needs. Interestingly, my client and his mother had almost the same perception of her situation. My client expressed it with much clarity through his play, and his mother expressed it verbally with little prompting. His mother cared about him, but what appeared to be missing was that she had very little understanding of his situation. Sharing his theme with her helped her to see his perspective.

Determination of Progress in Themes

Identifying themes and then observing the child's play behavior through the theme helps determine progress in play therapy. Again, measuring progress deserves it own thorough discussion in the next chapter but themes can play a part in evaluating progress. Although play behaviors might continue to be similar week after week, a play therapist looks for differences in progression of the theme. Is the child using a different tone of voice now? Is there resolution to a problem? Is there a difference in intensity when the play behavior occurs? Is the theme delivered in more or less time? Is there more or less verbalization with the theme? Monitoring changes in play themes requires the use of video recording of sessions. Play therapist memory is riddled with human error. A review of recordings helps to notice differences in children's play.

In this case, the client played out similar scenes of a devouring of the mother figure by two other figures and an abandonment of one figure for several weeks. The play scenes progressed to where the mother figure retreated to protect herself and the smaller figure, previously abandoned. This play occurred for several more weeks. It appeared that the mother figure was trying to figure out how to stay safe. As mentioned, the client began each play session with a war scene that was cleared out before the thematic abandonment play began. After several weeks of playing out the abandonment theme, the client merged the two play behaviors. The mother figure was in a cave with her smaller child. She was completely surrounded by soldiers who were finding multiple ways to get her out so they could kill her. Suddenly, many more soldiers of a different color surrounded the attacking forces. The client even sang the cavalry theme as he placed the soldiers strategically. The cavalry forces killed all the opposing forces and the mother and baby were allowed to come out of the cave safely. The client did not verbalize an end but it was clear to me that this was his ending. In subsequent sessions, he no longer played with the mother/child figures although he continued to play with the two spider and snake figures that were constantly wreaking havoc in the playroom.

Observing the changes in his play each week allowed me to see that he was progressing in his theme from feeling abandoned to finding ways to protect his mother so that she would not abandon him. This change in play can be interpreted in many different ways but it coincided with less aggression in his home environment and improvement in his mother's depressive symptoms. I believe that he used the play behaviors to work through his theme of abandonment and figured out a way to cope with his mother's depression.

Thematic Case Notes

When a play therapist has identified play themes, these impact therapeutic case notes. Instead of just providing a list of play behaviors that have very little meaning to the therapist upon review, or certainly to outside sources, noting themes can help give clarity to the client's progress. Here is a brief example of how themes might be noted in session summaries:

> Session 3: Child displayed intensity when engaged in play regarding feeling abandoned by his mother. He appeared to relate feeling abandoned with his younger siblings. Child demonstrated little hope of feeling connected.
>
> Session 5: Child continued to display fear of being left alone and abandoned by his mother figure. He appears to blame his younger siblings for being left alone.
>
> Session 7: Child displayed similar fears of abandonment from previous sessions but attempted to find protection so that he would not be abandoned. He appeared to demonstrate an understanding of his mother's emotional state.
>
> Session 9: Child is exploring multiple ways to help protect his relationship with his mother. He is spending a greater amount of time providing protective sources instead of destructive forces.

Cautions Regarding Theme Work

Working with themes is not necessary to the effectiveness of CCPT. The relationship between therapist and child is the most healing factor of the play therapy process. However, themes provide the therapist with a way to understand clients more fully and hopefully lend themselves as a way to deepen the therapeutic relationship. I also greatly appreciate the use of themes in working with parents. But the exploration of themes lies within the context of the healing relationship and therapeutic environment. They should never supersede these factors and should only work to enhance them.

Therapists are cautioned about the analytical nature of working with themes. Identifying themes requires thinking about the client from an objective therapeutic perspective. Because it is a cognitive process, it has little benefit in the playroom. Effective play therapy involves "being with" the client in the moment. If play therapists engage in cognitive conceptualization during play sessions, they risk losing connection with the child, which is where true understanding is found. For thematic work to be beneficial to a client, the therapist conceptualizes outside the playroom. Through consultation and the review of video recordings, a therapist begins to form thematic hypotheses that can then be used in the playroom in the form of more focused responses, if deemed appropriately effective.

All of this "thinking" takes place outside the playroom so that the therapist is prepared when entering the playroom to convey understanding and acceptance of the child in the present moment.

Themes are not definitive constructs. They are changing and flexible, just as clients are changing and flexible. What appears to be a clear theme in one session might appear quite murky in the following session. The therapist demonstrates flexibility in hypothesis testing to arrive at a theme that is resonant with the client. Again, supervision and consultation are extremely helpful in providing alternative thematic ideas that might not occur to the play therapist in the relationship.

Finally, the person of the therapist influences the conceptualization of themes. As with all humans, play therapists are influenced by their previous experiences and their perceptions of those experiences. A self-aware play therapist acknowledges the impact of past experiences on current practice and conceptualization of clients. Play therapists lacking in self-awareness can be dangerous by placing their own themes onto clients. I once supervised a play therapist who brought me three different cases over a month's time where she was certain that the child was being sexually abused in each case. As I observed and processed recorded sessions with her, I became concerned that she projected much more meaning into the children's play than I would have expected. After the third case, I shared my concerns with her, including her focus on sexual abuse and her apparent anger with the clients' parents. She revealed that she had been sexually abused as a child. Although she was in therapy during adolescence, she had not participated in counseling as an adult. Her new occupation of play therapist was bringing up past issues and perceptions that she acknowledged as impacting her judgment with clients. She took a break from her counseling training and entered into therapy. When she came back a year later, she was much more effective in her role as therapist and was able to openly discuss when she felt her past was influencing her professionally. This is an example of a more serious case but I have observed lesser projections onto children from other therapists, such as when a therapist has control issues and believes that clients are challenging him personally instead of recognizing the child's theme as separate from the therapist. Identifying and working with themes requires flexibility and self-awareness on the part of the therapist if it is to benefit the client.

Behaviors and Themes

To clearly distinguish between play themes and play behaviors, I have put together a list of common themes and behaviors. This is by no means an exhaustive list but it might help guide a therapist in identifying themes.

Table 7.1 Examples of Play Behaviors

Exploratory — Exploring Toys in Playroom	Aggression	Good Guy vs. Bad Guy
Death	Burying	Drowning
Burning	Breaking and fixing	Cleaning
Messiness	Destruction	Containment
Rescue	Escape	Feeding and care taking
Organizing	Sexualized	Parent play
Conflict	Failure	Attainment
Gift-giving/creating	Stealing	Hoarding
Physical contact with therapist	Competition	

Examples of Play Behaviors

Aggression is a primary example of a play behavior that lends no meaning in understanding the client. Aggressive play is defined as physically acting out against objects or people in the playroom. Sexualized play is also a behavior that is often confused with a theme. Children might engage in sexual acts, act out sexual acts with toys, dress up or dance in a sexually provocative way, or talk about sex. None of these concrete behaviors help us understand the child's theme regarding the sexual play. For example, a 5-year-old boy places a male adult doll on top of a male child doll and acts out anal intercourse. This reveals that the child has been exposed to sexual knowledge and possible experience beyond what is developmentally appropriate. The play therapist will need to respond by taking appropriate action to make sure the child is safe. However, thematically, the play therapist would be looking for more context to the play. When the child acts out intercourse with the dolls, does he take the adult voice or the child voice? Is someone being hurt? Is someone enjoying hurting someone else? Is anyone fighting to stop? Is anyone crying? Is it completely silent? These contextual clues help figure out the meaning for the child. From this sexual experience, the child might identify with the aggressor and derive a theme of power/control. Or the child might take on a powerless/hopeless theme that there is no way to help self. There could be countless ways a child has derived meaning from the experience; and to be most helpful in play therapy, play therapists would need to identify this meaning, not just label it as sexualized play. Table 7.1 is a list of common play behaviors that may indicate several different themes.

Examples of Play Themes

Table 7.2 presents a list of common play themes seen in play therapy. Each theme is listed with an accompanying statement that helps explain the child's perspective. Again, this is by no means exhaustive and there could

Table 7.2 Examples of Play Themes

Theme	Internal Statement
Relationship	It's important to me that we are connected. I want to connect with you or others.
Power/Control	I must be in control of my environment to feel safe. I must have power over you or others to be worthy.
Dependency	I can't do things on my own. I am not capable. Others must help me.
Revenge	I need to hurt others to feel that I am worthy. I must get back at others for hurting me.
Safety/Security	I must figure out ways to stay safe. It's up to me to make things secure.
Mastery	I must accomplish things to feel competent. I must do things right to feel worthy.
Nurturing	I want to give to others to help them. I want to take care of others to be connected with them. Giving to others helps me feel that I am giving to myself.
Grief/Loss	I am hurting because I have lost someone or something that was important to me. I am trying to figure out why I lost someone or something that was important to me.
Abandonment	I have been left alone. I am alone.
Protection	I must protect myself from someone or something. I must protect others from someone or something.
Separation	I am hurting because I have experienced being separated from someone or something that was important to me. I am trying to figure out why I have been separated from someone or something that was important to me.
Reparation	I can figure out how to make things better. I am capable of building ways to make things better.
Chaos/Instability	I am confused by my world. I don't know how to bring order to my world. It's out of my control.
Perfectionism	I must do everything right to be worthy. I am a complete failure if I make any mistakes.
Integration	I see how good and bad fit together. I can make sense of different parts of my world coming together.
Hopelessness	I have given up. Nothing will get better for me or others. There is no one who can help me.
Helplessness	I am incapable of taking care of myself. Others must take care of me.

Continued

Table 7.2 (*Continued*) Examples of Play Themes

Theme	Internal Statement
Anxiety	I am fearful of the world/my world.
	I am fearful of not being worthy.
Self-sufficiency	I don't need anyone. I can make it on my own.
Resiliency	I can make things better.
	I can make it through tough times.

be many more identified play themes seen in play therapy. This table only serves to help the play therapist identify internal statements that are being communicated by the child.

Conclusion

This chapter has presented the meaning of themes, how to identify them, and how to use them in play therapy. In addition, I attempted to explore the difference between play behaviors (actions in the playroom) and play themes (meaningful metaphors of internal statements). The exploration of themes in play therapy is experimental, and this chapter attempted to communicate my conception and experiences with children in play therapy at a deeper level of understanding. Play themes may serve the advanced play therapist by offering a comprehensive framework for understanding and conveyance of that understanding.

CHAPTER 8
Progress and Termination

Child-centered play therapy (CCPT) is predicated on the valuing of each and every individual child who enters therapy. The child is a unique person with a growing sense of self in relation to the environment. The goal of therapy is not to solve a problem or set of problems, but rather to serve the child. There is no ideal state that is the objective of therapy because person-centered therapy emphasizes the process of becoming fully functional, as characterized by openness to experience, living in a state of awareness, and trusting the organism (Wilkins, 2010). There is no end to growth and change. One implication of holding such a noble belief in the continued growth of humans is a limited ability to measure progress in terms of traditional medical model methods. Measurement of change is challenging in CCPT. Although a therapist might experience a felt sense of qualitative change in session, he or she might be pressured to provide objective evidence of that change with little success.

The medical model applied to therapy categorizes intervention as a problem-solving method in which a client enters therapy with symptoms that need to be diagnosed; then a treatment will be applied to the symptoms and a cure will emanate. The medical model is rejected by person-centered philosophy as inapplicable to CCPT because therapists are working with people, not symptoms. In addition, there is little to no evidence that the medical model is effective in the intervention of feeling, thought, and behavioral stressors (Whitaker, 2010; Wilkins, 2010). The use of diagnosis serves as a method for assessing change in many therapeutic approaches. Because therapists diagnose according to behavioral criteria, progress is determined by an observation of decreasing symptoms. Person-centered therapists have eschewed the procedure of diagnosis as part of the medical model's attempt to diminish the person of the client. However, it is recognized that diagnosis is a reality of current mental health practice and CCPT therapists will be required to diagnose in some settings. Wilkins (2010) summarized the person-centered approach to diagnosis and assessment in three main points: (1) diagnosis is irrelevant to person-centered therapy and may be harmful to the client or relationship, (2) diagnosis is a reality in current psychotherapy and person-centered therapists must take this into account, and (3) when assessment focuses on the client and involves the client's knowledge of self, it can be advantageous in person-centered therapy. Therefore, person-centered therapy differentiates between the process of diagnosis and the process of assessment. Assessment of client experience and progress can be beneficial to the process of therapy.

Process and Stages of Play Therapy

Assessment of play therapy is useful when aligning the evaluation process with the process described in person-centered therapy. The first step in assessing person-centered therapy is to evaluate the six conditions necessary for change. Prior to and throughout play therapy, the therapist assesses the client and counselor's level of contact, the client's level of incongruence, the therapist's level of congruence, the therapist's experience and communication of empathy, the therapist's experience and communication of unconditional positive regard, and the client's ability to receive the therapist's attitudinal qualities. Wilkins (2010) suggests specific questions for the therapist as follows:

1. Are my potential client and I capable of establishing and maintaining contact?
2. Is my potential client in need of and able to make use of therapy? That is to say, is my potential client in a state of incongruence and vulnerable and/or anxious?
3. Can I be congruent in the relationship with my potential client?
4. Can I experience unconditional positive regard for this potential client?
5. Can I experience an empathic understanding of the potential client's internal frame of reference?
6. Will my potential client perceive at least to a minimal degree my unconditional positive regard and empathy? (pp. 183–184)

The CCPT therapist will continue to assess these six conditions throughout the therapeutic relationship with each child. Assessment of the conditions is especially warranted when the child appears to be regressing in presentation or increasing her or his problematic behaviors outside the play session.

The process of play therapy is not easily defined. In 1942, Rogers outlined the process of therapy in terms of what the therapist provides and what could be expected from the client over the course of therapy. Later, Rogers (1961) attempted to define the steps of personality change as observed in clients. Rogers (1942) presented a 12-step process of person-centered therapy that explains when and how change occurs. He developed his conceptualization of the process from experience and clearly stated that each step of the process can be mingled with one another. Steps were not intended to be strictly linear but occur in approximate order. The following is a presentation of the steps with an attempt to align them to play therapy.

1. The child comes for help. In adult therapy, this is seen as the adult taking responsibility and seeking support for change. However, in child therapy, the child is often not requesting help nor has awareness of needing help.
2. The helping situation is defined. For play therapy, this is structured as the initial statement: "This is the playroom. In here you can play with the toys in lots of the ways you like."
3. The play therapist encourages free expression of feelings by offering a permissive environment with few limits and by reflecting the child's feelings, thoughts, and actions without judgment.
4. The play therapist accepts, recognizes, and clarifies negative feelings through sending a felt sense of warmth to the child and reflecting the child's feeling and meaning behind negative or aggressive actions.
5. The child will begin to show positive expression of feelings. This can be reflected in the child's play or verbalization, or possibly a nurturing expression to the therapist.
6. The play therapist accepts positive feelings in the same manner as negative feelings. The child's positive expression is not praised, but accepted as equal to negative feelings and a valued part of the personality.
7. This step acknowledges the development of insight and acceptance of self by the client. For children, this step entails a growing sense of self-acceptance evident through an expression of patience or approval of created works of art, accidents, or failures.
8. The child will clarify possible courses of action or decisions. Play scenes may encompass the selection or expression of different solutions or coping skills. Sometimes the child is able to verbalize actions available to them outside the session.
9. Child begins to initiate positive action outside the therapy session. Actions are often small and go unnoticed by caretakers (therapists

should keep a keen eye on any such missed actions). The child might ask to do a chore or initiate a conversation with a peer.
10. Child continues to grow in self-acceptance and understanding of self. This is referred to as insight for adults. Child's expression of self-acceptance will be displayed through play and action, and sometimes verbalization.
11. Positive action increases inside and outside of session. Children will increase positive actions, especially if encouraged by the consequences. Relationship between child and therapist is warm and reciprocal.
12. Child experiences a decreased need for the relationship with therapist, although still feels warmly toward therapist. Child is experiencing self-confidence in and out of session.

In working toward understanding and assessing the process of play therapy, a therapist seeks to determine at what stage she is in a relationship with the child. Recognizing where a relationship is in the process provides information on how the therapy is progressing and how a child might be responding to the relationship. Rogers (1961) further contributed to understanding the process of therapeutic change by concentrating on explaining the growth that occurs with the client throughout the development of change. He described a seven-stage process of personality change that also can be applied to children in play therapy:

Stage 1. Child is defensive and resistant to change. Child may exhibit several behaviors to express this resistance, such as refusal to go to the playroom, refusal to play, or diffuse aggression expressed through damage to playroom, self, or therapist.

Stage 2. The child becomes slightly less rigid and will begin exploratory play or benign conversation. Child may engage in play that is repetitive of movies, video games or television shows, with seemingly little emotion.

Stage 3. Child begins to engage in meaningful play but in a way that still allows for emotional distance. Play disruptions might occur often during this stage as child moves toward a sense of safety.

Stage 4. Child engages in consistent meaningful play for at least a few minutes each session. Child will share affect in play and possibly with therapist. Verbalization with therapist may increase as relationship with therapist increases.

Stage 5. Child regularly shares a variation of emotions. Play progresses toward being self-directed and self-enhancing. Coping skills and decision-making skills are used with more confidence. Child accepts more responsibility for actions. A common occurrence in play therapy during this stage is for children to catch themselves when they are about to break a limit, something like (as child fills up the fourth bucket of water), "Oh, the sand is only for three containers of water; I'll pour this back in the sink."

Stage 6. Child moves toward congruence and demonstrates unconditional positive regard for others. This is demonstrated through less demanding behavior of adults and a developing sense of patience with self.

Stage 7. Child is a fully functioning self-actualized individual who is empathic and shows unconditional positive regard for others, within the limitations of developmental appropriateness.

Wilkins (2010) summarized that adults in Stages 1 and 2 are unlikely to be in therapy because there is no realization of a need for help; it is within Stage 3 that adults are likely to initiate therapy; Stages 4 and 5 represent the most active stages in therapy; Stage 6 typically represents the onset of irreversible personality change; and in Stage 7, adults no longer need a therapist. This summary as applied to children is somewhat different because children are likely to be in therapy from the beginning of Stage 1 due to a parent or caretaker's initiative. The therapist may have to access patience as the child naturally develops a safety level within the relationship before moving into the more active change-evident stages.

Two play therapists, Clark Moustakas (1973) and Louise Guerney (2001), developed theories of process change in play therapy related to child-centered or relationship-based play therapy. Moustakas (1973) observed through qualitative analysis that maladjusted children appeared to go through stages of change in play therapy. In the explanation of Moustakas' play therapy stages, children enter play therapy with undifferentiated emotions that are mostly negative; gradually their hostility becomes more focused and is directly expressed; anger becomes more ambivalent and positive emotions emerge; and finally, they engage in positive play and express a balance of positive and negative emotions. Moustakas' stage theory has been applied to working with aggressive children and is discussed in greater detail in Chapter 10.

Guerney (2001) developed a broad categorization (early, mid, later) of play therapy stages in her early work with children. She later defined these stages in the following order: Warm-Up, Aggressive, Regressive, and Mastery. In the Warm-Up stage, children orient themselves to the playroom, the therapist, and the structure of play therapy. Their play may be less focused or more tentative. During this stage, the child is concentrating on developing a relationship with the therapist and there are growing signs of trust and rapport building. In the Aggressive stage, children have moved beyond the adjustment to sessions. They feel secure enough to deal with the therapeutic issues underlying the presenting problems. Children will engage in aggressive behaviors, which will rise to a peak in this stage. The level of aggressive behavior depends on the baseline aggressive behavior presented initially by the child. Children who are not aggressive may exhibit mild aggression while children who present as aggressive may engage in destructive aggression levels during this stage. The expression of aggression is a sign that the child is feeling secure in the therapeutic relationship. The Regressive stage is marked by a decrease in or extinction of aggressive behaviors. Children may exhibit regressed play behaviors below what is expected for their age. They may also demonstrate play in which they seek to be nurtured or they nurture others, possibly the therapist. Children in this stage may also demonstrate dependency on the therapist. At the final Mastery stage, regressive play decreases as mastery behaviors appear. Children may engage in games, playing honestly and responsibly. They may also attempt to provide help to the therapist. Children at this stage demonstrate competency themes in their play behaviors and in their interaction with the therapist.

Rogers, Moustakas, and Guerney clarified in presentations of their process theories that stages did not apply to all clients, nor do they always develop in a linear fashion. The hallmark of person-centered theory is the assumption that no single explanation can be applied to all individual clients. Table 8.1 provides a visual table to help compare and contrast the four theories as applied to play therapy. I find that each of the theories is useful and somewhat accurate in its own way. I apply a different stage theory when assessing progress in a therapeutic relationship according to the individual context and case of the child. I have not found any of them to be applicable to all play therapy relationships, as would be expected from a child-centered play therapist.

Measuring Progress

To summarize thus far, the first step in measuring progress is to understand the theory and process of play therapy, which can be applied to the therapist's recognition of client change. However, no one theory appears to be able to define the multitude of processes that occur on an individual case-by-case basis. Thereby, measuring progress becomes more of a challenging prospect because it will need to be applied individually. Each child is considered individually by the therapist based on the child's presenting concerns, personality, expression of thoughts and feelings through play and verbalization, and the relationship between child and therapist. These considerations are used to fully conceptualize the child in a holistic way and provide guidelines for recognizing progress.

Table 8.1 Stages of Therapeutic Change in Person-Centered Therapy and CCPT

Rogers (1942) (Conceptualized for Adult Therapy)	Rogers (1967) (Conceptualized for Adult Therapy) Client:	Guerney (2001)	Moustakas (1973)
Individual comes for help The helping situation is defined Counselor encourages free expression of feelings in regard to the problem	Is defensive and resistant to change Is slightly less rigid; talks about external events or people Talks about self but as an object; avoids the present	Warm-Up: • Child orients to playroom, therapist, and structure • Child builds relationship with therapist • Play may be unfocused	Diffused emotions: • Emotions are undifferentiated and mostly negative • Emotions are magnified, generalized, and easily stimulated and evoked
Counselor accepts, recognizes, and clarifies negative feelings Full expression of negative feelings leads to tentative expressions of positive ones	Talks about deep feelings; develops relationship with therapist	Aggressive: • Child deals with issues underlying symptoms • Aggressive behavior at its peak, relevant to baseline	Direct hostility: • Attitude of hostility becomes gradually sharpened and more specific as relationship with therapist is clarified and strengthened • Anger is expressed more directly and related to particular persons • As expressions are accepted, the feelings become less intense and affect the child less in total experiences

Continued

Table 8.1 (*Continued*) Stages of Therapeutic Change in Person-Centered Therapy and CCPT

Rogers (1942) (Conceptualized for Adult Therapy)	**Rogers (1967) (Conceptualized for Adult Therapy) Client:**	**Guerney (2001)**	**Moustakas (1973)**
Counselor accepts and recognizes positive feelings Client experiences understanding and acceptance of self Clarification of possible decisions and actions Emergence of small positive actions Development of further insight Increasing positive action by client Client experiences decreasing need for help	Expresses present emotions; relies on self decision making; takes more responsibility Shows rapid growth toward congruence; develops unconditional positive regard for others Is fully functioning; self-actualized	Regressive: • Aggressive behaviors decrease or disappear • Regressive behaviors appear • Nurturance or dependency may be themes Mastery: • Regressive behaviors decrease or disappear • Mastery play becomes predominant • Child may show leniency or care for therapist • Child demonstrates competency behaviors	Anger and ambivalence: • Anger is still specific but a variety of ambivalences appear • Fluctuate play between aggression and more positive forms of expression Positive feelings: • Play is more realistic • Positive and negative attitudes are more separated

In an early attempt to develop criteria for measuring progress in play therapy, Haworth (1982) presented the following guides:

1. Is there less dependence on the therapist?
2. Is there less concern about other children using the room or seeing the therapist?
3. Can the child now see and accept both good and bad in the same person?
4. Have there been changes in attitude toward time, in terms of awareness, interest, or acceptance?
5. Has there been a change in reactions to cleaning up the room—less concerned if meticulously clean before, and more concerned if messy before?
6. Does child accept self?
7. Are there evidences of insight and self-evaluation? Does the child compare former actions with present ones?
8. Is there a change in the quality or amount of verbalization?
9. Is there less aggression toward, or with, toys?
10. Does the child accept limits more readily?
11. Have the child's forms of art expression changed?
12. Is there less need to engage in infantile or regressive play?
13. Is there less gorging on cookies? Does the child now offer some to the therapist?
14. Is there less fantasy and symbolic play, and more creative-constructive play?
15. Has there been a diminution in the number and intensity of fears?

Through these questions, Haworth attempted to address the individuality of the child by acknowledging that some children will want to move in one direction while others will move in a different direction, in both cases moving toward progress. A simple example of this acknowledgment of individuality can be seen in the example of messiness. When Sophia enters play therapy, she gets out each toy, one by one, and puts it back before playing with another one. She makes sure that each time she puts a toy back, it is in exactly the same position. When she paints, she makes sure to not drip any paint. When Sophia accidentally gets a slight brush of paint across her thumb, she quickly runs to the sink to wash it off. She seems anxious if anything is out of place. When Megan enters therapy, she slides all the toys off the shelf and throws them in the sandbox. When she paints, she mixes all the paints together until there is a blob of black paint left on the paper. She flicks paints across the room and accidentally spills paint as she is painting. She then empties all the glue onto the painted paper and attempts to put it into the sandbox but complies when the limit is set. Sophia and Megan are exemplary of the child-centered rationale toward individual measurement of progress. Progress for Sophia would be measured by her ability to freely flow in her play from toy to toy. She would exhibit a sense of ease when a slight mess occurs on her or in the playroom. Progress for Sophia is exhibited through increased messiness. Progress for Megan would be measured by her ability to apply a sense of order to her play. She would exhibit the ability to organize and move through play in a way that is focused to allow for full expression. Progress for Megan is exhibited through decreased messiness.

In searching for a method to examine progress on an individual level, I developed a continuum of play behaviors that may occur in play session (see Figure 8.1). Measurable characteristics or behaviors demonstrated by the child in play session are marked on a continuum between dichotomous categories. Table 8.2 lists the categories and explanations for each end of the spectrum.

The purpose of listing the dichotomous characteristics is to provide a continuum of measurement for the play therapist. For each characteristic, the play therapist rates the child on the continuum based on the child's behavior in individual play sessions. It is assumed that the child will move in one direction or another for the characteristics that are significant for that individual child. There is no assumption of value on either end of the continuum. The play therapist assesses growth according to movement in the direction that is helpful to the child. The Play Therapy Progress Worksheet (Figure 8.1) allows the play therapist to rate multiple sessions on one form. The rating of multiple sessions provides the therapist with a progressive look at the child over time in play therapy. Figure 8.2 presents an example of the Play Therapy Progress Worksheet when it is completed. In the case of Courtney, the worksheet indicates that across 10 sessions she demonstrated less aggressive behaviors, more sustained play, more constructive and clean play, more frequent response to limits, more meaningful play, more positive affect, increased mastery play, higher frustration tolerance, and less giving-up behaviors. She remained consistent in her self-directed play, energy level, verbal frequency, demonstration of affect, and age-appropriate play. She varied inconsistently in her involvement of the therapist, both in verbalization and play. Issues where Courtney remained consistent or varied inconsistently were not of concern to the play therapist at the initiation of play therapy and hence did not pose a problem for progress assessment. Figure 8.2 demonstrates the individual nature of assessment for play therapy and how it can be applied in a systematic manner that informs the play therapist of progress.

Use of Formal Appraisal in the Assessment of Progress

The continuum of play therapy progress offers an individual model for assessing progress that takes into account the uniqueness of the child and also integrates a holistic observation of the child. However, traditional methods of assessment include the use of tests that are considered reasonable and valid objective measures of appraisal. Although testing is not commonly welcomed by person-centered therapists due to the use of objective measures inaccurately applied to subjective beings, Bozarth (1998) listed three conditions for person-centered assessment, including the client might request to take tests, policies of the setting might demand testing of clients, and testing might be an objective way for the client and counselor to consider a decision for action. In CCPT, the client will rarely request to take a test or rarely will testing be used as a way for the client and counselor to consider a specific action. However, CCPT therapists often work in settings where testing is demanded. For certain settings, testing is used to provide evidence of effective practice.

I would like to add one more condition when testing appears to be beneficial for CCPT. Testing, especially testing data collected from parents, can be helpful in developing a working relationship with parents. Most data collected on children is reported by parents or caretakers. Hence, data serves not only to give information about the child but it also provides information about the parent and the parent/child relationship. For example, a frequently used assessment in child therapy, the Parenting Stress Index (Abidin, 1995) prompts parents by asking what behaviors engaged in by the child are stressful to the parent. Results indicate not only what child behaviors generally concern, but also what behaviors are most problematic for the parent. This particular assessment gives a snapshot of family dynamics and how the parent copes with the stress produced from the parent/child relationship. In addition, CCPT therapists can use testing data to provide information to parents about concrete change observable in the child. Often parents do not consciously notice behavioral changes in their children due to daily interactions that might be challenging. But they will report differences when specifically prompted by behavioral measures of assessment. CCPT therapists share testing results with parents to illustrate demonstrative change that has been noticed and reported by parents themselves. This can be a powerful tool in parent consultations.

Yet, from a person-centered perspective, testing should never be used in isolation to make therapeutic decisions. The Play Therapy Progress Worksheet (Figure 8.1) offers a three-prong approach to determining progress. In the first section, an individual observation system for continuum change is utilized. In the second section, the therapist uses two sets of data to inform change based on behavior and relationships outside of therapy. First, the play

Child/Age: ______________ Play Therapist: ______________ 1st Session Date: __________ Today's Date: __________ # of Sessions: __________

ASSESSMENT OF IN-SESSION PROGRESS

Continuum of Play Therapy Progress (Rate the characteristic for each session by session number)

	<——————————>							
Aggressive								No aggressive behaviors
Self-directed play								Dependence on therapist for play initiative
Low energy								High energy
Sustained play behaviors								Inability to sustain play or carry out play scene
Destructive								Constructive
Messy								Clean
Highly verbal								No verbalization
Responds to limits appropriately								Breaks limits
Involves therapist in play								Plays alone
Involves therapist in verbalization								No verbalization or verbalizes as narrative without therapist interaction
Play is thematic, seemingly meaningful								Play is rote, and seemingly meaningless to child
No affect observed								Intensity of affect expressed
Positive affect (laugh, smiles, content)								Negative affect (anger, cries, sadness)
Age-appropriate play								Regressed play
Mastery play								No mastery play
Inability to tolerate frustration								High level of frustration tolerance
Keeps trying when play is difficult								Gives up when play gets difficult

ASSESSMENT OF OUT-OF-SESSION PROGRESS:

Parent Report: ______________________________

____

Other Adult Reports: ______________________________

____

Assessment:	Pre-Date:	Post-Date:	Circle one:	Improvement	No Improvement	Decline
Assessment: ________	Pre-Date: ________	Post-Date: ________	Circle one:	Improvement	No Improvement	Decline
Assessment: ________	Pre-Date: ________	Post-Date: ________	Circle one:	Improvement	No Improvement	Decline
Assessment: ________	Pre-Date: ________	Post-Date: ________	Circle one:	Improvement	No Improvement	Decline
Assessment: ________	Pre-Date: ________	Post-Date: ________	Circle one:	Improvement	No Improvement	Decline
Assessment: ________	Pre-Date: ________	Post-Date: ________	Circle one:	Improvement	No Improvement	Decline

Figure 8.1 Play therapy progress worksheet.

Table 8.2 Continuum of Play Therapy Progress Characteristics and Descriptions

Category	High	Low
Aggressive	Child exhibits high number of aggressive behaviors	Child exhibits no aggressive behaviors
Self-Directed Play	Child initiates play with confidence and thoughtful planning	Child does not play at all or completely dependent on therapist to direct play
Energy	Child exhibits high level of energy throughout session	Child exhibits no energy for play or verbalization
Sustained Play Behaviors	Child is focused in play and carries out full play scenes	Child is easily distracted and unable to play in any one behavior for more than seconds or a minute
Destructive	Child is highly destructive toward playroom, materials and therapist	Child is constructive in play, building and creating throughout session
Messy	Child is very messy.	Child is very clean.
Verbalization	Child frequently talks throughout session	Child says nothing
Response to Limits	Child immediately complies with any limits set	Child breaks all limits set by therapist
Play involvement of therapist	Child involves therapist in all play	Child plays alone
Verbal involvement of therapist	Child verbally interacts with therapist throughout entire session	Child says nothing directly to the therapist
Meaningful Play	Child demonstrates focus and concentration in play. Child plays out at least one consistent theme played out with toys or verbalization	Child shows no interest in play scenes
Affect	Child expresses intense emotions throughout session	Child demonstrates no observable emotions
Positive Affect	Child demonstrates positive affect throughout session, such as smiling, laughing, or appearing content	Child demonstrates negative affect throughout session, such as anger, crying, sadness
Age-Appropriate Play	Child exhibits play behavior expected of a child his or her age	Child engages in regressed play behaviors, below the expected age level

Table 8.2 (*Continued*) Continuum of Play Therapy Progress Characteristics and Descriptions

Category	High	Low
Mastery	Child engages in play behaviors that demonstrate competency	Child demonstrates no mastery play and even sets self up for failing in behaviors
Frustration Tolerance	Child is able to tolerate a high level of frustration, continuing to try or staying calm when things get hard	Child cannot tolerate any level of frustration or failure
Effort	Child keeps trying behaviors after they become challenging	Child gives up immediately when play becomes difficult

therapist notes change, or lack thereof, as reported by parents or other adults involved in the child's daily interactions. Second, the play therapist notes differences in testing scores between testing periods, concluding whether there has been improvement, no improvement, or worsening of scores. Figure 8.2 offers an example of Courtney's out-of-session progress. The therapist documents the mother's report that Courtney has decreased tantrums and showed positive behaviors of helping with chores. Yet, she still has approximately two tantrums a week. Courtney's teacher reports that she has not sent Courtney to the office since last report but Courtney still exhibits minor but frequent behavioral problems. Finally, the therapist documents appraisal results from two measurements: the Child Domain of Parenting Stress Index (PSI; Abidin, 1995) and the Aggression subscale of the Child Behavior Checklist (CBCL; Achenbach & Rescorla, 2001). On both assessments, Courtney scored toward the desired range showing an improvement.

The use of testing data with reliable instruments can aid the play therapist in working in settings that require traditional measurement and in working with parents to identify areas of need for parent education and support, as well to demonstrate observed progress. Table 8.3 (at end of chapter) lists assessments that are frequently used in working with children in play therapy and represent legitimate sources for the collection of data. The Play Therapy Progress Worksheet offers a format where the therapist can collect qualitative and quantitative data to make an informed and individualized decision regarding the effectiveness and progression of play therapy.

Termination

As discussed, when a therapist believes that the release of the self-actualizing tendency determines ultimate functionality and health, reaching

Child/Age: *Courtney Willis* Play Therapist: *Dee Ray* 1st Session Date: *09/10/11* Today's Date: *12/15/11* # of Sessions: *10*

ASSESSMENT OF IN-SESSION PROGRESS

Continuum of Play Therapy Progress (Rate the characteristic for each session by session number)

	<———						———>	
Aggressive	1,2	4	3,5,9	6,7,8	10			No aggressive behaviors
Self-directed play	1,2,3,4,5 8,9,10	6,7						Dependence on therapist for play initiative
Low energy					6,8,10	3,5,7,9	1,2,4	High energy
Sustained play behaviors		9,10		7,8	6	4	1,2,3,5	Inability to sustain play or carry out play scene
Destructive	1,2,3,4	5		6,7	8,9,10			Constructive
Messy	1,2,3,4	5		6,7,8,10		9		Clean
Highly verbal	1,2,3,4,5,6, 7,8,9,10							No verbalization
Responds to limits appropriately	9,10	7,8	1,6		4,5		2,3	Breaks limits
Involves therapist in play		1	8,9,10	2	5	3,4	6,7	Plays alone

Involves therapist in verbalization	8	10	7,9	4,5,6	1,2,3			No verbalization or verbalizes as narrative without therapist interaction
Play is thematic, seemingly meaningful	1,2,3,5,8,9,10	4,6	7					Play is rote, and seemingly meaningless to child
No affect observed					5,6,10	7,9	1,2,3,4,8	Intensity of affect expressed
Positive affect (laugh, smiles, content)			6,7,9,10	8	4	5	1,2,3	Negative affect (anger, cries, sadness)
Age-appropriate play	1,2,3,4,5,7,9	8,10					6	Regressed play
Mastery play		9,10		6,7,8		4	1,2,3,5	No mastery play
Inability to tolerate frustration	1,2,3,4		5,8	6,9	7,10			High level of frustration tolerance
Keeps trying when play is difficult		10	6,7,9	5,8			1,2,3,4	Gives up when play gets difficult

ASSESSMENT OF OUT-OF-SESSION PROGRESS:

Parent Report: *Mother reports a decrease of tantrums at home, and two incidents where C. asked to help do a chore. C. still has about 2 tantrums a week but down from daily reported at intake.*

Other Adult Reports: *Teacher reports no incidents where C. was sent to office but usually goes down a color on behavioral chart every couple of days due to yelling out in class or arguing with other students.*

Assessment: *Parenting Stress Index CD* Pre-Date: *9/10/11* Post-Date: *12/15/11* Circle one: **Improvement** No Improvement Decline

Assessment: *Child Behavior Checklist Agg* Pre-Date: *9/10/11* Post-Date: *12/15/11* Circle one: **Improvement** No Improvement Decline

Assessment: ______________ Pre-Date: __________ Post-Date: __________ Circle one: Improvement No Improvement Decline

Figure 8.2 Play therapy progress worksheet (completed).

termination decisions is challenging. Many child therapies support termination when certain symptoms or behaviors become extinct or fall into a nonclinical range on objective assessments. West (1996) concluded that a therapist considers termination when a child exhibits greater self-confidence, decreased problem behaviors, is realistic about problems and challenges, and shows improvements in peer relationships and school. She further noted that play in session is age appropriate, organized, and constructive, and there is a trusting relationship between child and therapist. Because a child is much more than the sum total of behaviors, termination decisions in CCPT are made according to holistic standards, bringing together a conceptualization of the child in session, at home, and at school. West (1996) proposed the following questions when deciding upon termination:

1. Is there improvement in most of the child's presenting problems?
2. Is the child feeling better?
3. Is the child getting along well at home and school?
4. Does the child have a reasonably realistic understanding of family background?
5. Would the child benefit from referral elsewhere?
6. Is play therapy proving unhelpful, or is it rejected by the child or caretakers?

Using a combination of the child progress assessment and West's questioning, a therapist can come to a conclusion regarding whether or not termination is indicated. Many CCPT therapists may consider it a fortunate circumstance to consider mutual termination. Often, therapy is terminated abruptly at the will of the parent without therapist or child consent. The abrupt ending to therapy is disconcerting for a child and may result in the child's interpretation that she did something wrong or that the therapist no longer wants to see her. CCPT therapists first address termination in initial parent consultations, explaining the need for a planned approach to ending therapy. When parents decide that termination is in order before the therapist or child agrees, the therapist makes a concerted effort to contact the parent to plead the case for one last session with the child.

In ideal cases, the child has come to a natural end of therapy wherein he is expressive and constructive in session; maintains warm relationships with some adults and children, including the therapist; and engages in self-enhancing behaviors. Upon deciding that termination is appropriate, the therapist discusses the possibility of termination with the parent. When therapy is going well, parents may be hesitant to terminate because they worry about possible regression on the part of the child and are also concerned about suffering from a lack of support when they no longer see the therapist. CCPT therapists are very encouraging during this phase of therapy, reminding parents of their growth that correlated with the child's development. The play therapist will discuss options for returning if the parent feels that the child is in need of therapy following termination. Therapists inform children of termination 3 to 4 weeks prior to the final session. A longer period of time may result in increasing the child's anxiety regarding the impending separation, and younger children are usually confused by lengthy timelines. A shorter period of time does not allow the child time to emotionally prepare for separation. Children should be informed of termination at the beginning of a session so that the therapist can observe and support any possible immediate or shortly delayed reactions.

Play therapists are often surprised, sometimes disappointed, by a child's reaction to termination. A child may respond with a simple "okay" and it is never spoken of again. At the final session, the child may simply wave goodbye to the therapist without any demonstrative sadness or upset. Although this may be hurtful to the play therapist's feelings or bruising to the ego, this type of ending is developmentally appropriate. In addition, a simple ending to the relationship indicates that the child was ready to end and progress to the next stages of self-actualization without dependence on the therapist. Play therapists will often ask if they should give the child something or do something different in session to mark termination. Again, as in all CCPT, the child takes the lead. If the therapist decides to do something to mark the ending of therapy, it is purely for the therapist, not for the client. In alternate scenarios, children may want to give something to the therapist. In these cases, if the child asks first, "What do you want me to give you for our last time?" I will respond, "Anything that you make is something I will like." This answer is clearly out of alignment from nondirectivity, but I do find that the need for congruence overrides nondirectivity when ending therapy. If a child wants to celebrate the ending of the relationship with a symbolic token, I, as me, truly want to participate in that celebration. I attempt to avoid any encouragement for the child to buy a gift; but if a child arrives at our final session with a gift (of small monetary value), I will usually accept such a gift as a way of honoring the child's intention. Whether or not the child acknowledges termination, I commemorate our relationship by taking a few minutes to review the child's file and reading through all the documents in a personal way before filing that final termination summary.

Table 8.3 Frequently Used Assessments in Child Therapy

Attention Deficit Disorders Evaluation Scale Third Edition (ADDES-3)

Author: S. McCarney
Description: ADDES enables educators, school and private psychologists, pediatricians, and other medical personnel to evaluate and diagnose Attention-Deficit/Hyperactivity Disorder in children and youth from input provided by primary observers of the student's behavior.

Behavioral Assessment System for Children (BASC)

Authors: C. Reynolds & R. Kamphaus
Description: The BASC is a set of rating scales and forms using multiple raters to help understand the behaviors and emotions of children and adults. Scales include Teacher Rating Scale (TRS), Parent Rating Scale (PRS), Self-Report of Personality (SRP), Student Observation System (SOS), & Structured Developmental History (SDH).

Child Behavior Checklist/1½–5/LDS & Child Behavior Checklist/6–18 (CBCL)

Authors: T. Achenbach & L. Rescorla
Description: The CBCL/1½–5/LDS obtains parents' ratings and descriptions of problems, disabilities, what concerns parents most about their child, and the best things about the child.
The CBCL/6–18 obtains reports from parents, other close relatives, and/or guardians regarding children's competencies and behavioral/emotional problems.

Child Interpersonal Relationships and Attitudes Assessment (CIRAA)

Authors: R. Holliman & D. Ray
Description: The CIRAA is an instrument designed to measure outcomes and progress related to child self-control, interpersonal relationships, coping skills, and internal locus of evaluation.

Children's Depression Inventory (CDI)

Author: M. Kovacs
Description: The CDI measures cognitive, affective, and behavioral signs of depression in a child.

Children's Play Therapy Instrument (CPTI)

Authors: P. Kernberg, S. Chazan, & L. Normandin
Description: CPTI is an observational tool to measure activity in play therapy sessions to aid in diagnosis and progress measurement.

Conners' Rating Scales-Revised (CRS-R)

Author: K. Conners
Description: CRS is an instrument that uses observer ratings and self-report ratings to help assess attention-deficit/hyperactivity disorder (ADHD) and evaluate problem behavior in children and adolescents.

Continued

Table 8.3 (*Continued*) Frequently Used Assessments in Child Therapy

Developmental Assessment of Young Children (DAYC)

Authors: J. Voress & T. Maddox

Description: The DAYC is a battery of five subtests, including cognitive, communication, social-emotional development, physical development, and adaptive behavior designed to measure different but interrelated developmental abilities.

Direct Observation Form (DOF)

Authors: S. McConaughy & T. Achenbach

Description: The DOF is designed to assess problems and on-task behavior observed in settings such as classrooms, group activities, and recess.

Eyeberg Child Behavior Inventory (ECBI)

Authors: S. Eyeberg & D. Pincus

Description: ECBI is an instrument that measures disruptive behaviors in children and the frequency with which they occur.

Functional Emotional Assessment Scale (FEAS)

Authors: S. Greenspan & G. DeGangi

Description: The FEAS is used to observe and measure emotional and social functioning in infants, young children, and their families. Observation of functioning includes interactions, self-regulation, problem solving, imagination, and pretend play, to name a few.

Gesell Developmental Observation (GDO)

Authors: F. Ilg, J. Keirns, & S. Iba

Description: The Gesell Developmental Observation (GDO) is a comprehensive developmental screening tool that assists parents, educators, and other professionals in understanding characteristics of child behavior in relation to typical growth patterns.

Index of Teaching Stress (ITS)

Authors: R. Abidin, R. Greene, & T. Konold

Description: The ITS measures the stress a teacher experiences in interaction with a particular child regarding the student's behavior, the teacher's perception of the teaching process, and the teacher's perception of support from others.

Parenting Stress Index, 3rd Ed. (PSI)

Author: R. Abidin

Description: The PSI measures the stress a parent experiences as a result of interaction with a child. It identifies parent/child relationship problem areas in parents of children ages 1 month to 12 years.

Piers-Harris Children's Self-Concept Scale, Second Edition (Piers-Harris 2)

Authors: E. Piers, D. Harris, & D. Herzberg

Description: The Piers-Harris 2 provides an overall view of an individual's self-perception and helps identify children, adolescents, and teenagers who may require further testing and possibly treatment.

Continued

Table 8.3 (*Continued*) Frequently Used Assessments in Child Therapy

The Pictorial Scale of Perceived Competence and Social Acceptance for Young Children (PSPCSAYC)

Authors: S. Harter & R. Pike

Description: The PSPCSAYC measures a child's perceived competence and perceived social acceptance in the four domains of cognitive competence, physical competence, peer acceptance, and maternal acceptance.

Self-Perception Profile for Children (SPPC)

Author: S. Harter

Description: The Perceived Competence Scale for Children assesses children's perceived competence in scholastic competence, social acceptance, athletic competence, physical appearance, and behavioral conduct. In addition to a self-reported concept score, administrators can administer an importance scale for each domain to establish its centricity to the child's overall self-esteem.

Student-Teacher Relationship Scale (STRS)

Author: R. Pianta

Description: The STRS measures student/teacher relationship patterns in terms of conflict, closeness, and dependence, as well as overall quality of the relationship by measuring the teacher's perception of the relationship with a particular student.

Teacher Report Form/6–18 (TRF) & Caregiver-Teacher's Report Form/1½–5 (C-TRF)

Authors: T. Achenbach & L. Rescorla

Description: The C-TRF obtains ratings by daycare providers and teachers on 99 items, plus descriptions of problems, disabilities, what concerns the respondent most about the child, and the best things about the child.

The TRF is designed to obtain teachers' reports of children's academic performance, adaptive functioning, and behavioral/emotional problems.

Trauma Play Scale (TPS)

Authors: J. Findling & S. Bratton

Description: TPS is an observational scale designed to detect differences in the play therapy behaviors of children with a history of interpersonal trauma.

Revised Children's Manifest Anxiety Scale: 2nd Edition (RCMAS-2)

Authors: C. Reynolds & B. Richmond

Description: RCMAS measures the level and nature of anxiety, as experienced by children today.

Source: Table originally compiled by Dee Ray, Ryan Holliman, Sarah Carlson, and Jeffrey Sullivan.

References

Abidin, R. (1995). *Parenting stress index* (3rd ed.). Lutz, FL: Psychological Assessment Resources.

Achenbach, T., & Rescorla, L. (2001). *Manual for the ASEBA school-age forms and profiles.* Burlington, VT: University of Vermont, Research Center for Children, Youth, & Families.

Bozarth, J. (1998). *Person-centered therapy: A revolutionary paradigm.* Ross-On-Wye: PCCS.

Guerney, L. (2001). Child-centered play therapy. *International Journal of Play Therapy, 10*(2), pp. 13–31.

Haworth, M. (1982). Assessment of individual progress. In G. Landreth (Ed.), *Play therapy: Dynamics of the process of counseling with children* (245–246). Springfield, IL: Charles C Thomas. (Reprinted from *Child psychotherapy: Practice and theory*, by M. Haworth, 1964, New York: Basic Books).

Moustakas, C. (1973). *Children in play therapy.* New York: Jason Aronson.

Rogers, C. (1942). *Counseling and psychotherapy.* Boston: Houghton Mifflin.

Rogers, C. (1961). *On becoming a person: A therapist's view of psychotherapy.* New York: Houghton Mifflin.

West, J. (1996). *Child centred play therapy* (2nd ed.). London: Hodder Arnold.

Whitaker, R. (2010). *Anatomy of an epidemic: Magic bullets, psychiatric drugs, and the astonishing rise of mental illness in America.* New York: Crown.

Wilkins, P. (2010). *Person-centred therapy: 100 key points.* New York: Routledge.

CHAPTER 9
Parent Consultation

Play therapists often cite working with parents or guardians as the most challenging aspect of counseling with children. To have access to working with children, play therapists must forge a positive and collaborative relationship with their parents. When parents feel alienated, blamed, or ignored in the therapy process, they will typically terminate services. Whether viewed as right or wrong, this is the legal right of a parent. Hence, play therapists benefit from keeping the acknowledgment of this legality at the forefront of their work with parents. By respecting parents' legal rights, play therapists will naturally move to creative means to keep the parent involved so that the child remains in play therapy.

Legal rights clarify the power of the parent regarding children, yet there are great therapeutic benefits to involving parents in play therapy. First, parents are the primary caretakers of children. They are the most important figures in a child's life. The absence or involvement of a parent in a child's life is critical to the child's development and emotional stability. Although Axline (1947) believed that play therapy is effective without parent involvement and this has been documented in research, research has also demonstrated that play therapy has greater effects with parental involvement (Bratton, Ray, Rhine, & Jones, 2005). The process of involving parents is not clearly understood. There is a question regarding whether parent involvement is more successful because the therapist is facilitating changes in the system by enhancing the parent/child relationship, or the parent is utilizing new skills taught by the therapist, or the parent is feeling better because of emotional support provided by the therapist and can thereby give more emotional support to the child, or other facilitative factors. Not enough research has been conducted in this area to isolate how parent involvement is helpful. More than likely, benefits are enhanced because of a combination of factors. It appears common sense that play therapy will make a bigger difference if play therapists can engage parents in the process.

Attitudes for Building a Successful Therapeutic Relationship With Parents

To work with parents, play therapists benefit from exhibiting attitudes that provide a basis for a collaborative relationship. A play therapist's goal is to develop a relationship with parents in which parents feel accepted, understood, and safe so that they will be open to encouragement, skill building, and change in parenting style. The following attitudes are listed as integral in building a working relationship. These attitudes are necessary when parents have access to a child and it appears that they will continue to have access. However, it is noted that at times, the play therapist may be forced to act in a role that limits the relationship between a parent and a child when the child is in danger.

1. *Respect for the parent's role.* Play therapists will be much more effective if they recognize the role of the parent as the most important relationship in the child's life. Although the therapist has much to offer a child, what the parent offers is of much more importance in the overall development of the child.
2. *Respect for the parent's knowledge of the child.* Even the most neglectful of parents often possess intimate knowledge of the child and the child's development needed by the play therapist to enhance the effectiveness of the therapist. The therapist may be the expert regarding children but the parent is the expert regarding the specific child in therapy. Parents provide factual information such as the child's developmental milestones and family interruptions during the child's lifetime, but they also provide perceptual understanding such as relationship factors between child and adults and early personality characteristics of the child. Gathering this information helps guide the play therapist in conceptualizing the child's overall case and specifying systemic interventions that will facilitate growth.
3. *Affection for the parent as a person.* In working with children who have experienced traumatic parenting or a lack of parenting, play therapists may often become less likely to present as caring and nurturing to parents. As child advocates, play therapists often struggle with anger and frustration toward parents who are perceived as damaging to their children. However, play therapists

will be more effective if they can overcome such feelings and work toward a true care for the parent. As learned in basic counseling courses, people respond when they feel cared for and safe. In my years of counseling children, I have developed a belief that most parents are operating at least 10% better as parents than how they were parented. Although I have no evidence that this is a true, this belief helps me accept parents where they are and develop compassion so that we can work collaboratively.

4. *Patience.* The relationship between parent and play therapist is enhanced when the play therapist maintains an attitude of patience. Play therapists may be eager to make quick systemic changes by immediately teaching skills and solving problems. However, working at the parent's pace is most effective. Some parents need several consultation sessions before they feel safe enough to move forward with change. Some parents are eager for quick fixes to big problems and pressure play therapists to respond quickly. In this situation, play therapists might respond by building the relationship with the parent through reflection and processing of the parents' feelings of frustration. Teaching and skill building are most effective within the context of a safe relationship.
5. *Clear focus on child as the client.* In the model presented in this book, the child is the client and parents are seen as systemic partners in therapy. Hence, this is a different philosophy from other theoretical models where the family might be seen as the client. In a consultation model, play therapists define the child as client. Such clarity allows the play therapist to act accordingly with parents. All interactions between play therapist and parent are initiated to facilitate growth in the child. In this approach, when the play therapist or parent identifies needs for additional sources of help, such as counseling for the parent for individual issues that might be impacting their parenting or any issues of concern for the parent, the play therapist will refer the parent for those services. This helps clarify that the play therapist is the child's therapist, not the parent's. Although in my experience, one outcome to the consultation relationship is that parents feel supported and understood, which helps with their feelings regarding parenting and self-concept issues.
6. *Therapist as expert.* In child-centered play therapy (CCPT), the relationship a therapist builds with the child and parent is the base for all change. Because of this core belief, some play therapists view the parent/consultant role as one in which the play therapist acts only from a relational model of genuineness, acceptance, and empathy. There is a lack of agreement regarding whether this is the

most effective role for the play therapist consultant. Some parents will absolutely respond to this type of relationship by transferring their experiences with the therapist to the child and change will occur. Yet, parents seem to need some sense of external confidence provided by the therapist in order to be open to relational factors. In other words, the play therapist needs to exhibit knowledge and experience regarding children and play therapy so that parents will feel safe enough to share their vulnerabilities and concerns. Just to be clear, I am not advocating that play therapists lecture, give advice, or direct parents. I am advocating that play therapists provide such expertise as knowledge of development, typical child behavior, and/or parenting skills that have worked in similar situations when parents are open to new information in which they have been lacking. This type of expertise is appreciated by many parents and helps build their confidence in the play therapy process.

Process of Consultation

The parent consultation model requires consistent contact between parent and play therapist for the purposes of providing support, teaching knowledge or skills, and monitoring progress. The recommended frequency of parent consultations is to hold a parent consultation every three to five sessions of play therapy. Frequency may be increased if a child or parent is experiencing a situational crisis and needs more support. If the parent consistently requests weekly consultations for support reasons, this might be a sign that the parent could benefit from personal counseling. Alternately, play therapists should be wary of limiting parent contact beyond five sessions (translated here as 5 weeks) because of the length of time in which the parent has no access to the therapeutic process.

The length and placement of parent consultation sessions is varied among play therapists and is often based on individual cases. Typically, a parent consultation is between 30 and 50 minutes. The most pertinent consideration in making the decision about length of parent consultation is the possible interference with the child's play therapy session. For practicality reasons, play therapists hold parent consultations either before or after child play therapy sessions so that the parent only has to attend therapy once. When this is the case, the child's time is likely to be infringed upon. I personally prefer to keep my parent consultation sessions to a maximum of 30 minutes. I also hold parent consultations following the child's play therapy session to ensure that the child gets the full session time; and if parents choose to extend the parent consultation time, it is interfering with their time or my time, not the child's time. Optimally, the play therapist holds parent consultations separately from the play therapy session time, and without the child present. This allows the play therapist to spend up to a full therapy hour with the parent and there are fewer distractions because the child is not waiting. Yet, this scenario is not practical for most play therapy cases.

For the benefit of the child, the play therapist seeks to involve all major caretakers of the child in consultation. This can include biological parents, stepparents, adoptive parents, custodial grandparents, or others. The goal is to involve in the therapeutic process those adults who spend the most time with the child. Hence, configurations of attendees of consultations might look different. Some consultations might involve mother and stepfather while others might involve father and stepmother or mother and grandmother. Just as the therapist has a plan for therapy for the child, the therapist should also have an organized plan for parent consultation based on the needs of each case.

Regarding the child's involvement in parent consultation, again play therapists act differently. Traditionally, young children do not participate in parent consultations because consultations are verbally based and it would be developmentally inappropriate to ask a 3- to 6-year-old to sit quietly as other people are talking about him. As children grow older, a play therapist might consider involving children in parent consultations, especially to participate in family problem solving or family therapeutic activities. Play therapists also need to consider the parent's ability to communicate effectively with the child. If the parent's method of communicating with the child is to negatively attack the child, then the play therapist might consider working with communication skills with parent before involving the child in parent consultations.

First Parent Consultation

The first parent consultation has one primary goal: to develop a relationship with the parent so that the parent brings the child in for a first play therapy session. The play therapist works to align with the parent for the beginning of a safe relationship that invites parent vulnerability, honesty, willingness to learn, and confidence in the process of play therapy. The first parent consultation is often lengthy, at a minimum of 1 hour but may extend to 2 hours, depending on the depth of the case. Because parents refer children to therapy with whom there might have been significant conflict or who have experienced trauma, it is recommended that children do not attend the first parent consultation. This allows the parent and therapist to speak freely without concern for the child's perception of the consultation. There are several features that contribute to a successful first parent consultation, including gathering developmental history, listening and conceptualizing parent concerns, defining and explaining play therapy, and addressing termination.

Developmental History Most play therapists operate within similar guidelines for initiation of therapy, including attaining background information and informed consent. These are ethical and legal requirements for most licensed mental health professionals. In addition to these components of paperwork involved with therapy, play therapists need full developmental histories for their clients. As covered earlier in this book (Chapter 2), development knowledge is a principal component of working with children. Not only does the play therapist need to understand typical development, but the play therapist should also have a thorough understanding of each client's developmental history. Developmental history involves a detailed understanding of a child's developmental milestones such as labor and birth, walking, talking, motor skills, potty training, reading, writing, and building of interpersonal relationships, just to name a few. Therapists must also be able to place these milestones within the context of the child, specifically family configurations, mobility, births and deaths, and other environmental factors. This type of thorough history allows the therapist to conceptualize possible barriers to the child's development and systemic factors affecting development. Table 9.1 offers an example of a thorough developmental history questionnaire. Please note that this form is intended as a structure for developmental history and does not replace a thorough background form that would request information regarding parent history, household information, and details regarding current diagnoses and medications.

For practical reasons, play therapists will start the first parent consultation by conducting a developmental history interview. The initial focus on development sends a subtle message to the parents that play therapy will go beyond just problem solving and consider the whole child. Second, beginning with the developmental interview sets a positive tone of looking at the child's growth, instead of the traditional focus on the child's problem. And finally, as parents answer developmental history questions, they reveal their concerns in a more detailed way regarding the child. Often, when a play therapist has completed the developmental history interview, parents have expressed their concerns in detail and this shortens the second phase of the consultation involving discovering parent concerns.

Parent Concerns After the developmental history, play therapists should specifically address the concerns of the parents regarding the child. This phase might begin by the therapist summarizing the concerns that were revealed during the developmental history and then asking if there are any further concerns. Another helpful step in clarifying parent concerns is to ask parents what they hope to see as a result of therapy. Clarifying parent expectations is an especially important step prior to the introduction

Table 9.1 Developmental History Questionnaire

1. Was the pregnancy planned? Any drug or alcohol use during pregnancy?
2. Were there any complications during the labor or delivery of child?
3. Did delivery occur as expected? On time, late or premature?
4. How long did the baby stay in the hospital after birth?
5. What was the baby's birth weight? Height?
6. What was the baby's Apgar score?
7. Were there any complications following delivery?
8. Were there any difficulties feeding during infancy?
9. How well did baby sleep initially? What are child's current sleeping patterns?
10. Did caregivers feel bonded to child throughout infancy?
11. What was the child's temperament throughout infancy?
12. Who did the baby interact with in early childhood? Or spend the most time with?
13. Were there any disruptions in child's caregiving relationships?
14. Describe caregivers' relationships with child.
15. Describe siblings' relationships with child.
16. Did you notice any differences in child's development compared to other children?
17. When did child start sitting up?
18. When did child start walking? Any complications?
19. When did child start talking? Any complications?
20. When was child toilet trained? Describe that process.
21. Does child experience any toilet complications currently?
22. If over 3 years of age:
    a. Does child know numbers or letters?
    b. Does child know how to read?
    c. At what level does the child read?
    d. Any complications with reading?
23. If over 3 years of age:
    a. Does child write?
    b. Any complications with writing?
24. How does child perform in physical activities? Involvement in sports?
25. If child is in school, how has child progressed in school?
26. How does child get along with authority figures such as teachers?
27. Does child have friends? How many? What are those relationships like?
28. Who does child currently interact with on a daily basis? Describe those relationships.
29. How many times has child moved throughout childhood? Describe those moves.
30. How many schools has child attended? Describe each transition.
31. Has child experienced any significant losses of family members, friends or pets?

of play therapy to the parent. The therapist will utilize these expectations later when explaining the play therapy process to parents.

Frequently, the parent's concerns are not aligned with the child's concerns; this becomes evident after the play therapist begins seeing the child. This mismatch between what parents would like to see differently in the child and what the child is working on in play therapy needs to be conceptualized by the therapist in a holistic way in order to address the needs of all parties. This will be discussed in more detail later in this chapter as part of subsequent parent consultations. At this time, the point is that therapists should be keenly aware of the parents' expectations from the very beginning of play therapy to establish an effective relationship.

Defining Play Therapy After the play therapist has explored the child's history and parents' concerns, the play therapist moves into the explanation of play therapy. This step is critical to the play therapy process because this is the parent's first exposure to how play therapy works and skepticism often runs high. Because the parent is unsure of the process, the play therapist needs to exhibit confidence in how to define play therapy, explain how it works, and explain how it will specifically address each child's needs. The effective play therapist has a memorized two- or three-sentence definition of play therapy that can be recited at any requested time. And each play therapist needs to use his or her own words to define the process.

Landreth (2002) defines play therapy as

> [A] dynamic interpersonal relationship between a child and a therapist trained in play therapy procedures who provides selected play materials and facilitates the development of a safe relationship for the child to fully express and explore self through play, the child's natural medium of communication, for optimal growth and development. (p. 16)

Although this is a thorough definition of play therapy, play therapists need to alter their definitions to fit their audiences. Throughout this book, several different definitions of play therapy can be found that were created for specific audiences. Parents will usually focus on children's behaviors, accomplishments, or self-confidence. Also, play therapists should be aware of the educational level of parents, including average vocabulary. Finally, I have experienced that child-centered play therapists often present themselves as passive participants in the play therapy process, using such terms as "I allow the child to…," "I let the child…," etc. This presentation of passivity does not inspire confidence from parents and also underestimates the work of the play therapist in the session.

Another definition that might address the above issues is

> Play therapy is a way of working with children in which they express themselves through play and toys. When I facilitate play therapy, I provide an environment where children experience safety and learn to feel self-confident, limit their problem behaviors, and tap into their potential.

This is not so much a definition as it is a goal statement of play therapy and should be used to initiate the explanation of play therapy. The goals listed in the definition statement are different phrases to present basic child-centered concepts such as self-responsibility, self-concept, self-direction, self-enhancing decision making, and internal self-evaluation.

Subsequent explanation of play therapy will integrate child-centered concepts with specific parents concerns. The following is a case example:

In the first parent consultation, David's parents express that they are worried about David's level of aggression toward family members and his disrespect toward them. They describe him as "out of control," "could care less about others' feelings," and "never takes responsibility." After hearing these concerns, the play therapist begins to describe play therapy and how it might help David.

Play Therapist: "It sounds like you're really worried that David doesn't care about others or you. In play therapy, he will be able to express himself through play and toys. When I facilitate play therapy, I provide an environment where children experience safety and learn to feel self-confident, limit their problem behaviors, and tap into their potential. For David, this means that he will be in a place where he can fully express what keeps him from expressing his care for others. As he expresses this freely, he can then develop a sense of self that is free to care and show care. I will provide a space for him to practice these expressions and skills, which means he will also experience limiting his behaviors that are out of control and learn better coping mechanisms to get his needs met. I cannot guarantee that this goal will be met, nor I can tell you when it will be met. I will have more information as David and I get to know each other. But this is how I expect it to work successfully for David."

The trick to providing an effective definition and explanation of play therapy is that the therapist is knowledgeable about the philosophical framework that guides CCPT. Because CCPT is based on a theory of humankind, it can be addressed to each client specifically. From presenting problems that involve severe interpersonal trauma to superficial externalizing problems, CCPT provides an understanding of how play therapists facilitate change and how clients change (see Chapter 3).

Other critical aspects of play therapy that need to be explained during the first parent consultation include the need for confidentiality, parent consistency, and possible challenges with progress.

Confidentiality As highlighted earlier, the play therapist's client is the child. As such, the child is owed confidentiality within legal and ethical limitations. The concept of confidentiality regarding children, especially young children, is difficult for some parents to understand. Under most legal standards, mental health confidentiality regarding children belongs to the parent. However, under most ethical guidelines, mental health professionals who work with children are required to maintain confidentiality with the child for the benefit of the child, but not to the detriment of the child. In other words, verbal and nonverbal expression of the child in session will be kept confidential unless the expression is perceived by the therapist to be harmful if not revealed to authorities or parents. Clear limitations of confidentiality are delineated as revelation of harm to self or others, or legal request for information. However, many other areas are not so clear and are decided by individual therapists as to whether the child would benefit from sharing information with the parent.

The solution to confidentiality issues relies on informed consent of the client; and in the case of children, informed assent. The play therapist should work toward explaining confidentiality as clearly as possible to the both the parent and child. For parents, it is helpful to discuss confidentiality from their perspective. As mentioned, most parents do not see the value of confidentiality for their children. The play therapist should address children's needs for a safe environment where they can express themselves freely without regard to others' feelings or rules of right and wrong. This safe environment will allow the child to feel fully accepted as is so that change can occur. Another concrete analogy that sometimes works with parents is to ask them to imagine going to therapy themselves where they reveal intimate details about their lives and then imagine that their therapists bring in their spouses or significant others to discuss what they revealed. This analogy usually helps create empathy on the part of the parent. If all else fails in trying to create understanding of confidentiality by the parent, the play therapist may ask the parents to trust the process for the first few weeks and see if confidentiality is still a concern for them.

Parent Consistency An additional concept for the play therapist to address in the first parent consultation is the need for parent consistency in bringing the child to play therapy. Although this concept can be addressed in a brief statement, it is a critical piece of information for the parent to receive. For play therapy to be effective, the parent needs to commit to the child's regular attendance at play therapy. Sporadic attendance interferes with child progress and severely limits progress.

Challenges to Progress One hypothesis about play therapy that is well known by play therapists but not known by parents is the idea that "things might get worse before they get better." In his explanation of the process of play therapy, Moustakas (1955) concluded that children's play and expression were typically negative and unfocused in the first two phases of therapy. Recently, Ray (2008) provided some evidence that although gains are made early in play therapy, the earliest sessions may possibly result in parent reports of worsening behaviors. And anecdotally, Axline (1964) provided a case example of a mother who reported that her son's behavior seemed to be more problematic after participating in therapy, even though great gains were made by the end of play therapy. Theoretically, Moustakas explains this expression of negative feelings as part of progress. Because a child does not understand the nature of negative feelings or problem behaviors, the initial response to being in an accepting therapeutic environment is to lash out indiscriminately before figuring out how to focus energy on a specific problem area or relationship. As children learn to directly express negative feelings, they also allow positive feelings, and ultimately a predominance of positive feelings prevails.

The play therapist may wonder how this lesson on play therapy progress is relevant to the first parent consultation. It is relevant because parents may become concerned that play therapy is not only not working, but it is actually harming their child if they do not have access to this information. Children may start to reveal strong negative feelings after two to four play therapy sessions in which they lash out at parents or those closest to them. When a parent experiences a display of this negativity, he worries that play therapy is actually making his child worse, not better. A common result is that the parent never shares this information with the play therapist but terminates the relationship with no explanation. A more proactive approach is for the play therapist to express this scenario as a possible occurrence that happens early in play therapy; and although it might be disturbing to the parent, it can be viewed as a sign that play therapy is working effectively.

Case examples about this particular dynamic abound in my current clinic. When play therapists do not explain this process early on in parent consultation, they might receive angry calls from parents regarding how harmful play therapy has been and a quick termination to therapy. Alternately, in one recent case, the play therapist explained this possibility in the first parent consultation. After 2 weeks of play therapy, the parent called the therapist to say thank-you and how great play therapy was going. As the parent and therapist talked, the parent revealed that the previously quiet and withdrawn child screamed "I hate you" to his mother.

The mother shared how she could not believe how the play therapist knew this would be happening and she was thrilled to see the progress. Rarely do play therapists get to experience such enthusiasm from such occurrences. Also, it should be noted that the child went on to make positive and effective progress at home and in session.

Termination As in all therapy, termination should be at the forefront and in discussion from the initiation of counseling services. The play therapist needs to briefly address termination in the initial parent consultation. Sometimes, discussion regarding termination is initiated by the parent, who asks how long it will take before the child is better. This is a great lead-in to talking about termination. Discussion regarding termination helps to alleviate parents' fears that there is something profoundly "wrong" with their child or that they will always be dealing with their child's problems. Discussion of termination leads to hope. Play therapists want to instill hope in parents in every way possible.

The discussion of termination also allows the play therapist to address the best way to terminate if the parent feels that services are not helpful. Play therapy is different from adult therapy in that when an adult decides to terminate, it is the adult's decision about his or her own life. However, in play therapy, the adult is deciding for the child. This is problematic because sometimes the adult decides to terminate when the child has developed a strong therapeutic relationship with the therapist. Hence, the need for a termination discussion is required early in parent consultation in case of situations where the parent is not happy with services; the play therapist needs to provide a path for how to best address this situation. The child will benefit if the play therapist acknowledges that not all parents will grow to believe in play therapy or in the play therapist, and this is understandable by the therapist. Yet, the play therapist emphasizes the need for the child to be able to properly terminate with the therapist. The following is an example of a short termination discussion that might take place in a first parent consultation.

Parent: "How long will play therapy take? How long until David is better?"

Play Therapist: "You're concerned about when you might see changes in David and you're hoping to be able to make plans around this. I'd like to assure you that I will also be working toward the time when your child no longer needs to come to therapy. Every 3 to 5 weeks, we will meet and we will discuss how things are going and what progress is being made. We will review what's best for David. Ultimately, it is your decision about whether David continues in play therapy, and I hope that I can provide the best input to help with that decision. If for some reason you are not happy with his progress or what is going on in therapy, including that you may not be happy with how I do things, I ask you to please let me know. It is understandable that at some point you may not feel your child is benefiting, and I'd like for us to feel free to talk about that. Also, if at any point you decide to terminate services, I will understand and will respect your decision. However, I do ask that you allow at least two sessions between the time that you tell me about termination and the time of actual termination. This will allow me to properly close my relationship with David so that no therapeutic damage is done."

Wrapping up the First Parent Consultation As apparent in the explanation of the first parent consultation, this is a lengthy and informative interaction between parent and play therapist. The parent gives information regarding the child's background, development, and parent expectations, and the therapist gives information regarding play therapy. All of this information is exchanged in the context of the ultimate goal of relationship alignment. One caution regarding first parent consultations is not following the urge to give advice or present education. Parents often present with significant concerns and a sincere request for help. They will describe specific situations and ask for help on how to address them. Because the relationship has not been fully formed, the first parent consultation is not the best time to present education. As will be seen in the following paragraphs addressing ongoing parent consultations, there will be time to present skills and knowledge to parents according to the therapist's conceptualization of the parent. When a play therapist has a solid relationship with and understanding of the parent, he will be more successful at presenting parenting information. Another reason to not present education in the first consultation is simply because it is too overwhelming for both the parent and the therapist. Even if the parent is requesting help, the parent consultation has lasted 1 to 2 hours already and any extension reaches the point of exhaustion. A lot of information has been shared so that to try and add more to the consultation is risking that some will be lost by sheer magnitude. And finally, because the play therapist has not met the child, any parenting information would be extremely limited in its effectiveness. One way to respond to a parent's request for help in this circumstance would be

> I hear that you are feeling very overwhelmed and lost on what to do. I want to promise you that in the next few weeks we will address all of these concerns. However, right now, I feel that without meeting David, I would be very limited in how much help I could provide you. I know it's hard but I'd like to wait a couple more weeks and then we will meet and discuss some of these specific situations.

Ongoing Parent Consultations

The first parent consultation depends on a fairly consistent structure across most presenting problems with most parents. Subsequent parent consultations are more complicated because they address the specific concerns of specific parents. Even though it is difficult to provide a structure for ongoing parent consultations that will fit for all cases, there are a few components that appear to be effective when tailored to each case.

List of Concerns In the first parent consultation, the play therapist clarifies parents' concerns about the child and expectations for therapy. This list is helpful for the design of ongoing parent consultations. Through collaboration with parents, the play therapist should prioritize which problems or expectations are most concerning for the parent. Although the play therapist may not be in agreement with some of the concerns or the priority of concerns, parent consultations are more effective when the play therapist can address parent concerns. When the play therapist has different concerns from parents, these concerns can usually be integrated into parent concerns so that multiple goals can be met. Here is one example:

Play Therapist: "You've identified several concerns about David such as his disrespect, his lack of care for others, his aggression and a few others, which ones are you most concerned about?"

Parent: "I think it's that he just doesn't do what I ask him to and then he talks back or argues. This causes the most fights in our house."

Following this interaction in the first parent consultation, the play therapist notes the parent's concern. During the first play sessions, the play therapist observes that David sets up doll figures who yell at each other and interrupt each other, both parent and child figures. The play therapist becomes concerned that two-way communication between parent and child appears to be a major problem. As a result, the play therapist decides that teaching the skill of reflective listening is the most helpful for both the parent's concern and the play therapist's concern. During the second parent consultation, the play therapist starts the education phase with the following:

Play Therapist: "When we last met, you expressed concern over David not obeying and talking back to you. I noticed in David's play sessions that this same issue appears to be a concern for him, specifically not feeling heard or listened to. I'd like to talk to you about a skill that we call reflective listening that will be the first step toward intervening with this specific problem...."

The play therapist then moves to teaching a short segment on how to reflect when a child talks or nonverbally expresses a feeling.

The list of parent concerns is an agenda set between play therapist and parent that will help lend structure to parent consultations. The play therapist will consistently check in with the parent to check the current relevance of the list and add play therapist concerns to the list that might be additional to the parent's concerns. It is important that the play therapist remain flexible with parent concerns yet also not allow week-to-week detailed interactions with the child to sporadically change the list. Allowing concerns to change from week to week is essentially allowing a crisis modality to prevail in parent consultations and does not work toward the accomplishment of more relevant long-term goals. The play therapist can guide the process to address the more specific weekly concerns to fit in with overall goals such as in the following example:

Parent: "This week he was out of control. He yelled at his teacher when she gave him an F on his homework. They sent him to the office and then he threw a chair in the secretary's office. When I came to pick him up, he told me I was stupid and it was my fault for not helping him with his homework."

Play Therapist: "That sounds really frustrating. And I can see how you are really angry with him. As I think about the goals we've been working on, including listening better, being respectful, and not being aggressive, which part of this incident would you place as your biggest concern?"

This helps the parent see that each incident is not isolated but sits within the overall context of therapeutic goals. The ability to help parents see beyond each incident contributes to the establishment of hope.

Steps for Ongoing Parent Consultations Parent consultations require play therapist attitudes that were presented earlier in this chapter, a solid base set by the parent consultation, and collaboratively working with parents regarding concerns. When these components are present, the play therapist can typically follow a structure that will help guide ongoing parent consultations. Steps include checking in with the parent, informing the parent of progress occurring in play therapy, teaching one skill concept, and role-playing that concept with the parent.

Step 1: Check in with the parent. In ongoing parent consultations, the first step is for the play therapist to check in with how things are going with parent and child. A typical introductory question is, "How's it been going since the last time we met?" This is a qualitatively different statement than "How are you doing?," which implies that the play therapist wants to hear only about the parent. Remembering that the child is the client, asking about something related to the relationship, child, or events sets the tone that the play therapist is focused on helping with the child and/or the parent/child relationship.

Upon being asked the introductory question, parents are often quick to answer with lengthy scenarios, possibly bringing up significant events but often sharing multiple and minor problems. Step 1 is usually the longest phase of an ongoing parent consultation. At this point, the play therapist will need to use therapeutic judgment to decide whether the parent consultation time should be used for support and relationship building or if the play therapist should guide the consultation to the succeeding steps. To make this decision, the play therapist might consider several factors, such as significance of events upon the child and/or parent (Was the child/parent harmed/traumatized from the event?); emotionality of parent in the moment (Is the parent emotionally stable?); or solidity of the therapist/parent relationship (Would listening/supporting parent be more effective for the relationship than moving to other steps?). There are times when the play therapist must simply move into the role of supporting the parent in order to support the child. This should be a conscious decision made by the play therapist, and caution should be used not to move into this role too often or on a permanent basis. Moving solely into the role of parent supporter indicates that the parent needs a personal counselor, which is not the play therapist role in this model.

When a play therapist decides to respond to parent sharing in Step 1 by planning to move to other steps, the play therapist will respond to the parents' stories and concerns by reflecting, clarifying, and integrating concerns into the ongoing list of concerns. The play therapist will then guide the parent to Step 2.

Step 2: Inform parent of progress in play therapy. Moving into Step 2 requires a transition statement such as, "I'd like to talk a little about my experience with David" or "I've noticed a few things about David I'd like to share with you." Another powerful method of transitioning to Step 2 is to link Step 1 concerns with play therapy progress. Something like, "When you talked about David yelling and throwing the chair, I was thinking that I've seen some of this type of impulsive aggressive behavior in his play sessions." The purpose of Step 2 is to share the play therapist's observations, experiences, conceptualizations, or other client information that will be helpful to the parent in understanding the child. A prerequisite for Step 2 is that the play therapist has thoroughly thought about the child, the context of child, the actions and words in play sessions, and the parent/child relationship. Optimally, the play therapist has developed a full conceptualization of the child and has thoughtfully reviewed how to verbalize the conceptualization to the parent. Step 2 is benefited by identification of play themes as discussed in Chapter 7 and an explanation of those themes to the parent. The play therapist keeps Step 2 short because too much conceptualization or explanation of themes might be overwhelming to the parent, and this is usually a time when the therapist wants the parent to take in important information. Here is one example, starting with the sentence used above as a transition in a second parent consultation.

Play Therapist: "When you talked about David yelling and throwing the chair, I was thinking that I've seen some of this type of impulsive aggressive behavior in his play sessions. When things don't go his way, he has a very physical and loud way of expressing his frustration. So far, he has found a way to express this appropriately in play session, but I can see how it would be a problem at home and school. He appears to be a child who externalizes his feelings, which just means, if he feels, others will see the good and the bad. In the following weeks, we will keep working on how David can express these feelings but in a way that will be more appropriate to his setting. I think we're on our way."

I would like to dissect this response a bit for understanding. In the first 3 sessions, David has demonstrated several outbursts, such as he threw blocks across the room when he could not get them to stand up the way he wanted, and he threw paint at the wall when the black paint ran through his yellow painted sun. In both of these incidents and a few others, the play therapist set the limit and David followed the limit. The play therapist conceptualized that David has a difficult time appropriately handling his frustration and anger, but that when approached with reasonable limits, he was able to respond appropriately. When he's happy, David tends to sing or dress up or talk a lot. Most of his actions and words in the playroom indicate his need to externalize his feelings. Because it has only been three sessions, it is difficult for the play therapist to determine if David has a need to act externally on the environment because he is developmentally impulsive, needing power and control, only knows how to express himself physically, or many other possibilities. Because the play therapist is unsure but has some hypotheses, the play therapist shares what is known to the parent in a way that will help the parent understand the child better. The one little fact that David externalizes his feelings will help increase understanding of the parent. Although this conceptualization does not solve any behavioral problems, it is hopefully contributing to improving the parent/child relationship and encouraging the parent. The point of this explanation is that even if play therapists do not have themes or conceptualizations figured out, they can still offer something helpful to parents based on their experiences with child clients.

A play therapist may be tempted to skip Step 2 due to the time used for Step 1 or possibly not being confident about what to share in Step 2 because of limited contact or understanding of client. I caution play therapists against skipping Step 2. Although parents may appreciate the understanding and support of the play therapist, they also expect to learn about their child from the play therapist. If the play therapist does not share progress or conceptualizations derived from sessions, parents may leave feeling that play therapy is not helping their child. I have often observed parents really "liking" their play therapist, but terminating because they never heard how play therapy was actually helping their child.

Step 3: Teach one skill-based concept at a time. Steps 1 and 2 focused on relationship building with the parent, and understanding the child or parent/child relationship. Step 3 moves the parent consultation into education. Parents are often lacking the skills needed to build a positive relationship with their children. It is a common saying that "you need a driver's license to drive a car but anyone can have a child." This type of saying has been culturally embraced because of its common truth that most parents have never received education regarding how to be parents yet they are expected to do it well. There is no other job for which this attitude is true. Hence, it seems to make sense that play therapists would take the opportunity of parent consultations to teach basic parenting communication skills.

However, some play therapists make the mistake of attempting to teach parents multiple skills at one time. Again, going back to cultural norms, would it make sense to teach addition, subtraction, multiplication, and division within a month's time to a second grader? Play therapists know that basic skills for communication need to move from the most basic to more advanced types of skills. Parents need to be taught skills as building blocks to enhance their relationship with their child. The end goal of teaching these skills is that child problematic behaviors will decrease as parent skills increase, and a positive relationship between parent and child is pervasive. But slow and steady teaching is the base for parents learning to integrate skills into everyday interactions with their child.

Play therapists are advised to teach one skill at a time for each parent consultation. Tackling one skill at a time allows for better parent understanding, integration, and later accountability. In addition, only addressing one skill at a time is practical for the time limitation of a parent consultation. Most skills can be taught within 5 or 10 minutes and do not need extensive lecturing or explanation. The skill-building step of each parent consultation starts with reviewing the accomplishment of the skill from the previous parent consultation. The play therapist will check in with something like, "Were you able to use reflective listening this week?," "How did that go?," "Can you give me an example?," "Did you think it was helpful?," "How did David respond when you did it?" If the play therapist determines that the skill was not learned or utilized, the parent and play therapist can review the skill again until the parent feels confident in its use. If the play therapist sees that the skill was accomplished, then the play therapist can move on to the next relevant skill. Following the outline of parent consultation steps, I will list skill concepts that I have found helpful with parents. Although a few of them are pertinent to all play therapy cases—such as reflective listening, encouragement, choice giving, limit setting, and problem solving—others might be utilized only for specific cases. In addition, the order of presentation of skills is up to the collaboration between the therapist and parent. I highly recommend that reflective listening be taught to all parents first; but beyond this recommendation, the play therapist would need to determine the specific needs of the parent and child.

Step 4: Role-play skills concept. Role playing with the parent in teaching skill concepts is integral to learning the concept. In my experience, parents may nod and feign understanding of the concept but when they actually try to enact the skill, they often demonstrate a lack of ability to use it. In Step 4, the play therapist will typically give two or three scenarios using the concept and act as both the child and the parent. This gives the parent a concrete demonstration of words and actions. After the play therapist acts out scenarios, it is time to involve the parent. The play therapist can give the parent the option of playing the parent or the child, whichever is easier at first. The play therapist provides scenarios that might happen at home, and then the play therapist and parent act out the scenario several times with the parent sometimes playing parent and sometimes child. The parent's ability to play out both sides (as parent and child) increases empathy toward how the child might perceive the parent. The therapist then asks the parent to identify a typical scenario at home in which the skill might be used. The therapist and parent act out the scene from both sides. As the play therapist's relationship builds with the child, role-play scenarios become more powerful because the play therapist may accurately respond as the child would. The parent consultation ends with the play therapist encouraging the use of this skill during the coming weeks and reminding the parent that the therapist will check in at the next parent consultation. The play therapist might also encourage the parent to call the therapist during the week if she would like to discuss the use of the skill—good or bad outcome. Finally, the play therapist sets up the next parent consultation so that the parent is assured of the next meeting but, of course, recognizing the need for flexibility as things progress in the child's life and therapy.

Skill Concepts

The following is a list of concepts that have been found helpful to parents in enhancing parenting skills and the parent/child relationship. This list is by no means exhaustive but is compatible with CCPT philosophy by helping the parent develop an environment of growth for the child. Play therapists can use a variety of presentation methods to teach skills. Videos, handouts, refrigerator pin-ups, and books are just a few of the visual methods that help enhance parent learning.

Reflective Listening Reflective listening involves listening with intent and verbalizing back to the person what was heard as accurately as possible. Reflective listening requires eye contact, limiting distractions, and focusing on the person who is talking. This is how I teach this concept to parents:

Play Therapist: "I'd like to talk to you about reflective listening. It's one of the first skills we teach parents. It sounds simple but it makes such a big difference in how your child responds to you. When you use reflective listening, you will try hard to concentrate on your child so you will look at your child, put down your cell phone or turn off the computer or TV, or whatever is distracting to you. Your child will be talking to you and you will be looking and listening. When your child is done, you will summarize what your child said or, in other words, you will say back what you heard your child say and it can be much shorter. So, for example, if I said, 'Mom, I hate school. I never want to go back. You can't make me.' For reflective listening, as a mom, I'm going to forget that you have to go to school and that this might be a problem and I'm only going to concentrate on trying to understand. So, I might say, 'It sounds like you really don't want to go to school.' And you might see your child explain further what the problem is instead of getting into a fight about making him go to school. Can we try a few examples?"

After a few examples and role plays…

Play Therapist: "That's great. You were really trying to come up with ways of showing me that you heard me. And this also works if your child is not talking, like when your child is storming around the room or is throwing something. It might help David to know that you care by saying something like, 'You seem really mad.' See how this might get a different response from David than if you said, 'David, pick that up and don't throw anything in the house.' You can always deal with the behavior a little later. Right now, you just want to show you notice that he's feeling bad or maybe good. So, if I ran into the room and said, 'Mom, my soccer team won and I kicked in the final goal.' How could you respond to let me know that you understand how I'm feeling?"

As can be read, this teaching and role playing (Steps 3 and 4) can be conducted in a short amount of time but actually covering an important concept.

If the parent is having a difficult time with role playing, the therapist might extend teaching the concept to the next parent consultation. Reflective listening is the cornerstone of effective communication, and play therapists will find it worthwhile to ensure the parent's integration of this concept.

Limit Setting When teaching limit setting to parents, play therapists teach parents in the same way they were taught: the ACT method (Landreth, 2002). Limit setting was discussed thoroughly in Chapter 6. The same steps and concepts apply when teaching limit setting to parents. Parents need to start by Acknowledging Feeling. This process began when the play therapist introduced reflective listening, so the parent should already see the value in starting with reflection. The second step is Communicating the Limit. When teaching this step, play therapists will help parents brainstorm limits that are helpful and enforceable in the home environment. And the third step is Target an Alternative. Again, parents often need help from the play therapist to create appropriate alternatives for behaviors at home. Teaching limit setting requires a significant amount of role playing and applying the ACT method to typical limit-setting problems in the home.

This particular concept might also need more than one parent consultation to help parents fully integrate the use of the skill at home. Because limit setting is one of the key skills parents need but one they are least effective in conducting, the play therapist should be wary of a quick review of limit-setting skills and moving on to more advanced limit setting. While it is true that some children are going to need more advanced limit-setting methods, when done correctly, ACT will take care of most limit problems and should not be discarded until it is proven that a particular child is in need of another method.

Self-Esteem Building and Encouragement At this point, it is becoming obvious that the play therapist is teaching the same skills learned by the play therapist to facilitate a setting of growth in play therapy. The play therapist is now using those skills to teach the parent how to facilitate the growth environment at home. The skill concept of self-esteem building and encouragement was discussed as a play therapist skill in Chapter 5. Because parents are taught by self-help books or common culture to praise their children, the concept of encouragement is often new to them and difficult to differentiate from praise. Play therapists will find it helpful to present this particular skill concept by giving parents actual words to use for encouragement. A handout is often helpful with sentence starters such as, "You really tried hard…," "You like how you…," "You are proud of …," or "It didn't turn out like you wanted, but you stuck with it." Other resources that are helpful in how to teach encouragement to parents can be found in Kottman (2003) and Nelsen (2006).

Choice Giving Choice giving is a concept that was introduced as an advanced skill in play therapy limit setting (Chapter 6). In CCPT, choice giving is often limited to an extension of limit setting. As a parent concept, choice giving can be used in a much broader way. When parents give children choices, they are allowing children to develop a sense of responsibility and understanding of consequences. Choice giving can begin early in child development to help children learn the skill of decision making but in play therapy, it is often introduced by the play therapist to the parent as a new skill. Even if choice giving is introduced for older children, it still has a positive effect but will take more time for the child to adjust to a new way of making decisions within parental limits. Choice giving involves allowing the child to begin to make choices regarding simple decisions and moving to more complex ones. Here is one way to teach choice giving to parents:

Play Therapist: "I noticed that you and David appear to struggle when it comes to him obeying your rules. As I've gotten to know David, I've observed that he has a real need to be in control and when he feels out of control, he exerts himself physically by yelling or throwing things. From what you told me, this method has come to work for him because you usually walk out of the room, or you scream back until you are in tears and give up. There might be a way to help David gain a sense of control without resorting to aggression and also give you back some control in your relationship. It is called choice giving. For choice giving, I will be asking you to come up with times when you feel that it would be okay to give choices to David regarding something at home. It could be something simple like, 'What do you want me to fix for dinner tonight, chicken or fish?' or a little more complicated like, 'You have homework for tomorrow. Would you like to do it now right after school or after dinner?' The trick is that you have to be okay with any of the choices you give so that when he picks one, you will be in agreement. This will allow David to feel that he has some control over his own life and doesn't need to resort to physical aggression to gain a sense of control. But it also allows you to be the parent and establish what choices are reasonable for him. In addition, David will learn to deal with the consequences of his choices, like if he chooses to do his homework right after school, he chooses to watch his favorite television show that night; but if he chooses to do his homework after dinner, he has chosen not to watch his television show. These are the small choices we make to get ready for adulthood and realize we are choosing our own consequences. Can you think of times when you would be able to offer David choices at home?"

Choice giving allows the parent and child to work together to teach the child how decision making works in easy and hard situations. It also takes some pressure off the parent by reminding the child that consequences occur as a result of personal choices. More details regarding choice giving can be found in additional resources such as Landreth and Bratton (2005) and Nelsen (2006).

Freedom Phrases or Returning Responsibility The concept of returning responsibility is tangentially related to choice giving. Again, returning responsibility is a basic skill learned in play therapy in which the goal is to send a message to the child that she is capable and worthy of making self-enhancing decisions. Ginott (1965) referred to this type of response as freedom phrases, which is an empowering title to use with parents. Freedom phrases include "It's up to you…," "You can decide…," and "It's your choice…." Freedom phrases imply that the parent is in agreement with whatever the child decides for a particular situation; but instead of making the decision for the child by giving a "yes" answer, the parent is returning responsibility to the child for the choice, thereby encouraging a sense of freedom within the child.

Circles of Communication The concept of circles of communication is presented by Greenspan (1993) as way of improving communication between children and adults (specifically, parents and teachers). Circles of communication are somewhat of an extension of reflective listening by concentrating on the patterns of communication between parents and children. This way of communication involves opening and closing circles instead of creating new strings of conversation. For a circle to be opened and closed, a child will initiate a conversation about a topic, the parent will respond directly to the topic by reflecting or commenting on the topic, and the child will respond on the same subject. This pattern continues until the circle is closed. An example of a closed circle is the following:

Child: "Steve and Kara got in a fight today at school."
Parent: "Oh, that sounds big. What was the fight about?"
Child: "Kara tried to steal the ball from Steve during the soccer game and he kicked her."
Parent: "What did you think?"
Child: "I think they shouldn't take it so seriously. It's just a game."

This might seem like a typical parent/child conversation but many parents and children do not effectively concentrate on their conversations enough to hold meaningful interactions. Here is how a typical problematic relationship might play out:

Child: "Steve and Kara got in a fight today at school."
Parent: "What do you want for dinner tonight? I've got to get your brother to a baseball game."
Child: "I've got too much to do tonight. I want to watch TV. I'm not going to the game."
Parent: "Did you have any homework?"
Child: "Ms. Stevens is stupid. She gives the dumbest homework."

As can be seen in this example, parent and child are not communicating with each other and appear to be having their own private conversations sparked by thoughts from the other. This example is not atypical with the significant amount of stress among many families. But this example provides an understanding of how parents and children miss the opportunity to really connect or understand each other, as well as learn poor patterns of relating. Teaching the need for opening and closing circles of communication helps parents see the importance of how they respond to their children and how good communication patterns help avoid future relationship problems, possibly behavioral problems.

Problem-Solving Methods All families are in need of problem-solving methods. Learning to solve problems is a basic life skill but most people approach it spontaneously and without a plan in place. When significant problems such as negative parent/child interactions or acute child behavior start to interfere with functioning, parents do not have the skills to solve problems objectively. Hence, emotionality ensues and problems are increasingly encountered with no resolution. There are practical and effective methods for solving problems available in the literature. Nelsen (2006) and Faber and Mazlish (1999) provide clear, concrete steps for parents on how to work collaboratively with their children to solve problems. Play therapists need to identify what problem-solving method seems most effective for them and regularly teach this method to parents. As children grow older, play therapists can involve parents and children to solve problems during parent consultations. The method needs to be practical enough for parents to easily use in the home setting. Faber and Mazlish (1999) recommend several steps to problem solving for parents, including:

1. Talk about the child's feelings and needs.
2. Talk about the parent's feelings and needs.
3. Brainstorm together to find a mutually agreeable solution.
4. Write down all ideas, without evaluating.
5. Decide which ideas you like and which ones you do not like, and make a plan to follow.

Although collaborative problem solving will be most effective when children reach concrete operations around the age of 7 or 8, the play therapist can help parents figure out a way to modify the process to involve younger children. By having a procedure to follow, parents are likely to feel confident when approaching family problems, including child behavior problems.

Special Playtimes The recommendation that parents spend individual time with a child and allow the child to play and lead is promoted in several sources (Greenspan, 2003; Landreth & Bratton, 2005). From a CCPT perspective, the most effective parent intervention method is participation in Child Parent Relationship Therapy (CPRT; Landreth & Bratton, 2005). If a play therapist is interested in CPRT, resources are available to teach this particular intervention (Bratton, Landreth, Kellam, & Blackard, 2006; Landreth & Bratton, 2005). In lieu of participation in CPRT when it is not available or not recommended for particular cases, a play therapist may recommend special playtimes between parent and child as a skill concept. Play therapists will see benefits from even short playtimes in which the parent concentrates on the child and child's play without other distractions and practices reflective listening skills. Here is an example of how to present this concept to parents.

Play Therapist: "It seems like things are really stressful at your house and something is always going on. This type of stressful environment might contribute to David not feeling in control of his life. I'm going to ask you to do something that might seem like it adds to your stress at first, but in the end I think it might decrease your stress. I'd like for you to take 15 minutes after work sometime this week where you will only concentrate on David. During this time, you will just sit down by him when he's playing with some of his toys. As you're sitting, you will focus on him and use your reflective listening skills that you've been practicing. It will really be a time all for him. Make sure to turn off your cell phone, TV, computer, or anything else that will distract you. When 15 minutes are up, you can excuse yourself by saying that you've got to change clothes, make dinner, etc., but thank him for sharing his time with you. Can you think of a time this week that you could make this work?"

For older children, a play therapist might suggest that the parent offer to play a game or make a dessert together, something that the child usually enjoys doing. The only rule is that the parent must be focused on the child and use reflective listening skills. One-on-one time helps children feel important in the lives of their parents, and it helps parents learn to enjoy being with their children without the pressure to make them do something or say something.

Role Playing or Practicing As the play therapist teaches skills to parents through the use of role play, parents will hopefully learn to recognize the value of role play and will also develop solid role-playing skills. These skills can actually be generalized from the parent/play therapist relationship to the parent/child relationship. When parents would like their children to learn new skills, they can practice these new skills in low-stress situations before the problem occurs. For example, if a child has difficulty waking up in the morning, the parent can role play a new morning ritual with the child during the afternoon or evening when the child is not preoccupied with another activity or stressor. To teach the introduction of role play for children to parents, the play therapist may have the parent list the most persistent behavioral problems she is experiencing with her child. The play therapist and parent would then role play how to role play a new way of dealing with the problem with the child. Effective role plays to change behaviors require low stress, lots of practice (continuing the role play until the child is showing the new behavior), lots of reflective listening, and possibly limit setting or choice giving. An example of role play with a specific behavioral problem is given in Chapter 10.

References

Axline, A. (1947). *Play Therapy*. New York: Ballantine.

Axline, A. (1964). *Dibs: In search of self*. New York: Ballantine.

Bratton, S., Landreth, G., Kellam, T., & Blackard, S. (2006). *Child-parent relationship therapy treatment manual: A 10-session filial therapy model for training parents*. New York: Brunner-Routledge.

Bratton, S., Ray, D., Rhine, T., & Jones, L. (2005). The efficacy of play therapy with children: A meta-analytic review of treatment outcomes. *Professional Psychology: Research and Practice, 36*, 376–390.

Faber, A., & Mazlish, E. (1999). *How to talk so kids will listen & listen so kids will talk*. New York: Avon.

Ginott, H. (1965). *Between parent & child*. New York: Avon.

Greenspan, S. (1993). *Playground politics: Understanding the emotional life of your school-age child*. Reading, MA: Addison-Wesley.

Kottman, T. (2003). *Partners in play: An Adlerian approach to play therapy* (2nd ed.). Alexandria, VA: American Counseling Association.

Landreth, G. (2002). *Play therapy: The art of the relationship* (2nd ed.). New York: Brunner-Routledge.

Landreth, G., & Bratton, S. (2005). *Child-parent relationship therapy: A 10-session filial therapy model*. New York: Routledge.

Moustakas, C. (1955). Emotional adjustment and the play therapy process. *Journal of Genetic Psychology, 86*, 79–99.

Nelsen, J. (2006). *Positive Discipline*. New York: Ballantine.

Ray, D. (2008). Impact of play therapy on parent-child relationship stress in a mental health clinic setting. *British Journal of Guidance and Counselling, 36*, 165–187.

CHAPTER 10
Aggression In and Out of the Playroom

Aggressive behavior is of particular interest in play therapy. Young children are naturally aggressive and as they grow older, they begin to channel aggressive energies into more productive and self-enriching behaviors. Child development theories hypothesize that the growth of verbal expression lessens the need for children to express themselves through aggressive actions (Dionne, 2005). Play therapists are challenged to delineate between aggressive behaviors that are developmentally appropriate and those that appear to interrupt functionality.

In child-centered philosophy, a child moves as a holistic organism, progressing to feelings, thoughts, and behaviors that are self-enhancing. Rogers (1989) summarized that a person is

> ...basically trustworthy, member of the human species, whose deepest characteristics tend toward development, differentiation, cooperative relationships; whose life tends fundamentally to move from dependence to independence; whose impulses tend naturally to harmonize into a complex and changing pattern of self-regulation; whose total character is such as to tend to preserve and enhance himself and his species, and perhaps to move it toward its further evolution. (pp. 404–405)

This perspective encourages play therapists to view child aggressive behaviors as attempts by children to move toward greater actualization and functionality.

A view of aggression as a movement toward enrichment is counter to current culture where aggressive behaviors by children are viewed as actions to be deterred, stopped, and squelched. When a 2-year-old hits or bites another child in preschool, the most common reaction is a threat of dismissal. Instead of accepting intent of actions and redirecting to more positive expressions, adults label aggressive behaviors as worthy of a clinical diagnosis and vilify the child's need for expression.

Social learning theorists argue that aggressive behavior is a learned behavior that increases with acceptance and continued exposure to violent actions. Through positive experiences of power, pleasure, or weakening of internal inhibitions, allowed aggression is expected to increase (Schaefer & Mattei, 2005). Some play therapists oppose the expression of aggression in the playroom because they believe it will increase in intensity if allowed and will transition to increased acts of aggression outside the playroom (Drewes, 2008). They suggest that children need to be taught alternative forms of expression by the play therapist so that children will not attempt aggressive behaviors.

Development of Aggressive Acts and Play

Just as walking and talking are skills cultivated and honed as part of development, appropriate expression of aggression is also a developmental skill. Children reliably begin to manifest aggressive behaviors such as pushing, hitting, kicking, and throwing about 18 months of age (Peterson & Flanders, 2005). Aggressive behaviors occur early in development and appear to be normal expressions of emotions or desires. Developmental patterns indicate that aggression is part of most preschoolers' behavior but that the majority of children cease to use physical aggression by the end of elementary school (Archer & Cote, 2005). Most conflict at preschool ages involves competition for limited resources. Aggressive behavior peaks in kindergarten and then declines over time (Peterson & Flanders, 2005). Children become less physically aggressive and violent over time. Most children follow declining trajectories of physical aggression between kindergarten and grade 6 (Archer & Cote, 2005).

Gender differences regarding aggressive behaviors are also apparent in development. Early on, boys demonstrate a propensity for aggression over girls, indicating that differences may be innate. In one study summarized by Archer and Cote (2005), toddler boys were twice as likely as girls to hit another child frequently. Sex differences are present early on and do not appear to arise as a result of differential socialization. However, girls seem to learn more quickly than boys to inhibit or control aggressive behaviors (Archer & Cote, 2005).

Archer and Cote (2005) studied data among thousands of children regarding the development of aggression and concluded there was no statistical evidence to indicate that children become more aggressive over time. Social learning theory would expect children to become more aggressive as they become older through exposure to social influences such as violent television programs, aggressive role models, or deviant peers. If aggression were the result of cumulative social influences, Archer and Cote expected a statistically significant group of children would emerge as children who began to use physical aggression during elementary school years. They were unable to identify such a group. The majority of those at risk for later violent behavior were already on high trajectories of physical aggression in kindergarten (Archer & Cote, 2005).

This research implies that kindergartners would be the most violent among all people. And this implication is a half-truth. Based on research, kindergartners display the most aggressive acts among all developmental levels. However, due to the lack of intentionality, ability to plan, and access to weapons, kindergartner actions are not the most violent. Their actions are typically impulsive and intended to express an immediate feeling or desire. As children who continue to express themselves through aggression grow older, they gain planning abilities and access to materials; hence, the consequences of their aggressive acts become more disturbing.

In normal development, children develop coping skills to express needs in appropriate ways that do not involve aggressive actions. However, sometimes there are interferences in the developmental trajectory and aggressive acts continue to increase, rather than decrease. Often, when children act aggressively, the expression is mistaken for an outburst of anger. But in my experience, aggression is minimally associated with anger but highly related to an internal sense of power and control over self or environment. Oaklander (1988) conceptualized aggressive acts as deflections of real feelings, not direct expressions of anger. Often, aggression is inspired by an inability to cope with the environment or an attempt to establish a social connection in the only way that is responded to by adults, however negatively. Eastman (1994) proposed that aggressive acts are triggered by anything that threatens to lower the sense of status and control, such as challenges to one's power base, including not being able to have one's way, having to follow a class rule, or having to complete an assignment that is boring.

Mediation of Aggression

Experts have identified internal and external processes that regulate the development of aggressive acts (Peterson & Flanders, 2005). These processes have been observed in both animal and human species. The internal process that regulates aggression is empathy identified as an innate characteristic. The ability to identify with the feelings and thoughts of others subdues the need to be aggressive with others who are perceived as similar. The social process that regulates aggression is associated with a dominance-hierarchy structure. In the social process, humans have a primal need for belonging and will limit or increase aggressive behaviors based on social acceptance.

Aggression in Play Therapy

Aggression and the accompanying skills and processes needed to sublimate aggressive tendencies into productive functioning are documented throughout child development literature. What appears to be more controversial is the need for aggressive expression in play therapy. In the child-centered approach, expression of aggression is accepted and understood as the need to bring all facets of self into awareness. The following is an explanation of the developmental trajectory from a child-centered perspective. Early in development, a child has the need to express desires or feelings in forceful ways, choosing methods "to be heard" such as aggressive acts. This is seen in a 2-year-old who does not ask for a cookie due to limited language ability or a perception that the request will be denied. Instead, the 2-year-old runs up to another child, pushes the child, and takes away the cookie. This is a very typical and normal action of 2-year-olds around the world. What is then very specific to each child is the reaction of others who respond to the action of the child. There are an infinite number of reaction possibilities, such as the other child starts to cry, an adult begins to yell, or possibly the adult pushes the child to teach a lesson. In each case, the child internalizes a message regarding aggressive acts. The internalized message might be, "I will be hurt if I hurt others;" or "When I pushed, I showed I didn't care about others;" or "I have to push to ever get what I want." Whatever the message, it becomes the child's internalized message about the role of aggression. Children who are frequently aggressive often operate under the belief that the need that motivates the aggressive act is the problem, not the act itself. This belief results in a distorted view of self, such as "my needs are wrong" or "my feelings are wrong" and culminating in any number of dysfunctional patterns of behavior. In CCPT, the goal for children who are aggressive is to facilitate the expression of the needs behind the aggression. However, by the time children are referred to play therapy, they have experienced the confusion between need and aggressive act so many times that they are unable to distinguish between them, as evidenced by using the aggressive act as an automatic reaction to expressing feeling or desire. They simply are not aware of the difference between having a desire and expressing that desire aggressively. Hence, it is very difficult for them to problem-solve other methods to express needs.

The effectiveness of mental health interventions relies on the therapist's facilitation of an environment that accepts the need to express aggression and encourages its expression for self-enhancing purposes. Based on this understanding, CCPT allows the child's expression of aggression as a first step in helping reveal the child's needs behind aggressive acts. Because the child does not differentiate between need and act, allowing the child to be aggressive in the playroom sends the message to the child that the child's need is valued. Once the child feels that this facet of self is understood and valued by the therapist, the child will also begin to accept and value these parts of self. This is the role of empathy that mediates aggression in play therapy. Based on principles of self-actualization (the cornerstone of CCPT), the child will then naturally find more self-enhancing ways to express needs. It is the quality of the relationship and the expression of aggression in the presence of an accepting, understanding, empathic adult that results in the expression being assimilated by the child differently than occurs in other settings (Trotter, Eshelman, & Landreth, 2003). Although this theory of aggression is poetic in its positivity, it is often difficult to accept in practicality.

As CCPT therapists work with children who are aggressive and allow time for the process to be successful, children's acts may intensify or increase in frequency, threatening the therapeutic relationship. Some children are extremely aggressive toward self, therapist, or others and might push the limits of play therapy to great frustration. Aggressive acting-out children depend on their self-protection mechanisms to provide a sense of security as a way of coping with the world. Feeling threatened by the intimacy of a therapeutic relationship, the child will likely be skeptical and resistant to a therapist who is perceived as trying to change the child's behavior. This unfamiliar quality of the relationship may be perceived as a threat by the child; therefore, the therapeutic relationship can be an external stimulus to aggression at first (Johnson & Chuck, 2001). Many play therapists experience difficulty in appropriately responding to a child who directs physical aggression toward them (Johnson & Chuck, 2001).

Moustakas (1973) and Mills and Allan (1992) have described the process of working with aggressive children in the playroom (Table 10.1). Moustakas (1997) observed that disturbed children enter the playroom with strong emotions that are typically diffuse and undifferentiated. As the child develops greater trust in the therapist, anger, hostility, and aggression will become more focused, directly related to particular persons. When these expressions are accepted by the therapist, the child's feelings become less intense and are less influential on the child's behaviors. Positive expressions begin to appear, mixed with aggressive play. In the final stages of play therapy, the child's play is more marked by positive feelings and play becomes more realistic. Mills and Allan (1992) described a similar process but noted the child's anxiety toward the therapist at the beginning stage. The therapist's acceptance, being newly experienced by the child, becomes a source of anxiety and the child is unable to tolerate the physical proximity of the therapist. The therapist sets limits with the child to create feelings of security and the child responds by testing

Table 10.1 Play Therapy Stage Theories for Working with Aggressive Children

Play Therapy Stages	Moustakas (1973)	Mills & Allan (1992)
Stage 1	**Diffused emotions:** Emotions are undifferentiated and mostly negative. Emotions are magnified, generalized, and easily stimulated and evoked.	**Establishment of accepting environment and relationship:** Therapist accepts child's need for aggressive play. Child is anxious. Therapist sets limits.
Stage 2	**Direct hostility:** Attitude of hostility becomes gradually sharpened and more specific as relationship with therapist is clarified and strengthened. Anger is expressed more directly and related to particular persons. As expressions are accepted, the feelings become less intense and affect the child less in total experiences.	**Limit–testing:** Child engages in least tolerable behaviors and tests acceptance of therapist. Child experiences ambivalence.
Stage 3	**Anger and ambivalence:** Anger is still specific but a variety of ambivalences appear. Fluctuate play between aggression and more positive forms of expression.	**Working stage:** Child engages in more interaction with therapist and may exhibit higher self-confidence. Aggressive behavior declines.
Stage 4	**Positive feelings:** Play is more realistic. Positive and negative attitudes are more separated.	**Termination:** Child moves from aggressive behaviors to socially acceptable behaviors. Sensitivity may increase.

limits, feeling confused by the unfamiliarity with this type of adult relationship. As the therapist continues acceptance and limit setting, the child engages in more interactive play and less aggressive play. Both descriptions of the play therapy process emphasize the healing factor of the relationship between the child and the therapist in reducing aggressive behaviors.

Facilitation of Aggression in the Playroom

The first step in allowing expression of aggression in the playroom is offering materials that encourage a wide range of expression. Kottman (2003) suggested that toys labeled as aggressive can be used to help children express feelings of anger and fear, learn to act out aggression symbolically, explore issues of power and control, protect themselves symbolically from dangers, build a sense of competence, explore ways they can keep themselves safe, and develop self-control in a safe environment. Therapists choose toys for the playroom based on their ability to be used in many different ways as decided by the child. There are certain toys that have historically been labeled aggressive but they serve diverse purposes in the playroom. Some of these toys include a punching bag/bop bag, weapons (guns, knives, swords, etc.), toy soldiers, rubber bats, plastic shields, handcuffs, and rope (Kottman, 2003; Landreth, 2002). The inclusion of these toys in a playroom is critical to appropriate expression of aggression. A playroom full of dolls and stuffed animals limits child expression of aggression; just as a playroom full of guns and knives limits the expression of nurturing (Trotter, Eschelman, & Landreth, 2003). If aggressive toys are not available to the child in the playroom, yet toys such as dolls, bottles, and stuffed animals are present, the child receives the message that there is no room for expression of aggressive drives or feelings. And for some children who operate very aggressively, this message is internalized as "there is no room for me in the playroom."

Working toward the goal of allowing and accepting aggressive acts in the playroom, the therapist may have opened a Pandora's box of impulsive and consequential behaviors. Referring back to the chapter on limit setting, the CCPT guideline still applies that feelings are always accepted but all behaviors are not. Play therapists (Willock, 1983; Moustakas, 1973; O'Connor, 1986) have acknowledged a variety of aggressive behaviors that occur in the playroom, including spitting, kicking, hitting, obscenities, biting, yelling, shooting dart gun, throwing objects, acting out killing/death scenes, and destroying materials. For many children who are aggressive, these acts are not one-time occurrences. Some children move from one aggressive act to another during one session, requiring constant limit setting from the therapist.

As with all children, children who are aggressive often respond quite appropriately to limit setting. The limit-setting procedure presented in Chapter 6 is applicable to this population. The first step is to offer the ACT initial limit setting (Landreth, 2002), which includes acknowledging the child's feeling, communicating a definitive limit, and targeting an alternative action for expression. The second step is choice giving, which is followed by the final step, rarely ever used, the ultimate limit of ending the session. The continual and consistent use of the limit-setting process will eventually contribute to the process of appropriate expression of aggressive feelings and needs.

Therapist Reaction to Aggression

Perhaps the issue that interferes most with the effective facilitation of play therapy with children who are aggressive is the therapist as a person. The child's aggressive behaviors may stir up negative feelings in a play therapist, such as feeling ineffective, helpless, and unlikable. Those feelings, as a result, may produce anger or fear in a therapist, which often becomes a major struggle for a therapist.

The initial stage of working with children who are aggressive is to explore the therapist's belief system about children and the therapeutic role. The following are some common beliefs that I help play therapists explore when they are challenged by a case:

1. My job is to make children feel better.
2. Each time I see a child, he or she must feel better than when we started.
3. Children should follow rules.
4. Children should follow rules with minimal disruption.
5. If children do not follow rules, it is my job to enforce the rules.
6. I have the power to control a child's behavior.
7. If I do not control a child's behavior, I am ineffective/a failure.

These are common beliefs of not only play therapists, but also adults in general, regarding children. An agreement with any of these beliefs will lead to challenges in CCPT, especially with children who act aggressively. At the risk of being repetitive, CCPT facilitates the expression of all needs and feelings, recognizing that problematic behaviors are outcomes of distorted or unrecognized needs and feelings. Hence, behaviors are expressions and should be conceptualized as such by the effective play therapist. Instead of focusing on how to stop a behavior or change a behavior, a CCPT therapist focuses on the intention of the child and how to facilitate the appropriate expression of intention. Of course, limit setting is part of helping appropriate expression but the therapist's overarching goal is to allow expression. Another challenge to the possible beliefs listed above is the practical application of the belief. Short of being physically forceful with children, there is no way to "make" them follow limits. Following limits is an individual choice that each person makes. The therapist's role is to offer the limit, but it is the child's role to decide upon staying within the limit. When a therapist accepts the role of facilitating expression and recognizing the practical limitations of enforcing a limit, he will increase his effectiveness with children who are aggressive.

Once therapists have explored attitudes and belief systems related to working with children who are aggressive, following the limit-setting procedures should become less emotional (for the therapist) and result in more successful outcomes. However, the therapist will need to remain patient. A child's attempt to build new internal representation of self and self in relation to others can be a slow and complex process (Mills & Allan,

1992). There are other recommendations that are helpful in working with children who are aggressive that will enhance the process:

Continual use of empathy. Miller and Eisenberg (1988) defined empathy as "vicarious experiencing of emotions consistent with those of others" (p. 325) evoked by the affective state of another person. There is a negative relationship between the presence of empathy and exhibition of aggressive behaviors. Empathic understanding is the essential ingredient in effectiveness with children who are aggressive. Therapists demonstrate empathy by understanding the meaning behind aggressive behaviors and expressing it. Examples include "This is very new to you and you feel scared" and "You feel like you don't know what to do." Although not the only tool to demonstrate empathy, reflections of feelings can convey an empathic attitude.

Look for child's intent and respond. A play therapist should search for the intention of the child. What is the child trying to express? Is it a need for order, power, mastery, sense of self, connection to another? There are so many intentions, and it is the therapist's role to value the child as an individual person and respond to the individual need. Reflections of feelings and needs serve the double purpose of conveying both empathy and understanding.

Continue to patiently set limits. Limit setting can be exhausting when working with children who are aggressive. I have experienced and observed sessions where limit setting made up 80% of the therapist's responses. As mentioned, the process of restructuring self can be slow. The effective therapist trusts the process and repeatedly sets limits until progress is achieved. A helpful tip for therapists is to note any amount of progress. For some children, moving from 80% to 70% limit-setting responses is a noteworthy achievement and should be celebrated by the therapist. In setting limits with children who are aggressive, steps can be quickly used and the therapist is left with only the ultimate limit. It's important to slow down the process by being patient, consistent, and repetitive.

Consistently follow consequences of choices. Choice giving was explained in detail in Chapter 6 on limit setting. In utilizing choice giving with children who are aggressive, the therapist should be especially mindful of being consistent with following through on consequences. As soon as a child makes a choice, the therapist is responsible for enacting the consequence, such as asking for the gun or ball. When a child tries to cajole the therapist into changing the consequence, the therapist needs to remain consistent.

Ultimately, this demonstrates to the child that the world is a safe place with predictable consequences based on our choices.

Check voice. I have often observed that the single most damaging action by a therapist in setting effective limits is tone of voice. Based on fear or anxiety, a therapist might use a tone that conveys a need to control or a weakness/vulnerability about how to handle the situation. Limits need to be set with as much objectivity as possible. Children, especially children who are aggressive, are attuned to voice intonation and often respond more to tone than to actual words. The therapist must convey a sense of confidence and objectivity for the child to believe that it is safe to follow the limit.

Do not approach the child physically unless absolutely necessary. Earlier, it was noted that limit-setting steps can be quickly exhausted in the process of working with children who are aggressive. As actions and words intensify, a therapist can easily find herself in a physical confrontation with a child, feeling the need to physically control the child. In these situations, any physical movement toward a child may be interpreted as a threat to the child. Just like any other person, a child who feels threatened will react accordingly by attempting to defend self and this often looks offensive, not defensive. Physical movement toward a child in a limit-setting situation should only be enacted if the child or another person is in real danger. This would not include running or yelling. And when deemed necessary, the therapist would only use physical self as a barrier, not as an offensive physical restraint. Negative physical interactions between therapist and child are disruptive to the therapeutic process and often take a long time from which to recover, if ever.

Contain! Contain! Contain! As an alternative to physical confrontation, preventive containment is often helpful with children who are aggressive. Children tend to feel comfortable in places where the physical environment also conveys that things are in control. For example, wide-open spaces are often difficult for these children to maneuver but enclosed rooms offer some sense of comfort. I have no evidence for this statement except for experience and observation. It seems that when children who are aggressive are placed in open areas, it contributes to their sense of chaos and lack of safety, yet they seem calmer in smaller rooms. By smaller, I am not referring to a closet but just a room with four walls. Hence, if a therapist is aware that a child often acts aggressively, making a plan for getting a child in and out of the playroom in the most orderly way possible with direct destinations is optimal. Waiting periods and transitions are not the strengths of children who are aggressive and should be minimally used when working with them.

Working with Parents of Aggressive Children

Studies reveal that there is a crucial relationship between the quality of parenting that children received in their infancy and young childhood, and the occurrence and prolongation of their aggressive behaviors (Mills & Allan, 1992). The process of working with aggressive children takes time in play therapy. The timeliness of progress is influenced by the child's depth of feeling or need for aggressive behaviors. Establishing an environment of safety, fairly quickly done with most children, sometimes takes longer with children who are aggressive. I have worked with a small number of children who were unable to participate in any play other than aggression for up to 8 to 10 sessions. During this time of trusting the process, parents will often feel anxious about the play therapy process.

It is important to keep parents involved and encouraged through consistent parent consultations. During consultations, play therapists should note any progress at all to the parent and help the parent search for any progress at home. Because many behaviors that children engage in are disturbing and disruptive, the parent will often have a difficult time seeing slow signs of progress. Signs, such as children lessening aggressive responses to actions by one or two a day, being slower to reach a full tantrum, or making small unsuccessful attempts to positively relate to the parent, are often overlooked by a frustrated parent.

Tips for Working With Parents

1. *Consistent consultations.* The play therapist should hold a parent consultation every three to five sessions; and for these children, three is closer to the minimum. When children act aggressively in their environment, parents need extra support.
2. *Normalize the child's behaviors for the parent.* Although the child's aggressive behaviors are challenging and sometimes lead to serious consequences, parents need to be reassured that the child is not a monster or so completely different from other children. Play therapists can help parents by explaining possible intentions and motivations of the child. It is also helpful for a play therapist to reassure the parent that the behavior is not something new for the play therapist. In the example from Chapter 6 on limit setting about the girl who was physically removed from the clinic due to her aggressive behavior, the play therapist called the parent following the incident and used the following statement: "I know today was tough and Tanika was quite aggressive, but I just wanted to

let you know that this is something we're prepared to deal with and Tanika is not the first child who we've worked with who is aggressive. We'll keep working at it until she is able to find a better and more appropriate way to express herself." These kinds of statements let parents know that the play therapist is in the trenches with them and the child is not an uncontrollable foreign entity.

3. *Engage in problem solving.* The play therapist should be prepared to work with crises described by the parent on a weekly basis. When parents cite specific incidents, the play therapist should go through the events detail by detail to help figure out what solutions might help the parent for the next time. The focus becomes how to help the parent deal with the child's behavior in a proactive way, instead of consultations that seem to be focused on complaining or trying to emptily reassure the parent that everything will get better.
4. *Role-play use in consultation and for home.* Parents of children who are aggressive are especially susceptible to not knowing how to intervene when a child is the midst of an aggressive action. They will typically respond by disengaging and disconnecting or by engaging the child in a power play-off, which typically leads to more aggression. Parents need the play therapist's support to figure out different ways to respond when a child acts aggressively on a regular basis. The following process is "Active Practice" and the steps were modified from a procedure described as an academy by Levy and O'Hanlon (2001). They have been modified to fit a child-centered philosophy to deal with a child's problematic behaviors, and this approach was briefly mentioned in Chapter 9 on Parent Consultation.
   a. Role-play follows a specific incident where parent considers the child aggressive, disrespectful, etc.
   b. Pick a calm time period when both parent and child are relaxed.
   c. Play out the specific incident from beginning to end.
   d. Remain empathic by reflecting feelings but firm by continuing to role play until desired result.
   e. Parent must remain calm for experience to be a success and it can even be fun.

The following is a specific example of using the role-play technique.

Incident: Getting ready for school. This morning, as representative of most mornings, Jake's mom tried to wake him up. Jake did not wake up, even after several attempts, ranging from nice reminders to screams and threats. Mom finally physically pulled Jake out of bed. Jake responded by screaming, kicking, and cursing. Mom and Jake then battled for Jake to get dressed to be ready to go to school. Screaming continued until Mom dropped Jake off at school 10 minutes late. Steps for active practice in this case include:

1. In the evening, Jake is watching TV, playing computer, playing outside, or involved in another calm activity. Mom is also calm, with no stressful obligations for the next few minutes.
2. Mom presents to Jake, "We had some trouble this morning, and we need practice to make it better. After we successfully practice, then you can watch TV again."
3. Mom briefly explains that Jake needs to get out of bed, put on his clothes, and brush his teeth without arguing or screaming.
4. Mom asks Jake to get in bed, turn out the lights, and start the normal morning process.
5. Mom says in light tone, "Good morning, Jake. Time to get out of bed."
6. Each time Jake responds negatively, Mom should reflect, set the limit, and start over.
7. "You're angry that we are practicing, but I'm not for screaming at. You will need to get back in bed and start over."
8. Mom continues until Jake successfully completes the entire morning routine. This may take quite a while. Mom needs to remain calm, not talking any more than needed to remind Jake of the task.
9. When one successful practice occurs, Mom moves on without punishments or lectures.
10. The next morning, Mom starts the day with "Good morning. Jake. Time to get out of bed."
11. If Jake gets out of bed and gets through his routine with minimal disruption, active practice has worked.
12. If Jake engages in aggressive behaviors, Mom attempts to get through this stressful morning period with minimal aggression and anger. Mom then repeats the active practice process later that day when she and Jake are calm.

Active practice is time consuming and tests the patience of parents. Parents are in need of support and encouragement to continue the active practice process until change occurs. For children with excessive needs for power and control, active practice may appear unsuccessful for a lengthy period of time. Yet, if a parent will continue and remain as objective but caring as possible, active practice will help improve the child's behavior as well as the parent/child relationship.

Research on Aggression and Play Therapy

The claim that CCPT is effective in reducing aggressive behaviors is supported by preliminary research. Sloan (1997) found that after 11 children participated in aggressively charged play therapy sessions and 11 children participated in 10 traditional play therapy sessions, children who participated in aggressively charged play therapy did not exhibit more aggression in the playroom as compared to the children who received traditional play therapy. Kot, Landreth, & Giordano (1998) found that 11 children who participated in 12 individual sessions of CCPT exhibited less aggression following play therapy than 11 children who were assigned to a control group. In one of the first studies to focus on children with aggressive behaviors, Schumann (2010) investigated 37 children, kindergarten through fourth grade, referred by teachers and parents for aggressive behavioral problems. Participants were rated at-risk or clinically significant on the Aggressive subscale of the Behavioral Assessment System for Children (BASC) by a parent or teacher. Twenty children participated in 12 to 15 CCPT sessions, and 17 participated in 12 to 19 small group guidance using the evidence-based Second Step Violence Prevention Program for schools. Results revealed that both groups statistically significantly improved aggression with a medium effect size on the Aggressive subscale of the BASC and Teacher Report Form as measured by teachers and with a small effect size as measured by parents on both the BASC and Child Behavior Checklist. Ray, Blanco, Sullivan, and Holliman (2009) researched 41 children referred by teachers for aggressive behaviors in the classroom. The treatment group received 14 sessions of CCPT, held twice weekly. The control group was placed on a waitlist and received no treatment. Parents reported a moderate decrease in aggression for the treatment group over the control group according to effect size (N = 32). Teachers reported that both groups significantly improved over time (N = 41). In post hoc analysis, it was revealed that children assigned to CCPT showed a statistically significant decrease in aggressive behaviors, and children assigned to the control group demonstrated no statistically significant difference.

Conclusion

Aggression is a normal part of child development and is typically expressed by all children at young ages. As children grow older, they develop abilities to meet their needs without acting aggressively toward others. However, some children do not learn or utilize the necessary skills for meeting their needs and continue an aggressive trajectory. Play therapy allows children to express their motivations for aggression while limiting their harmful behaviors. Through child expression and therapist empathy and acceptance, children will instinctually move toward a more self-enhancing way of working within their worlds. The field of CCPT has demonstrated through theory and research that aggressive acts decrease as a child experiences the conditions provided in play therapy.

References

Archer, J., & Cote, S. (2005). Sex differences in aggressive behavior. In R. Tremblay, W. Hartup, & J. Archer (Eds.), *Developmental origins of aggression* (425–443). New York: Guilford Press.

Dionne, G. (2005). Language development and aggressive behavior. In R. Tremblay, W. Hartup, & J. Archer (Eds.). *Developmental origins of aggression* (330–352). New York: Guilford Press.

Drewes, A. (2008). Bobo revisited: What the research says. *International Journal of Play Therapy, 17*, 52–65.

Eastman, M. (1994). *Taming the dragon in your child.* New York: John Wiley & Sons.

Johnson, S., & Chuck, P. (2001). Play therapy with aggressive acting-out children. In G. Landreth (Ed.), *Innovations in play therapy: Issues, process, and special populations* (239–255). Philadelphia: Taylor & Francis.

Kot, S., Landreth, G., & Giordano, M. (1998). Intensive child-centered play therapy with child witnesses of domestic violence. *International Journal of Play Therapy, 7*, 17–36.

Kottman, T. (2003). *Partners in play: An Adlerian approach to play therapy* (2nd ed.). Alexandria, VA: American Counseling Association.

Landreth, G. (2002). *Play therapy: The art of the relationship* (2nd ed.). New York: Brunner-Routledge.

Levy, R., & O'Hanlon, B. (2001). *Try and make me.* New York: Rodale.

Miller, P., & Eisenberg, N. (1988). The relation of empathy to aggressive and externalizing/antisocial behavior. *Psychological Bulletin, 103*, 324–344.

Mills, B., & Allan, J. (1992). Play therapy with the maltreated child: Impact upon aggressive and withdrawn patterns of interaction. *International Journal of Play Therapy, 1*, 1–20.

Moustakas, C. (1973). *Children in play therapy.* New York: Jason Aronson.

Oaklander, V. (1988). *Windows to our children.* Highland, NY: The Gestalt Journal Press.

O'Connor, K. (1986). The interaction of hostile and depressive behaviors: A case study of a depressed boy. *Journal of Child and Adolescent Psychotherapy, 3*, 105–108.

Peterson, J., & Flanders, J. (2005). Play and the regulation of aggression. In R. Tremblay, W. Hartup, & J. Archer (Eds.), *Developmental origins of aggression* (133–157). New York: Guilford Press.

Ray, D., Blanco, P., Sullivan, J., & Holliman, R. (2009). An exploratory study of child-centered play therapy with aggressive children. *International Journal of Play Therapy, 18*(3), 162–175.

Rogers, C. (1989). *The Carl Rogers reader.* New York: Houghton Mifflin.

Schaefer, C., & Mattei, D. (2005). Catharsis: Effectiveness in children's aggression. *International Journal of Play Therapy, 14*, 103–109.

Schumann, B. (2010). Effectiveness of child centered play therapy for children referred for aggression in elementary school. In J. Baggerly, D. Ray, & S. Bratton (Eds.), *Child-centered play therapy research: The evidence base for effective practice* (193–208). Hoboken, NJ: Wiley.

Sloan, S. (1997). Effects of aggressive therapeutic play: Does it increase or diminish spontaneous aggression? (Doctoral dissertation, Alfred University, Alfred, NY, 1997). *Dissertation Abstracts International, B 59/07*, 3677.

Trotter, K., Eshelman, D., & Landreth, G. (2003). A place for BoBo in play therapy. *International Journal of Play Therapy, 12*, 117–139.

Willock, B. (1983). Play therapy with the aggressive, acting-out child. In C. Schaefer & K. O'Connor (Eds.), *Handbook of play therapy* (387–411). New York: John Wiley & Sons.

CHAPTER 11
Group Play Therapy

Group play therapy requires a level of commitment to children and to the process of play beyond what is required in individual play therapy. Slavson (1999) emphasized this point in his warning statement:

> The anxiety stimulated by the presence of other children and the support they give one another in their hostility toward the adult include hyperactivity and destructiveness seldom encountered in the play of one child. (p. 25)

Group play therapy employs the advanced skills of experienced play therapists. Individual play therapy allows the therapist the freedom to control many variables of the therapeutic process. The therapist sets the environment and makes decisions regarding how to respond to the individual child. Interactions are often predictable because the therapist anticipates how each of his responses will be received by the child. However, the modality of group play therapy requires that the therapist accept the inevitability of human contact over which the therapist has no control. Group play therapy demands not only the expertise of the therapist in play therapy, but also an expertise in facilitation and a secure level of acceptance with the interactions of others. Group play therapy offers a challenging environment for play therapists by requiring a comfort level with positive and negative interactions that take place between children, commitment to the belief that children can be therapeutic agents for each other, and additional skills beyond what is expected of a play therapist in individual therapy. The confidence of a play therapist is sometimes shaken by the mere increase in activity levels that occurs in group therapy when compared to individual play therapy. Play therapists may also have reactions to perceived lack of control, the inability to be therapeutic in response giving, and a reduced feeling of intimacy with clients that was experienced in individual therapy. To overcome these challenges and reactions, a play therapist will need to embrace the value of the group method, recognizing its effectiveness for therapy over individual methods in specific cases.

Benefits of Group Play Therapy

Although group play therapy is not indicated for all children, there are perceived benefits that improve its viability as a therapeutic modality for some children. The following are a few of its attributes:

1. *Comfort level of child.* Because other children are present, each child is able to reduce anxiety related to a new setting and a new way of interacting with the adult (therapist) (Ginott, 1961). The child will enter the play therapy environment with greater ease due to the presence of another child.
2. *Participation of child.* As children observe and interact with each other, they develop a sense of permissiveness provided by the setting. This level of permissiveness may allow the child to quickly engage in the process (Sweeney & Homeyer, 1999).
3. *Vicarious and induced catharsis.* By observing the play of others, a child may be emotionally stimulated to play out his or her own past and current issues of distress (Ginott, 1961). This compares to adult group therapy, wherein one adult begins to talk about issues of conflict and others will begin to share similar feelings and experiences. This same process occurs in group play therapy with the introduction of certain play materials and themes.
4. *Vicarious and direct learning.* As experienced in all group therapy, clients benefit by learning from each other. In group play therapy, children learn to problem solve with each other to reach individual or group goals, and they learn coping skills for when they do not get what they want from other children. These learning experiences are then transferred to the real-world setting where they implement new skills learned in group play therapy (Ginott, 1961).
5. *Therapist opportunity for observation.* Often in individual play therapy, a child progresses by working through play themes and activities, which is observed by the therapist (Ginott, 1961). Yet, parents will report a lack of social skills negatively affecting the child's functioning at school, home, etc. It is only through the observation of interaction with others that the play therapist can observe a lack of social skills or a manifestation of the child's

anxiety related to being with others. Group play therapy allows the play therapist to holistically see the child in the environment.

6. *Reality testing and limit setting.* Group play therapy offers a microcosm of society, which requires skills of interaction. Through group play therapy, the child can experiment with new behaviors of coping when negative experiences occur within a safe environment (Sweeney & Homeyer, 1999).
7. *Positive interactions.* Group play therapy offers an environment where children can experience positive interactions with one another (Ginott, 1961). On the playground, children may walk away from interaction or play out negative interactions with fighting or name calling. With the help of the play therapist, the group play therapy setting requires that children remain in physical proximity and can hear the reflections of threatening feelings and thoughts as voiced by the therapist. Interactions coupled with awareness may lead to an increase in positive experiences with peers.

Group Selection

Whereas most children can benefit from individual play therapy, all children are not appropriate for group play therapy. There are children who display personality or behavioral characteristics contraindicated for group, such as extreme aggression. Additionally, there are children who have lived through external experiences far beyond those of their peers and will use the playroom to work through those experiences, such as children who have been sexually abused, leading to an anxious experience for the previously unaffected children in the group. However, there is one common criterion necessary for group involvement to be successful. Slavson and Schiffer (1975) termed this criterion "social hunger" (p. 107), which is described as the potential to relate to others. Ginott (1961) elaborated on social hunger by defining it as "a person's desire to gain acceptance by his peers, to act, dress, and talk as they do, and to attain and maintain status in his group. In return for peer acceptance, a child is motivated to change behavior" (p. 17). For inclusion in group therapy, the therapist assesses the level of social awareness for each potential group member and the member's willingness to exchange behavior for acceptance. Without the individual child's awareness of social interactions and their relationship to acceptance, the group modality will yield less effective results. Questions that will guide the assessment of social hunger include

1. To what level does the child notice the presence of other children?
2. To what level does the child notice the behavior of other children?

3. To what level does the child attempt to interact with other children?
4. To what level does the child change her behavior to gain the attention of other children?
5. To what level does the child change her behavior to interact with other children?
6. To what level does the child change her behavior to gain the approval of other children?

If the answer is "to a great degree" for all of these questions, then the child is exhibiting signs of social hunger that indicate the utility of group. More than likely, the therapist will answer these questions on a continuum, assessing the child's level for each question. Based on the overall level of social hunger displayed, a therapist will make a decision regarding if the child is experiencing the basic criterion needed for group play therapy before moving to other considerations of group appropriateness.

Although there are cases that seem inappropriate for group play therapy, it is difficult to list hard and fast rules about when to rule out certain children for group. Instead, a therapist will want to consider certain variables to determine a child's appropriateness for group. The most effective method of determining appropriateness for group is to facilitate an individual session with a child prior to decision making. The following issues are considerations when deciding a child's match to a group intervention: age, aggression, attachment, sexual abuse, and social and relational issues.

Age. There are mixed opinions in the play therapy field regarding the age at which a group intervention becomes a reasonable option for children. At younger ages, children are less likely to display signs of social hunger; specifically, they are less likely to be aware of other children. Child development is marked by an initial observation of others within a child's periphery, moving to an observation of other children's behaviors, progressing to a desire to play with other children, and finally to change play behavior based on others' actions. Often, young children simply do not notice the presence or actions of other children. Even more often for younger ages such as 4 or 5 years, children may notice the play of others but it serves in no relationship to them, and hence does not work as a changing agent. As so frequently seen in preschool groups, one child will play with a harmonica while another child plays with a doll. If neither child interferes with the other, very little interaction will take place naturally. However, this is not always the case for young children. Some children are socially attuned from very young ages and will begin to practice social skills in order to get what they want. As in the above example, the child playing with the doll might notice the harmonica and desire to play with it instead of the doll. The child then moves toward the other child and asks if he can play, smiles and stares at the other child while playing, or grabs the harmonica out of the child's hands. All of these actions are prompted by the awareness of needing to act socially to get needs met, but of course, at different skill levels. There is no definitive age at which group play therapy is appropriate. What is known is that children are more likely to display social hunger at older ages, culminating in extreme social hunger needs at 11 to 12 years old for children operating within normal ranges. A play therapist may use this knowledge of development to initially look to group interventions, over individual play therapy, at around the ages of 7 to 12 years old.

Aggression. It has been a commonly held belief that children who exhibit aggressive behaviors are not appropriate for group play therapy. Again, taking definitive stands on criteria for group is not helpful to a play therapist. The criterion regarding aggression should be the degree to which a child engages in aggressive acts and the context that contributes to those acts. Children who have been historically aggressive can greatly benefit from group interaction. The following questions will help a play therapist in the assessment of appropriateness for group:

1. With whom is the child typically aggressive?
2. What is the nature of the typical aggressive acts? Does the child throw things around or attempt to hurt self/others?
3. To what degree has the child exhibited aggression? (e.g., hit another child and run away, choke a child until an adult interrupted)
4. In what context has the child exhibited aggression? Does the child become aggressive to get what he wants or when he is threatened by authority, or does it appear to be spontaneous and unprovoked?

A child who pushes, hits, or bullies to get her own way or items that she wants can be appropriate for group play therapy when paired with a child who is not easily intimidated. Interaction in group play therapy will help the child learn that certain social skills are needed to get what she wants and to maintain a friendship. A child who appears to be highly violent and has a history of seriously hurting others is not appropriate for group. Such a child would need to begin play therapy in an individual setting so that the therapist can offer a controlled environment for expression. A child who has few friends but only exhibits aggression toward parents may be a good candidate for group because the child is displaying a need for power and authority when interacting with parents. Group play therapy may address issues related to the lack of social skills without igniting the child's need to exert control in an aggressive way.

Attachment. Children who are assessed with a lack of attachment stemming from early childhood trauma or neglect are typically not appropriate for group play therapy initially. These children benefit from a long-term relationship with an adult attachment figure to work through early childhood trauma and learn to develop a secure relationship with a consistent adult. Placing children with attachment issues into groups is predictably overwhelming and anxiety producing. The group reinforces issues of mistrust, and a child may respond by withdrawing or acting out aggressively on the environment to establish a sense of safety. Yet, this warning regarding an initial use of group therapy is followed by the encouragement that following individualized counseling, group therapy can be beneficial for children who have experienced early childhood neglect or trauma. Once the child is able to form an attachment to an adult, group play therapy offers the opportunity to extend this attachment to other children and practice skills that had been lacking previously.

Sexual abuse. As with children experiencing attachment issues, children who have been sexually abused typically benefit from individual play therapy initially. The confusion that accompanies the experience of sexual abuse is best expressed in the safety provided by a consistent, therapeutic adult. Children who have been sexually abused may use the play therapy experience to play out the concrete actions of their abuse and express their perceptions of abuse. The interactions of peers in this process may be disruptive to the child who has been sexually abused and deter the child from full expression. Additionally, children who have been sexually abused are sexually knowledgeable beyond the knowledge level of most children. When a child shares sexual knowledge with a child who has experienced no context for that knowledge, the result can be disturbing and anxiety provoking. However, it should be noted that following individual play therapy, children who have been sexually abused can greatly benefit from interaction with peers, sexually abused or not, in group play therapy for the purposes of building peer support.

Social and relational issues. Common sense would dictate that group play therapy is most appropriate for children who are experiencing social problems with peers. Children who have no friends or conflictual peer relationships are prime candidates for group play therapy. Especially when children grow older and peers become more influential, a child's ability to initiate and maintain friendships is crucial to normal development. Group play therapy offers these children an environment in which another child is structured to stay in the room so that opportunities naturally occur for interaction and the practice of social skills. In the presence of a facilitative play therapist, group children learn to be more aware of each other; their needs, feelings, and thoughts; and how to act in a way that will sustain interaction.

Composition of Group

Once the play therapist has determined that an individual child is a good match for a group play therapy intervention, matching the child to another child or children becomes of greatest importance. Again, attempting to list exact rules of composition is not helpful. Some might say that a therapist should "always match a strong-willed child with a strong-willed child" or "always match a shy child with an outgoing child." My experience has been that group composition rules are unfounded and different cases call for different decisions. I will present possible considerations for the play therapist when matching children with others.

Number of children in group. Child-centered group play therapy allows for full movement and decision making by each member of the group. For each child present, there are verbal and nonverbal play behaviors, relationships to other children, and a relationship with the therapist. These behaviors and relationships are manifested in innumerable dynamics happening simultaneously in the playroom. Ginott (1961) and Axline (1969) recommended and cited examples of play therapy groups made up of five to eight children with one play therapist. The transcripts are compelling and demonstrate the advantage of facilitating a group of that size. However, for several reasons, I would recommend that child-centered group play therapy is most effective when limited to two or three children. There are practical factors related to the number of group members, including the size of the room. Children need enough room to separate from other children in the room, offering the ability for expansive play. Second, the logistics of scheduling several members for group is often daunting and discourages the play therapist from initiating group intervention; the more members involved in the group, the more scheduling required. Limiting the group number helps the play therapist offer a valuable intervention without becoming overwhelmed. Perhaps most importantly, when group size exceeds three members, it becomes difficult for the therapist to be fully attuned to the multiple dynamics taking place. Although children are serving as therapeutic agents for each other and the therapist is not the only facilitator of environment, it is still essential for the therapist to provide the attitudes for encounter, including genuineness, empathy, and unconditional positive regard. For many therapists, the multiplicity of relationship interactions, sound level, and activity level may interfere with the provision of therapist attitudes when more than two or three children are present.

Gender composition. Gender and age appear to be considerations that are intrinsically linked to one another. For young children, around ages 4 to 5 years, gender is less of an issue in play and verbalization. Girls and boys appear to mix well, without interfering with the expression of each other. Younger ages also usually account for greater acceptance of differences between children, including differences in gender. As children grow older and become more entrenched in gender patterns, differences in play and verbalized expression grow stronger and more distinct. Of course, this is not the case for all boys and girls, only in a generalized perspective. Older girls and boys become more inhibited in the presence of the opposite sex, especially in relationship to types of play behaviors. Boys tend to engage in aggressive and symbolic play beyond the age of girls' engagement in these types of play behaviors. Girls use extensive forms of verbalization as they grow older while boys often become less verbal, able to relate better through action. Because of these differences, it is recommended that play groups are composed of same-sex members beyond the age of 6 years old. Same-sex groups will presumably encourage expression, understanding, and acceptance among group members to a greater degree in comparison to mixed-gender groups.

Age. Age was previously addressed as a consideration for whether an individual child will benefit from a group intervention. If the therapist has decided that a child is an appropriate age for group, the therapist must then consider the most effective age for the matched child/ren. One well-known guideline is to match children within 1 year chronologically. Children are historically hierarchical in their relationships with each other, with age serving as the primary decisive factor in leadership and acceptance. Placing children of similar ages with each other avoids the inherent inequality that accompanies age differences. The 1-year guideline is typically a successful one and works effectively in my experience. However, there can be many exceptions. An older shy, bullied child might be matched with a younger child who can be more accepting and whose presence will help build esteem in the older child. The younger, impulsive child might gain maturity by interacting with the older child. The therapist will want to consider the uniqueness of the match for both children over and above any age restrictions.

Siblings. Sibling groups are a special case of group play therapy. Very few of the composition guidelines apply to the decision of placing siblings in the same group. Sibling play therapy groups are often of mixed gender and mixed age. For the case of siblings, a distinctive decision-making process is utilized to determine appropriateness for group. The nature of the presenting problem is the relevant consideration for siblings. Sibling rivalry, or intense fighting among siblings, can be traced to a lack of individual relationships occurring between parents and children. Placing children who are struggling to gain an individual relationship with an attachment figure (parent) in one setting to another setting where they will compete for a relationship with an attachment figure (therapist) is contraindicated. This type of presenting problem lends itself to individual intervention and, of course, parent intervention. Another common presenting problem for siblings is family trauma. They may have experienced abuse or the observation of abuse, neglect, or abandonment by parental figures. In this case, sibling group play therapy is often an effective intervention because it provides a place of safety with the therapist and fellow siblings to express the level of and response to trauma, while building a strong support system among siblings. The group play therapist will match the appropriateness of a sibling group with the individual and family needs of the siblings.

Personality, behavioral, and cultural characteristics. The most challenging consideration of group composition is the matching of children according to complementary personality, behavioral, and cultural characteristics. Is one child too aggressive? Is one child too withdrawn? Will an outgoing child help bring out or inhibit the participation of a shy child? Will children who are missing parents help one another or enter into their own worlds of grief? Will ethnicity make a difference when I place two African-American children with one Hispanic child? Will a child of poverty be able to relate to a child of privilege? These are the types of questions that therapists will ask themselves when composing groups of children. More than likely, the answers will be different for diverse cases with unique children at the core of the decision. I have found the following questions helpful in this type of decision making:

- Can one child pace the development of another child? In other words, can a characteristic of one child be a model for another child?
- Will one child be completely overwhelming to another child? Is the characteristic of one child, such as aggression or depression, so powerful that another child would shut down in its presence?
- When dealing with cultural differences, such as ethnicity, language, or socioeconomic level, will the mix of children be so fundamentally different from a child's background that the child is likely to withdraw in the presence of others? For example, if an African-American child has only interacted with other African-Americans in her development, will she be able to relate to two Caucasian children and a Caucasian therapist, or will this composition inhibit her ability to express herself?

Process of Group Play Therapy

There are many professional approaches and theoretical belief systems related to group counseling. In many group orientations, there is a drive toward structuring the group experience so that clients will quickly engage in interaction with less anxiety, leading to group cohesion, an ultimate goal. The focus of group play therapy is always the individual child (Ginott, 1961). Children are free to play independently or with each other. As in individual play therapy, the therapist follows the children as individuals throughout the session. If there are group goals or group rules, they are set by group members, *not* by the therapist. The mere presence of other children and probable ensuing interactions between children are considered the therapeutic factors of group play therapy, especially when joined with high levels of social hunger.

In group play therapy, the therapist does not structure for cohesion, primarily for two reasons. The first reason for an individual focus within group is that child-centered group play therapy is grounded in person-centered theory. The group leader models facilitative behaviors, including giving autonomy to persons in groups, freeing children for full expression of selves, facilitating learning, stimulating independence, accepting the emerging creativity of the child, delegating full responsibility, offering and receiving feedback, encouraging and relying on self-evaluation, and finding reward in the development and achievement of others (Bozarth, 1998). Each individual child has the innate potential for development of the self-actualizing tendency, leading to a productive approach to self and others. Rogers (1970) believed that the group process was much more important than the behavior and statements of the therapist, highlighting the need for attitudinal qualities over concrete therapeutic responses. In fact, the therapist sometimes interferes with the process of the group when he feels that he must lead or structure the group to some imagined end goal. Group members, even children, have the ability to be therapeutic for each other in a way that is distinct from the therapist's role. Their approach to each other is one of genuineness and naturally felt empathy, especially when children have experienced similar contexts, personality characteristics, or presenting issues. An empathic role that the "expert" therapist works for to connect to a child is often completely natural for other children.

A second reason for the lack of focus on cohesion is the developmental nature of children who have a propensity to be self-focused. When children are given the opportunity for free play, they want to move in their own directions. Based on age and level of social hunger, they move in and out of the worlds of other children, but prefer to maintain self-direction (a goal of person-centered therapy). The therapist's need to structure groups for cohesion will often feel artificial to children, as if they have to play "grown-up." In practice, when a therapist provides more structure, this usually translates to more limits, less flexibility, and more teaching by the therapist to sustain the structure. Therapist direction increases, while child direction decreases. What comes naturally to children, interacting and playing with one another, has now become disingenuous and for the benefit of the therapist, not the children. Children cease to experience natural interaction and consequences of interaction, as well as giving up opportunities for the natural building of social skills. For example, two children in group play therapy who both want the same toy will struggle over the toy and then ultimately move to some kind of resolution using their own resources that can then be transferred to the school playground. When a therapist intervenes to teach a few social skills for resolution, children will often comply and do as they are told but do not make the connection between what they feel they have to do for an authority figure in session and the next day's interactions with peers.

There is very little written on group play therapy. I would speculate that little is written because child-centered group play therapy is not widely used; and when it is used, it is not clear as to the processes that are working for change in the individual child. I believe that group play therapy is not widely used because of many diverse reasons, not the least of which is that the simple act of organizing group scheduling is time consuming for therapists. Other reasons are addressed among the special issues discussed later in the chapter. When an intervention is not widely used, there is a challenge in understanding the process taking place during the use of the intervention. This is true for group play therapy.

Our best resource for understanding the process of group play therapy is to return to the writings of Rogers (1970) on encounter groups. Although Rogers spoke specifically about encounter group experiences with adults, the process of group patterns he outlined appears to fit the dynamics of group play therapy with some clarifications about children. The process begins (a) with a milling around due to no directional responsibility in the group; then (b) there is an initial resistance to personal expression or exploration, followed by (c) surface description of past feelings, moving into (d) expression of negative feelings toward other group members that establishes safety to (e) express and explore personally meaningful material, leading to (f) expression of immediate interpersonal feelings in the group, which develops (g) a healing capacity in the group and fosters (h) self-acceptance and the beginning of change delving into (i) the cracking of facades that invites (j) individual feedback that leads to (k) confrontation that forms (l) helping relationships outside of the group sessions and then (m) the basic encounter (true experiencing of another person) occurs, encouraging (n) expression of positive feelings and closeness to develop the final step of (o) behavior changes in the group (Rogers, 1970).

This description seems deep for a child group but here are some other words for this pattern that fit the child process. Children will enter group play therapy with (a) little direction, playing with what is easiest for self or with others; (b) there is little revelation about self regarding meaningful events or thoughts, and (c) verbalization sticks with concrete facts ("my mother is in jail"); (d) interaction between group members begins to occur, leading to possible negative interactions (i.e., fighting over toys or storyline of play); (e) play behaviors and storylines begin to mirror the issues with which the child is struggling; (f) child works through play to reveal thoughts and feelings about self, (g) allowing others in the group to see the real self and demonstrate acceptance despite revelation, (h) and resulting in the child moving toward an acceptance of full self, including thoughts and feelings; (i) the child is now able to be self, revealing positive and negative characteristics; (j) interaction between children increases, (k) with genuine reactions between children (l) and increased sense of warmth and friendship outside and inside session, (m) leading to full acceptance of each other (the encounter), (n) the ability to express positive feelings toward one another when felt, and (o) behavioral change for the purposes of sustaining friendship. This pattern can be seen in group play therapy when the group is allowed to move in its own direction, given enough time for the process to take place and facilitated—not interfered with—by the therapist.

Group Case Example

I find it difficult to choose just one case to exemplify the characteristics of the group play therapy process addressed in this chapter. In sifting through my experiences, I have selected a case that most exemplifies the significance of providing unconditional positive regard for each child and trusting the group process to unleash the self-actualizing tendency.

Jacob was in March of his first grade year when I first met him. The school counselor at a local school where I had been consulting called to tell me that Jacob was selectively mute and had not talked in school since he began kindergarten. For almost 2 years, the school had tried technique after technique to get Jacob to talk. They were out of options and she asked if I would be willing to see Jacob in play therapy. When I met Jacob's mother and father, they were concerned parents. They described Jacob as extremely talkative at home, but as soon as he entered the school, or even saw anyone related to school, he immediately stopped talking. Going through Jacob's history, his parents related several developmental milestones that were met with difficulties. When Jacob's mother attempted to wean him from breastfeeding at 9 months, Jacob refused to take a bottle and ended up in the hospital with dehydration. When Jacob began to walk, he hit his head, fell down, and refused to try again for 6 months. As he grew older, his perfectionism grew to the point that he would destroy any product that did not meet his standard and then move into an aggressive tantrum. He was a talented artist, even at the age of 7. He would spend an inordinate amount of time for his age drawing his pictures until they were perfect. It became evident that Jacob was fairly inflexible and responded negatively to change by shutting down. Jacob's parents and I discussed characteristics related to general anxiety, such as inflexibility and perfectionism, which appeared to fit Jacob's history and present circumstances.

Regarding school history, Jacob's mother could not remember when he stopped talking or if he ever talked at all in school. She remembered that his preschool teacher expressed concern because he did not talk to her or to other children. By first grade, his teacher discovered that if Jacob's mother came to school, he would talk. So, they worked out a plan wherein Jacob's mother came to school three times a week so that Jacob could read aloud to her and could be assessed for reading level by his teacher. This was a hardship for his mother, who financially needed to work full-time and had to take several hours off each week to attend school. In addition, this plan did not solve problems related to other subjects or to Jacob's lack of social interaction with his peers.

I immediately started seeing Jacob in individual play therapy at the counseling clinic. He did not talk during therapy but he was quite communicative, using pointing and acting gestures to interact with me. He also drew quite a bit and attempted to spell words to tell me certain things. Jacob was immediately attracted to two figures in the playroom, a doll that he identified as Mario, the video game protagonist; and an action figure modeled after the television figure, Xena, princess warrior. In his play, Mario would often get into trouble and Xena would have to come to rescue him and figure a way out of his dire straits. At the end of each session, Jacob would make sure to write on the chalkboard, Quit and Save, a video game reference to his desire to continue the play scene for his next session. At the beginning of subsequent sessions, he would write, Game Continue. Jacob and I saw each other for several months in weekly individual play therapy sessions. He was in school for 2 months initially and then summer arrived. We saw each other twice weekly during summer and his play was quite enjoyable for him, indicating less anxiety through his relaxed body posture and increased nonverbal communication with me.

When he began second grade in the fall, I warned his mother that I was unsure if he was willing to talk in school. And not surprisingly, Jacob did not talk to anyone at school through October. In November, his mother related that Jacob had relaxed at home and was exhibiting less anxious behaviors, less perfectionism, and no tantrums. However, she related that Jacob's teacher was very concerned because Jacob would be attending an intermediate elementary school for third grade and there was no accurate way to assess his current academic level, as required for third-grade placement. I suggested that we move Jacob's play therapy to the school setting and I asked her permission to find another child of Jacob's choosing to join him in play therapy. She agreed. In our next session, I asked Jacob if he would be willing to choose another child to join him in play therapy. It could be any child from his grade and I would talk to the child's parents to see if they would let him or her play. The very next day, Jacob's mother called me to tell me that Jacob had chosen a child and she was concerned because the child was a boy who Jacob had never played with nor talked about at home. She was unsure if this would be helpful because Jacob and this child had never actually spoken. Agreeing with her that this seemed like a strange choice, I asked her (and attempted to convince myself) to trust his choice and give it a try. I spoke with the boy and his parents who, once assured that there was nothing wrong with their child, were quite open to his participation.

When the new boy, Aaron, entered therapy, I was quite excited by his presence. He was talkative and playful. He was curious about play therapy and immediately attempted to engage in play with Jacob. Without talking, Jacob showed Aaron all the toys and attempted to lead the play with Mario and Xena. The first group session was encouraging and I anticipated positive changes. In our second group session, a strange event occurred. Aaron stopped talking. For the entire session, neither Jacob nor Aaron spoke a word but they did play together. I was gravely concerned, imagining the worst possible consequence that I may have facilitated the development of a selectively mute child in Aaron. Throughout the following week, I explored my doubts and fears, questioning my philosophy and approach to play therapy, but I resolved to stick with the intervention for a while to see how things would evolve. In the third and fourth sessions, there was again no talking but the play began to change. Both boys would engage in building elaborate scenes to put Mario in danger. Aaron took on the role of Yoshi as a sidekick to Mario. Jacob would place Mario in precarious positions and Aaron, as Yoshi, would find a way to help him. As these scenes built in intensity, Jacob stopped looking for the Xena figure. He never acknowledged it; he just stopped playing with Xena. At the end of each session, he would make the point to still write, Quit and Save.

In the fifth session, Aaron began to talk again. There was no explanation for his not talking; he just naturally talked and responded to Jacob's nonverbal communication with verbal communication. After 8 weeks, Jacob's mother called me so that we could meet. She was very excited and reported that the teacher had seen Jacob talking on the playground. He had been sighted talking to Aaron in a whisper. Over the next couple of weeks, these sightings became frequent and Jacob was now talking to several class members, even engaging in a few conversations with his teacher. In our 10th session, both boys played out another elaborate scene of Mario getting into trouble. This time Mario got out on his own without any help. When Mario was safe, the boys celebrated by tearing up the entire scene. Jacob wrote in big huge marker letters, Game Over. Aaron verbalized, "It is finished" with enthusiasm and relief in his voice. I presented termination at our next session, and we saw each other two more times. During these 2 weeks, the teacher reported that Jacob was now talking as much as other children and fully engaged in the classroom.

By this time we were coming to the end of the school year and I informed Jacob's mother that I would be moving away from the area. She and I discussed that Jacob would probably struggle somewhat with anxiety throughout his development and new situations might initiate different anxious behaviors. I was especially concerned about his entry into a new school in the fall and explained that Jacob might return to mutism in this new setting. I asked her to call me if there were any problems. In early September, I received a voice mail from Jacob's mother, who asked me to call her but left no other details. I immediately thought the worst and guessed that he was not talking at his new school. When I returned her call, she did not answer. Because of my own worry, I picked up the phone to call the school, where I knew the principal well. She had also been informed of Jacob's situation and knew of my relationship with him through his mother. When the school counselor was unavailable, I asked to speak to the principal. When she answered, I inquired about how Jacob was doing and she exclaimed, "You are not going to believe this but I just did a walk-through in the cafeteria. I had to tell Jacob to hold it down because he was talking so much to his friends." We both laughed as we hung up and later Jacob's mom called me back to tell me how great Jacob was doing in school and how happy she was with his progress.

Several points are evident in this case example. First, Jacob responded to an environment where he could fully express his struggle, which appeared to be a fear or anxiety of handling his situation on his own. He used the Xena figure as his rescue figure, possibly seeing her as a maternal savior. Second, when offered group intervention, Jacob knew better than any adult who would be the most therapeutic for him. To this day, I do not know how Jacob knew but he intuitively chose a child who exhibited every sign of normal development and who demonstrated a significant amount of acceptance for Jacob. Third, Aaron was able to provide all the conditions necessary for change to Jacob. He intuitively provided empathy and acceptance through his lack of speaking. And finally, through group process, not through structured design, Jacob was able to develop a sense of self-regard that matched his environment. He could figure out how to save himself, and he needed to do it through his relationships.

Special Issues Related to Group Play Therapy

As discussed in the introduction to this chapter, group play therapy has the likelihood of producing new fears, threats, challenging experiences, and self-doubts within the play therapist. Therapists may experience conflict between providing the attitudinal qualities necessary for therapy and perceivably simple issues such as tolerance of noise/mess level to more personal issues such as lack of ability to control interactions or feeling left out of the group process when children begin to serve each other's needs. The following are a few challenging issues that I have observed over the years in working with group play therapists.

Noise and mess. Although most play therapists learn to deal with noise and mess in the playroom in the individual setting, the intensity in these areas when facilitating group play therapy is multiplied and is often upsetting to therapists. Therapists will often have difficulty staying present with children in session because they (the therapists) are distracted by the level of mess and noise. This issue can be addressed by problem solving the management issues, such as the therapist leaving enough time between play therapy sessions to clean the room or exchanging certain craft materials that are particularly messy to the group. If simple solutions such as these are not helpful, the play therapist may need to explore her general level of comfort with mess, a possible family background that affects this issue, and its effects on her current lifestyle.

Matching and timing. Because so much interaction is taking place in a group play therapy session, therapists often find it challenging to maintain a matched level of responsiveness and energy. New group play therapists, in particular, will find themselves a "beat" behind the level of interaction between the children, challenging their own ability to be immediate in session. This issue usually dissipates with experience as therapists learn to respond to more pressing interactions and less to general activity. Continued experience in group, review of such moments in video recordings of sessions, and consultations with discussion of responses are helpful in increasing the therapist's in-the-moment abilities.

Control issues. The need for control is perhaps one of the more dangerous personality needs embraced by play therapists. If a play therapist has a strong need for control, this need might be somewhat challenged by individual play therapy but it will be greatly challenged in group play therapy. When a play therapist displays a need to control the setting, the interaction, and the play of the child so that it is directed to the outcome desired by the therapist, play therapy can be negatively affected by disallowing the child to move toward a more helpful direction identified by the child. In group play therapy, children will directly challenge this need for control through their play, activity level, breaking of limits, attitude toward the therapist, and other destructive behaviors that place the focus of therapy on "winning." Ultimately, when a therapist actively engages with a child to establish control, everyone loses and the therapeutic process ceases to be therapeutic. Although limits are essential to the play therapy process, limits are set as necessary to enhance the therapeutic process for the child, not to establish control over the child by the therapist. In supervision, I have encountered many play therapists for whom the group process revealed their issues of control and impacted their ability to be effective. Upon recognition of the issue as a problem, the therapist explores personal conflicts surrounding the issue of control and their ability to directly deal with their needs in the context of their professional goals.

Limit setting. Not surprisingly, limit setting in group play therapy is a highlighted area of concern. The presence of more children inspires more concerns regarding the need for limits and how to set those limits. Typical concerns involving limit setting of group play therapists include "Is this behavior okay in group play therapy versus individual play therapy?", "How far do I allow them to go when I see that we're headed for a limit?", "How much responsibility do I turn over to them to solve the problem versus set the limit for them?", "When there is more than one, how do I enforce the limit?", and so on. There is no right answer to any of these questions, and they are usually addressed on a case-by-case basis. The basic underlying message of the therapist who is asking these questions is, "I'm scared things are going to get out of control and become nontherapeutic. How do I keep that from happening?" A play therapist is now exploring a sense of competency and confidence, as well as a belief in the attitudinal quality of unconditional positive regard. Consultation is especially crucial during these times of questioning and exploration. Limit setting in group play therapy requires quickness of response from the therapist because activity moves at such a rapid rate and the possibility of harm to another is greater. In addition to consultation, a play therapist will benefit from preventive work such as brainstorming possible scenarios and problem solving the best solutions.

Philosophy challenges. The issue of limit setting is directly related to the therapist's belief in the self-directed nature of children. There is no greater laboratory for experimenting with the question of a need for guidance for children versus a belief in their ability to positively self-direct their behavior than the group play therapy room. For child-centered play therapists, this is an especially salient issue. Child-centered play therapists embrace the belief that children have the ability to direct their behavior to positive outcomes, specifically in individual play therapy. However, in group play therapy, when a play therapist is forced to step in the middle of two children physically engaging in a fight, this belief system is challenged. The therapist must make the decision regarding the need for the introduction of a problem-solving method or the continued allowance of such aggression (while still stepping in when physical aggression is pursued) until the children tap into their positive nature and develop coping skills from an internal sense of doing what moves them toward self-actualization. Advanced play therapists use the group play therapy experience as an opportunity to explore and clarify belief systems about children that help the therapist become a stronger, more effective agent for change.

Role of therapist. When therapists choose to become play therapists, they are often attracted to the idea of serving as a therapeutic agent of change for a child. Play therapists often develop intimate, close relationships with their individual clients because children allow therapists, and sometimes only the therapist, to see their whole world. In group play therapy, the modality relies on the presence and interaction of other children who will serve as change agents for each child. Often, the therapist will take a "back seat" to the group of children in the expression and development of new coping skills. Although the group play therapist serves a critical role in providing the environment and facilitating group members' interactions, direct interaction and involvement is limited as compared to individual play therapy. Commonly, therapists are disappointed in this role and prefer to have the more intimate connection provided in individual play therapy. When this issue arises, advanced therapists explore their personal needs and motivations being fulfilled in play therapy and how these needs might be negatively affecting their abilities as play therapists.

Conclusion

Ginott (1961) warned that "Play therapy, particularly group play therapy, provides many opportunities for testing the stability of the therapist and for bringing even the most accepting adult to the brink of his endurance" (p. 128). Advanced play therapists recognize the value and benefits of group play therapy while also concurrently understanding the personal energy and commitment needed to effectively facilitate group process among children who are offered an environment of accepted expression. Group play therapy presents the individual child with an opportunity to express personal strengths and challenges related to self-regard in the presence of other children who will provide feedback, acceptance, and—hopefully—support. Through the group process, each child is able to build congruence between self-regard and environment in a microcosm of a typical childhood setting where peers are generally present and interactive. The advanced play therapist provides an environment where group members choose direction for self and group, knowing that such a setting will lead to a release of the self-actualizing tendency. Experiencing and communicating the attitudinal qualities necessary for change becomes more of a challenge for a play therapist in a group setting as compared to individual play therapy. Advanced play therapists who pursue group intervention are genuinely attuned to personal energy and focus as they experience empathy and unconditional positive regard for each group member and the group as a whole.

References

Axline, V. (1969). *Play Therapy*. New York: Ballantine Books.

Bozarth, J. (1998). *Person-centered therapy: A revolutionary paradigm.* Ross-on-Wye: PCCS Books.

Ginott, H. (1961). *Group psychotherapy with children.* New York: McGraw-Hill.

Rogers, C. (1970). *Carl Rogers on encounter groups.* New York: Harper & Row.

Slavson, S. (1999). Play group therapy for young children. In D. Sweeney, & L. Homeyer (Eds.), *Handbook of group play therapy: How to do it, how it works, whom it's best for* (24–35). San Francisco: Jossey-Bass Publishers. (Original work published 1948.)

Slavson, S., & Schiffer, M. (1975). *Group psychotherapies for children: A textbook.* New York: International Universities Press.

Sweeney, D., & Homeyer, L. (1999). Group play therapy. In D. Sweeney, & L. Homeyer (Eds.), *Handbook of group play therapy: How to do it, how it works, whom it's best for* (3–14). San Francisco: Jossey-Bass Publishers.

CHAPTER 12
Play Therapy in the Schools

Play therapy is the developmentally preferred modality for conducting counseling with elementary school-age children. Various mental health professionals are based in schools to provide services for children who are struggling academically, emotionally, and behaviorally. Schools typically employ mental health professionals for the sole purpose of helping children progress academically. Hence, for play therapists to justify their work in schools, it becomes imperative that they connect the intervention of play therapy to school success. There is general recognition that emotional and behavioral elements may benefit or impede academic progress. Often, play therapists will need to highlight the relationship between emotional and academic health.

The need for mental health services for children has been labeled a crisis in the United States (Committee on School Health, 2004; Mellin, 2009) and data suggests that if children obtain help, they are most likely to receive mental health services in the school setting (Foster, Rollefson, Doksum, Noonan, & Robinson, 2005; Rones & Hoagwood, 2000). The American Counseling Association, American School Counselor Association, National Association of School Psychologists, and School Social Work Association of America (2006) jointly called for interventions based on evidence to address the mental health needs of children in schools. Gilliam (2005) found that expulsion rates among preschoolers were higher than for school-age children and were partially attributed to a lack of attention to social-emotional needs. Furthermore, elementary-age children are more likely to be unhappy at school, absent, suspended, or expelled (National Center for Children in Poverty, 2006).

Historically, play therapists explained the link between play therapy and academic success as based in facilitation of an environment in which a child will feel safer, able to build positive school relationships, and freer to learn with less internal distractions. When children accept themselves and develop positive self-regard, they will be more open to learning from others. Landreth (2002) claimed that the goal of play therapy in schools is to "help children get ready to profit from the learning experiences offered" (p. 148). In Axline's (1949) early studies on the positive link between play therapy and child intelligence, she noted that play therapy allowed the child to overcome emotional limitations that hindered expression of intelligence and release the child to demonstrate full potential.

Early studies of child-centered play therapy (CCPT) measuring academic improvement suggested that play therapy helped to increase IQ scores and ability to learn in the classroom (Axline, 1949; Dulsky, 1942; Mundy, 1957; Shumkler & Naveh, 1985). Additionally, researchers (Newcomer & Morrison, 1974; Siegel, 1970) concluded that children with learning disabilities demonstrated significantly improved motor functioning and decreased learning difficulties as a result of participation in play therapy. In the past decade, research in play therapy has concentrated on disruptive behavioral problems, with no studies conducted on intelligence or academic achievement. Ray and Bratton (2010) questioned the focus on behavioral problems in schools as a dependent variable for play therapy research due to CCPT's focus on the inner world of the child.

Several recent CCPT research studies have been conducted in elementary schools, establishing a consistent pattern of incorporating play therapy in the school setting (Fall, Balvanz, Johnson, & Nelson, 1999; Fall, Navelski, & Welch, 2002; Garza & Bratton, 2005; Muro, Ray, Schottelkorb, Smith, & Blanco, 2006; Ray, 2007; Ray, Blanco, Sullivan, & Holliman, 2009; Ray, Schottelkorb, & Tsai, 2007; Schottelkorb & Ray, 2009; Schumann, 2010). These studies explored children's externalizing behaviors and relationships, specifically ADHD, aggression, and teacher/child relationships. Most recently, Blanco (2010) conducted an experimental study of play therapy effect on first graders labeled as academically at-risk. He concluded that first graders significantly improved on academic achievement following 16 sessions of CCPT over those who had not received play therapy, marking the first study in this century to link play therapy with academic achievement. Upon reviewing 21 CCPT research studies conducted in school settings, Bratton (2010) concluded that play therapy is responsive to the developmental needs of children and has been successfully applied with diverse and at-risk populations in schools.

Play Therapy Definition for Schools

Regional and school differences dictate a school's ease with the term "play therapy." Specifically, in the school counseling field, the term "therapy" is not encouraged due to assumed but artificial ideas regarding a difference between actions that take place in a counseling session versus a therapy session. To maintain a solidified definition of play therapy, I encourage the use of the term "play therapy" in all settings. However, when it appears that a school will reject play therapy simply due its title, I have used other terms such as "counseling with toys" or "play counseling."

As previously highlighted, the purpose of facilitating play therapy in schools is to benefit students academically. Hence, a definition that links play therapy with academic progress is highly encouraged. Here are a couple of examples:

> I use the method of counseling with toys based on the relationship between counselor and child. Elementary-age children have difficulty working through problems with words so I facilitate the process by providing a play environment from which they can work through those issues that impede their academic progress.

OR

> Play therapy is a way of working with children in their natural language of play. I facilitate an environment in which children can explore the connection between how they see themselves and how they are operating in their environment. Through play therapy, a child will develop coping skills, responsibility, decision-making skills, and self-control, which will help him or her be more successful in school by improving behavior to allow more learning to take place.

There are a few components of importance within these sample definitions. First, there is a concrete description of play therapy in which it is explained that the child will be playing with toys. Second, there is an explanation of development by emphasizing that a child better expresses self through play than through verbalization. Third, there is an implied active role of the counselor as seen in both definitions through the word "facilitate." This helps parents, teachers, and administrators know that the play therapist employs an active role in intervention. And finally, there is a tie to school through the use of common school language such as academic, learning, responsibility, and self-control. Using school language sends the message that the play therapist sees his or her role as part of the overall team working toward the student's academic success. These components are essential to a working definition that is enthusiastically accepted by school stakeholders.

Rationale for Play Therapy in Schools

The rationale for using play therapy in schools is similar to the rationale for using play therapy in any setting and has been explored thoroughly throughout this book. The unique aspect of providing a rationale for play therapy in schools is making the connection between the need for an emotional intervention and a child's academic progress. Again, using a rationale communicated through school language can be helpful. The American School Counselor Association National Model (American School Counselor Association, 2005) for school counseling outlines a delivery system consisting of four components: Guidance Curriculum, Individual Planning, Responsive Services, and System Support. Responsive Services is the component in which the school counseling program responds to students' immediate needs or concerns, and commonly involves counseling. Play therapy, as a responsive service, is the developmentally appropriate method of responding to the immediate needs of children who operate more fully in a nonverbal world. Play therapy aims to help children have stronger self-images, accept limits and consequences to actions, be more responsible for self and actions, be more independent and self-reliant, trust self better and gain a sense of control, and learn a variety of coping skills.

Working With School Administrators

Initiating a play therapy program in a school begins with the first contact with the lead school administrator, usually the principal. School counselors are encouraged to start a play therapy conversation in the first interview with a principal. In the structure of schools, school counselors usually report to the principal, who is also instrumental in deciding upon work duties applied to the school counselor. An address of play therapy in a first interview will provide an indication to the school counselor about the principal's openness to and knowledge of play therapy. Play therapy need not be presented as an unusual technique of a mysterious nature when addressed with the principal. A simple explanation, as provided in the previous definitions, or an emphasis that play therapy is a just a type of counseling that is most appropriate for children, will suffice when the school counselor presents play therapy as one component—responsive services—of the overall school counseling program. Too much focus on play therapy at the expense of other components of a school counseling program will possibly concern a principal that the school counselor will be short-changing other school counseling duties. Hence, the school counselor highlights play therapy as only one duty among many in a comprehensive school counseling program.

For other school mental health professionals who serve as adjuncts to academic services but may answer to an authority other than the principal, discussion of play therapy should also accompany initial interviews with school administrators. Students benefit when all school staff members are operating from the same goals and are supportive of methods in reaching those goals. School counselors, social workers, psychologists, and contract therapists begin and continue a dialogue with administrators regarding play therapy's place in improving academic achievement.

Another method of gaining support from administrators is to provide them with resources supporting the use of play therapy, including previous research, evaluation plans, and evaluation data. Chapter 15 includes a research summary of 80 years of research conducted in play therapy. This summary will aid the school-based play therapist by providing evidence of the effectiveness of play therapy. I attempted to compose a brief synopsis to help play therapists quickly access scholarly support for their work.

Evaluation plans are critical to securing support for play therapy work in the schools. Schools are under pressure to provide evidence, not only for the support of a school mental health intervention, but more importantly for the use of the intervention as contributing to school goals. Play therapists can connect their work to school vision by developing evaluation plans to that end. When children participate in play therapy, the play therapist should have a method of determining progress. Some of these methods were addressed in Chapter 8 on measuring progress. Specific evaluation methods that are utilized in schools include grades, teacher reports, standardized testing, discipline referrals, and psychological/behavioral testing. Grades and standardized academic testing tend to be poor indicators of play therapy progress due to the subjectivity of grades and time elapsed between collection of grades and testing. Discipline referral data, usually required by state education agencies, can be an easily accessible method of evaluation. Discipline referral data consists of the number of times a child is removed from a classroom for disciplinary problems. Data indicates an office referral to an administrator or further action taken by the school such as alternative placement or suspension. Because play therapy can have a substantial impact on a child's behavior and self-control, discipline referrals may decrease significantly throughout play therapy intervention. In addition, because discipline referrals are noted through structured data collection procedures for schools, data is considered objective and evidentiary. Improvement in discipline referrals is potentially influential with principals because it provides evidence that instructional time increases when less time is spent on dealing with discipline problems. Psychological testing is also a source of useful evaluation data, especially when measuring a decrease in behavioral problems as reported by teachers, or improvement in depression symptoms that might interfere with learning. Finally, schools often rely on simple evaluation questionnaires completed by teachers. Such questionnaires can be developed by school mental health professionals through the formation of 5 to 10 questions specific to a child's difficulties in school and then distribution to teachers on a pre- and post-play therapy basis. Although this type of evaluation is not empirically supported, it does help provide support to school officials who need evidence of effectiveness to continue sponsoring a school play therapy program.

Working With Teachers

Just as in the private sector where parents provide the gateway to children participating in play therapy, teachers are the key connection point for children in schools. Children are with their teachers for 6 to 8 hours per day, making them the most important adults in children's lives, second only to parents/primary caretakers. In addition, teachers are usually the first adults to notice that a child is in need of mental health intervention. It is incumbent upon play therapists to develop positive working relationships with teachers in order to better serve children.

An introduction to play therapy may be addressed through staff development days for teachers. Preferably, play therapists will reserve a block of time during staff development prior to the beginning of a school year. This early staff development time is often considered precious by administrators, and a play therapist must present a strong case to acquire the time. If it is impossible to acquire a block of time, then a play therapist must be assertive about garnering at least 30 minutes for presentation. Prior to the school year and any personal interaction with children is the time for play therapists to present the rationale and definition of play therapy to teachers. The play therapist will also present procedures for referral and walk teachers through the process of how the play therapist will be handling individual student cases. The presentation of toys can also be valuable, allowing teachers to have a concrete idea of what takes place in play therapy. In subsequent years, play therapists should provide teachers with evaluative data to support the play therapy program, including a presentation of how play therapy has aided teachers in their roles. Figure 12.1 is an example of an evaluation results data sheet that can be given to teachers and administrators. In this example, a play therapist would highlight that teachers themselves reported that children who participated in play therapy were demonstrating less aggressive behavior in the classroom.

Another method of gaining support from teachers is to purposefully integrate play into everyday school interactions. Each staff development may include a 5- to 10-minute group play activity led by the play therapist.

Play Therapy with Children Exhibiting Aggression in Schools

2009–2010 School Year

Children Served Franklin Elementary = 35; Lincoln Elementary = 14

Gender & Ethnicity

School	Franklin	Lincoln
Male	25	12
Female	10	2
African–American	6	1
Caucasian	16	7
Hispanic/Latin	11	4
Bi-racial	2	2

Aggression Subscale of the *Teacher Report Form*

Teachers reported that students who participated in play therapy significantly decreased aggressive behavior in the classroom

Treatment Group	PreMean	PostMean
Play Therapy	68.84	66.00*
Control	65.55	65.00

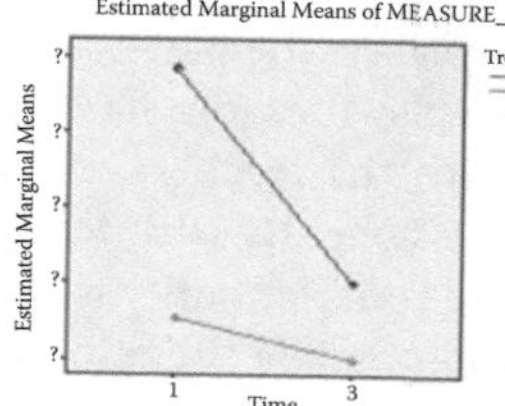

Aggression Subscale of the *Child Behavior Checklist* (completed by parent)

Parents of children who participated in play therapy reported an average decrease in aggressive behaviors exhibited at home when compared to children in a control group.

Treatment Group	PreMean	PostMean
Play Therapy	67.87	65.13
Control	61.76	60.59

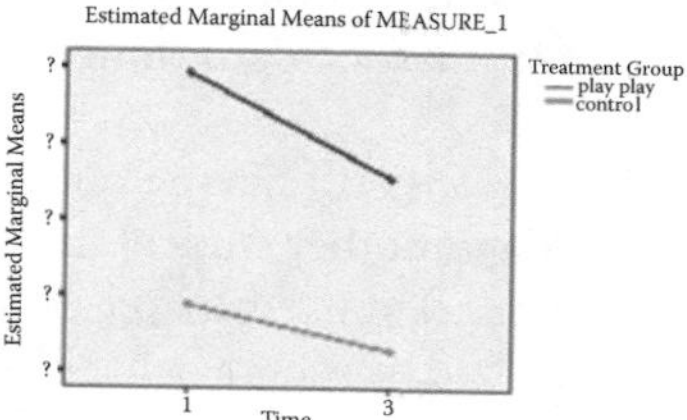

Figure 12.1 Sample school data.

Structured play activities, although not person-centered, highlight the importance of play in relaxing and enjoying the school environment for teachers. Some play activities can lead to better communication and expression of feelings. When teachers experience play at this level, they may be able to appreciate the implementation of a play therapy program for children. School play therapists will also want to provide play materials accessible to teachers, such as a small sand tray or hand toys for use when teachers just stop by for a few minutes. These materials again provide a release for teachers and demonstrate the healing nature of play in a personally experiential way. As a school counselor, I found that my small sand tray was quite popular with teachers. Many teachers stopped by just to rearrange a scene and engage in conversation. At one school I served, much to my delight, small sand trays began popping up on several teachers' desks.

Once teachers initially support a play therapy program, the play therapist must continue to communicate with teachers to sustain the viability of the program. When teachers refer a child for play therapy, the play therapist immediately responds to the teachers by engaging in a conversation regarding the teachers' concerns for the child. Play therapists will then inform the teachers of plans to make contact with the student. In some cases, a play therapist has an ongoing waiting list in the school and may have to delay contact with the child for several weeks. In these cases, the play therapist informs the teachers of anticipated contact. After a play therapist has begun facilitating play therapy with a child, contact with the teachers remains central to intervention. A play therapist regularly consults with teachers regarding a child's progress while still maintaining confidentiality with the child. Consultations should also offer support and possible suggestions to teachers specific to the child. The following is a sample excerpt from a play therapist/teacher consultation after three play therapy sessions.

Play Therapist: "Ms. Smith, I wanted to get back to you about Michael. I've seen him in play therapy three times now. He has demonstrated some of the behaviors you were concerned about. I feel like I'm getting to know him better. Have you noticed anything in the classroom lately?"

Teacher: "I'm so glad you started seeing him. He is still having outbursts when he doesn't get his way. Yesterday, another student took the yellow eraser off my desk, and Michael started to yell at him because it was the one he wanted. I had to send Michael to the isolation desk in the back of the room."

Play Therapist: "Yes, I noticed that he becomes frustrated easily and responds by expressing anger. When I reflect his anger back to him, like 'Michael, you're really angry that you didn't get what you wanted,' he seems to calm down."

Teacher: "That's hard to believe because he just gets louder when I tell him to stop being so angry."

Play Therapist: "It seems like my just saying calmly, 'You seem really angry' helps him actually get calmer. I wonder if that would work in the classroom."

Teacher: "I don't know but I'll give it a try."

Play Therapist: "Let me know how it works. I know he can be frustrating, especially when you have so many other kids to deal with. I'll keep seeing him and check back with you in a couple of weeks.

In this scenario, the play therapist initiates contact with the teacher to let her know that her concerns are being addressed. Also, the play therapist acknowledges the teacher's frustration with the student and provides empathy for the teacher's role. Instead of trying to suggest a list of recommendations for the teacher, the play therapist simply shares what has worked in play therapy. Teachers often resent a non-teacher's recommendations for the classroom. In order to be heard, a play therapist will softly reveal ideas that may or may not be helpful to the teacher, never presenting as the school expert on the teacher's classroom. And finally, a play therapist will reassure the teacher of continued support for the student and the teacher by pinpointing a time for next contact. It should be noted that this interaction took place in less than 5 minutes. Naturally, play therapists will need to conduct longer consultations as situations arise but contact can occur more frequently if the play therapist is respectful of the teacher's limited time and initiates brief and effective consultations.

One common occurrence in schools between play therapists and teachers is the teacher's refusal to allow the student to go to play therapy. Teacher thinking in these situations is similar: "The student has behaved badly or not completed work; therefore he doesn't deserve to play." "I cannot allow the student to be rewarded by playing after he has acted so poorly." The first intervention for this situation is prevention. If the play therapist has conducted education on play therapy, integrated play into teacher interactions, and been in regular communication with the teachers, the "not allowed to play today" scenario is less likely to occur. But sometimes the play therapist has provided all these preventive measures, and the teacher still responds negatively to the idea of play with a badly behaved child. Play therapists respond assertively to teachers in this situation, continuing to discuss the merit of attending play therapy even following the roughest of child behaviors. Below is a sample transcript from this scenario.

Play Therapist: (arrives at classroom) "I'm here for Antonia."

Teacher: (in an angry tone and in front of whole class) "Antonia won't be able to go to play today. I had to cancel her recess earlier because she yelled in class, and now she is refusing to do her work."

Play Therapist: (in front of class) "Sounds like a hard day. Can I talk with you in the hall?"

Teacher: (obviously irritated with play therapist but goes to the hall) "There is just no way I'm letting her leave to play after the way she has behaved today."

Play Therapist: "It sounds like she's been a handful. Really frustrating."

Teacher: "It's been awful. She's not getting rewarded."

Play Therapist: "And it seems like by going to play therapy she is being rewarded but this will actually be a time where she will be able to work through some of the problems happening in the classroom, like her staying angry and stubbornly refusing to do her work. A play therapy time might allow her to regroup and reenter the classroom with a better attitude."

Teacher: "I just don't feel right about it. She has broken so many rules already."

Play Therapist: "Somehow it just seems wrong to you but when we talked last week, you mentioned that these types of behaviors had decreased since she started play therapy. If we start being inconsistent or using play therapy as a type of reward system, I think we will see our progress stagnate."

Teacher: "Okay, fine, just take her."

The interaction between the teacher and play therapist in this scenario consists of several intentional features on the part of the play therapist. First, the play therapist quickly tries to remove the teacher from chastising the child in front of the classroom or using the conversation to punish the child. Second, the play therapist aligns herself with the teacher by acknowledging the teacher's feelings and sense of rightness. Third, the play therapist is assertive by pursuing the need for the play therapy session and not giving up even after the teacher has sounded emphatic. Fourth, the play therapist points out the benefits of regular attendance in play therapy and the consequences of missed sessions. Through calm reflection and explanation, the play therapist either convinces the teacher or wears down the teacher until the objective is met. I would highly recommend that in these types of situations, the play therapist seek further communication with the teacher under less stressful circumstances so that the play therapist/teacher relationship can be nurtured.

Working With Parents

Even in schools, parents are the ultimate decision makers regarding their child's participation in play therapy. School play therapists generally have less contact with parents than those in the private sector, yet positive play therapist/parent relationships are essential to the play therapy process. The school play therapist is particularly mindful of initiating contact with parents and finding ways to gain their support for play therapy.

The first step in beginning play therapy with a child is acquiring parental permission for counseling. Schools have various requirements and procedures for gaining parental permission that are adhered to by school play therapists. Figure 12.2 provides a sample consent form for a school

Dear Parent,

My name is Dee Ray and I am the school counselor for Franklin Elementary School. I am writing because you or your child has agreed to participate in counseling at Franklin Elementary School. As noted in the attached brochure, I provide counseling through play therapy. Play therapy is counseling for young children using play, children's natural language. In play therapy, I will meet with your child weekly or bi-weekly and facilitate your child's play for the purpose of engaging in greater emotional or behavioral functioning.

The counseling relationship is considered confidential, so information that your child shares with me is kept in confidence. There are rare cases, however, in which I might have to divulge information regarding your child, specifically if there is threat of harm to self or others, or if required by law.

I am happy to talk with you at any time regarding your child's participation in play therapy. Although I will not be able to share specific details of what your child says and does, we can discuss your child's concerns and progress.

If you would like to discuss the nature of counseling or have any further questions, you may contact me at (940) 555-2055.

- -

I have read and I understand this counseling consent form, and I agree to allow my child to participate in counseling at Franklin Elementary School.

____

Child's Name

____

Parent/Guardian Signature Date

Figure 12.2 Counseling consent form.

counselor providing play therapy. Because schools do not fall under Health Insurance Portability and Accountability Act regulations, a school counseling consent form has less formal language and detail, yet should still contain key elements of informed consent including an explanation of services and limits to confidentiality.

School play therapists also utilize brochures as a medium of communication. Brochures can be especially useful in defining and explaining play therapy. Figure 12.3 is a sample school counseling brochure that highlights the use of play therapy by the school counselor. Brochures are easily developed and can be distributed through hard copies or by placing them on the school website. Ensuring that parents receive information regarding the school counseling program and play therapy helps them understand the school counselor or play therapist's role in potentially helping their child.

Opening up the playroom to parents, teachers, and administrators allows stakeholders to experience the play therapy process on a first-hand

Franklin Elementary School Counseling Program

Welcome to Franklin Elementary School! My name is Dee Ray and I am Franklin's school counselor. At Franklin, we offer many services to help our children feel well and do well in school.

- Play Therapy to help children who are going through a rough time emotionally or behaviorally.
- Group Play Therapy to help children build social skills.
- Classroom Guidance to provide social and emotional education to all Franklin students.
- Parent Education to support parents in their roles as caretakers of our children.

Play Therapy

Sometimes children feel sad, angry, or confused. When children feel bad, they often do not learn well. They have difficulty paying attention in class or finishing their class work. Also, children might be struggling with their behaviors which get them in trouble with teachers and principals.

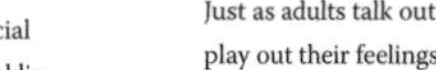

Play therapy is a counseling method for children to help them communicate in their natural language of play. Just as adults talk out their feelings, children often play out their feelings.

In play therapy, the school counselor will facilitate an environment in which children can explore the connection between how they see themselves and how they operate in their environment. Through play therapy, a child will develop coping skills, responsibility, decision-making skills and self-control which will help him or her be more successful in school. Play therapy is provided to help a child concentrate better and learn more in school.

Classroom Guidance

The school counselor will visit each classroom many times throughout the school year. During these visits, she will present a lesson on issues such as social skills, bullying, staying safe, or making good decisions. The goal of classroom guidance is to provide preventative education to all students of Franklin Elementary.

Parent Education

The school counselor will present parent education programs throughout the year. These programs will be based on needs of parents who complete a school-wide survey at the beginning of the school year.

Please contact me with any questions or ideas:

Dee Ray, School Counselor
(940) 555-2055
Dee.ray@franklinelementary.sch

Figure 12.3 Sample school counseling brochure.

basis. On nights when parents are invited into schools, such as open houses, meet the teacher, or parent organization meetings, the play therapist can open up the playroom for tours. I would suggest labeling sections of toys in the playroom, much like a kindergarten room. Nurturing toys are grouped and labeled, as are realistic toys, aggressive toys, and so on. For each label, an explanation for why that group is needed in the playroom is briefly given (see Chapter 5). During tours, the play therapist should be open and prepared for questions regarding play therapy materials and procedures.

In many regions, school play therapists are allowed to conduct play therapy without prior consent from a parent. Although this allows greater freedom in initiating contact with a child, I recommend contacting the parent as quickly as possible following a play therapy session if contact has not already been made with the parent. Children who begin play therapy are often quite excited and enthusiastically talk about the experience. Hearing that a child has been placed in play therapy without parent knowledge can be quite concerning for a parent. This notification should come from the play therapist, not the child. A play therapist contacts the parent as soon as possible for introduction and requests permission to continue to see the child in play therapy. Personal contact through a letter sent home is highly recommended. In addition to making initial contact, a school play therapist schedules regular contact with parents over the duration of play therapy. As is often the case in schools, parent consultations may be irregular and mostly conducted by phone. A play therapist makes every effort to contact the parent every 5 or 6 weeks in person or by phone. Regular consultation decreases the likelihood of miscommunication and involves the parent in the child's progress—not only in play therapy, but also in school.

Space and Play Materials

Chapter 5 presented toy and space needs for the ideal playroom, often not available to the school play therapist. Fortunately, play therapy can be effective in different sizes of rooms. Essential features of a playroom include shelves for placing toys above the floor and allowing more room for movement and at least some space for free movement. Optimal features include access to water through a sink, noncarpeted floors, and durable wall paint. Again, these are ideal conditions. School play therapists are able to successfully facilitate play in a conference room, bookroom, behind a cafeteria stage, or in a portable building. School counselors typically are assigned offices, some small and some large. In small spaces, school counselors should be creative with room placement. Shelves can be used to place toys within reach of children and still provide floor space. Desk room might be minimized to create more free space in the office. A conference table might double as a craft table. If a school counselor is one of the fortunate few who is assigned a classroom, dividers/shelves can be used to divide parts of the room. One example is to use bookshelves to divide a classroom into four equal spaces: one space for a desk area, one space for a play therapy area, one space for a guidance area, and one space for a conference area.

However, many school play therapists move around a school with no stable base from which to work with children. A portable playroom can be developed to allow a play therapist to operate out of almost any space. Toys can be stored in large tote bags or large plastic bins, preferably on wheels. For sessions, play therapists lay out toys in an organized way prior to the child's entry. If a play therapist is mobile, there are some key considerations for effective play therapy. The first is the attempt to provide some consistency to the child regarding setting. Even if play therapy is conducted in a borrowed classroom only free for a 30-minute session, the play therapist should aim to provide play therapy for that child in that same classroom for each session. Providing this type of setting consistency for the child will help send a message of safety, thereby improving the effectiveness of play therapy. Another consideration for the mobile school play therapist is confidentiality. The play therapist should ensure the confidentiality of the child by insisting that whatever space is being used only belongs to that child and therapist at that time. If a play therapist is providing play therapy behind a cafeteria stage curtain, the play therapist works with the administrators and custodians to make sure the space is not being used and that other children or staff cannot hear what is going on in session.

The same play materials are recommended for both clinical and school settings; these were presented in Chapter 5. Further considerations regarding play materials specific to school settings include the need to provide materials for a wide range of ages and the inclusion of aggressive toys. In elementary schools, the play therapist might be facilitating play therapy with a 5-year-old or a 12-year-old. Materials in the room should be functional for a broad range of ages. Whereas baby bottles are heavily used in play therapy with 5-year-olds, they may be met with disdain by a 12-year-old. And although glue and glitter may be used for expression with older children, they are dumped and smeared by 6-year-olds just for fun. School play therapists benefit from organizing materials into age groups and scheduling play therapy accordingly. Some craft materials may be placed in cabinets that remain locked except on Mondays and Tuesdays when the play therapist sees fourth and fifth graders, and some toy carts are rolled out on Wednesday and Thursday when the play therapist sees the kindergarteners and first graders. Versatility of space and materials is essential for effective play therapy in elementary schools.

A discussion of space and materials in schools would not be complete without addressing aggressive toys. My experience suggests that schools are more likely than clinical settings to present obstacles to the inclusion of aggressive toys in the playroom. Based on fear stemming from infrequent violence occurring in schools, teachers, parents, and administrators may respond negatively to the inclusion of a toy gun, knife, rope, or handcuffs in a playroom. The advanced play therapist anticipates a school's reaction to aggressive toys by being prepared with supportive rationale and examples of their use: "Guns represent the ultimate form of aggression in society and provide children with a symbolic way to represent powerlessness and anger." "Rope is often used to communicate a sense of closeness to the therapist, a valuing of the relationship." Once the play therapist has assertively addressed concerns regarding aggressive toys and there is still objection to their use, the play therapist can replace toys with less offensive symbols and still meet the needs of the children. Examples include using several thick sticks and string for "creating" guns or including a jump rope that can be used for handcuffs or a tying rope. Play therapists in this situation are inspired to be creative.

Organizing Play Therapy Intervention in the School Setting

The school setting is unique in that every school is made up of hundreds, maybe thousands, of children who can benefit from play therapy but only one or two mental health professionals who can provide it. Obviously, most children do not need play therapy for emotional and behavioral problems, but a majority of children could benefit from the experience. As a school counselor, I became overwhelmed with deciding how many and who could participate in play therapy. The school counselor role, similar to that of a school social worker or psychologist, consists of other components required for the job. Play therapy can only be provided to a comparatively small number of students when considering the total number of students in a school. To survive the school counseling role and provide play therapy intervention, I created a prioritization system for decision making that would at least offer a structure so that children could be served in an orderly, if not comprehensive, way. Table 12.1 lists the general steps for this decision-making structure.

Due to my background in clinical settings prior to my school counseling experience, I chose to implement a waiting list procedure. I organized my calendar to calculate how many play therapy sessions would be possible in a week's time. For my job at the time, I could conduct 12 sessions per week, 30 minutes per session. The number of available spaces meant that I could serve 12 children in individual play therapy or possibly more if I facilitated group play therapy. There were 650 children attending my school and I had identified at least 50 who appeared to need intensive intervention. Based on teacher reports, parent reports, child behavior,

Table 12.1 Steps to School Play Therapy Prioritization Schedule

Step 1	Calculate number of available play therapy sessions.
Step 2	List names of all referred children.
Step 3	Collect background information on children, including teacher and parent reports, and school files.
Step 4	Determine if any children can be referred to outside agencies or private practitioners.
Step 5	Rank-order each of the children based on the severity of the case and the threat of school failure.
Step 6	Schedule children in group and individual play therapy based on available session times.
Step 7	Assess each child at the end of six sessions to determine progress.
Step 8	If child has made reasonable progress in six sessions, terminate with child. Add next child on list to schedule. If child has not made reasonable progress, continue in play therapy for another six sessions.

and a lack of referral opportunities, I prioritized the 50 students. Using school priorities, students at risk for being sent to alternative schools were placed high on the list while students experiencing emotional and contextual problems were ranked lower. Through the scheduling of individual and group play therapy, I was able to start seeing 18 children each week in play therapy. My goal was to provide six sessions to each of the 18 children and then reassess each child for termination. When children were terminated, I then moved down the list to the next child and added him or her to the schedule. Surprisingly, this system was effective in eventually getting through the initial 50 children plus children who were added throughout the year. As could be expected, five children were seen for the entire year due to severe emotional and behavioral problems combined with the parents' inability to attain services outside the school.

As a counselor, I felt limited in my ability to deliver the necessary play therapy services; but as the only school mental health professional, I used this prioritization structure to at least reach as many students as possible under the circumstances. A play therapist might consider delivering play therapy multiple times per week instead of the traditional weekly session. Recent research in schools has highlighted the benefits of conducting two sessions per week over 8 weeks as compared to weekly sessions over 16 weeks (Ray, Henson, Schottelkorb, Brown, & Muro, 2008). Multiple weekly sessions might also be conducive to a school play therapist's schedule by concentrating play therapy interventions within a limited period of time.

One of the most positive aspects of working in schools, as compared to clinical settings, is the process of termination. In the school setting, termination can be approached with less trepidation than in clinical environments due to accessibility to the student. The termination process involves the judgment of the play therapist based on the observable progress of the child. In some cases, play therapists feel that it is risky to terminate only to observe significant signs of distress after termination. The benefit of working in schools is that play therapists can easily observe the child's stability following termination. If termination was premature, the play therapist can quickly reengage the child in play therapy with little harm done. One final note about termination in schools is that it is sometimes tempting to use semester and summer breaks as catalysts for termination. Just as in the clinical world, termination is based on observable therapeutic factors, which was addressed in Chapter 8. Decisions regarding termination are not based on arbitrary markers of time.

Therapeutic Conditions

Inconsistency is probably the leading threat to school play therapy. Elements that are considered requirements for clinical practice, such as therapist attendance, being on time, confidentiality, and lack of disruptions, may be disregarded in a school setting where children are treated with less respect and autonomy. Common sense would dictate that school play therapists are present and prepared for their scheduled play therapy sessions. Just as in private practice, a school therapist attends a scheduled session. Some readers may be wondering why I am making such an obvious point. In my experience, I have observed that sessions in schools are treated quite differently than in clinical settings regarding structure. A school counselor may be called to a teacher meeting and never show up for a scheduled time with a student. A school psychologist may be trying to fit in one more assessment with a child and miss a scheduled play session with another. Or, sometimes, the play therapist attempts to pick up the child an hour or two after the scheduled time. This difference is perplexing to me because a mental health professional who treats clients in this manner would never succeed in agency or private practice. Yet somehow this has become acceptable behavior in schools. I feel strongly that this behavior sends a message of disrespect to the child and is intolerable professional behavior. School play therapists should strive to be available and on time for scheduled sessions. Such behavior promotes trust in the relationship between therapist and child—the cornerstone for therapeutic change. When a school play therapist cannot attend a session because of unexpected circumstances, the play therapist should make personal contact with the child to reschedule. This is minimal respectful behavior toward a client.

Other threats to consistency include a lack of confidentiality and an inability to control session disruptions. Confidentiality is owed to our children and is represented in every mental health professional organization's code of ethics. In schools, where the culture encourages a lack of confidentiality, a play therapist may stand alone when not sharing details of a child's counseling sessions. Again, the child's ability to trust the counseling relationship is vital to its success, and counselor behaviors reflect this trust. Not only does a play therapist keep student information confidential, but the play therapist is also charged with ensuring that the child's play is kept confidential by being aware of the limitations to confidentiality that certain settings provide. If play therapy is being conducted behind a curtain on the cafeteria stage, the play therapist is responsible for ensuring that no one is present during the play therapy time. If play therapy is being conducted in a portable unit with a blocked-off playroom, reading tutoring should not take place on the other side of the shelves. Windows should be covered and door signs should be utilized to prevent disruptions. School sessions are especially susceptible to disruptions. Overhead speakers, classroom and office phones, and unlocked doors practically invite constant interruptions. School play therapists develop communication rules with office administrative staff and teachers marked by signs and displayed schedules to minimize disruptions.

Transitioning a child between the classroom and playroom can present challenges to the play therapist. Although the youngest of children quickly acclimate to the school environment and feel comfortable in transitioning to other schoolrooms, a play therapist is advised to pick up a child from the classroom for play therapy. Picking up the child helps transition in several ways. First, the play therapist can ensure timeliness of the play therapy session. Second, picking up the child avoids any miscommunication between the teacher, child, and play therapist regarding the proper time for session or the possible "no play today" scenario. And finally, picking up the child allows the play therapist a transition time with the child where small talk can take place in the hallway before starting the play therapy session.

Although providing a warning to the ending of a play therapy session is essential in all settings, the purpose of a providing a warning is especially salient in the school environment. When a child leaves a play therapy session in school, he or she is expected to reenter the classroom with an academic attitude. The 5-minute and 1-minute warnings provide the time needed for a child to transition back into an environment where there are high expectations, vastly different from the setting of the playroom. In some cases, children have participated in an emotionally charged session, and it is quite difficult for them to reestablish a connection with the school environment. I found that a walk through the school, sometimes running a school errand with the child to drop off something at a teacher's room, helps the child's reentry into the school world. In addition, I will often initiate conversations regarding academics with the child in the hallway, such as "How hard was your math homework?" or "Do you have a spelling test this week?" Again, this helps focus the child on the classroom environment that he or she is reentering. On one occasion, I facilitated a session with a young boy who had witnessed his father fatally shoot himself in the head. In this session, the boy picked up the gun several different times, pointed it at himself, and then put it down. At the 5-minute warning, the boy picked up the gun and shot himself in the head with the dart. He then fell down and laid quietly for the last few minutes of the session. Needless to say, it was problematic for me to send him back to his classroom. At the end of the session, he arose energetically to leave the room. I asked him to accompany me to deliver papers to two different teachers across the school from each other. During the extra 10 minutes it took to deliver the papers, we discussed his upcoming math test and how he had a difficult time with multiplication. By the time we reached his classroom, he seemed prepared to reenter.

Note Taking and Educational Planning

Because of the humanistic nature of CCPT, some play therapists struggle with the behavioral focus in the schools, including paperwork that is decidedly behavioral in requirements. The school counseling field has a history of avoiding the subject of note taking in schools. Due to the confidential nature of counseling, school counselors may have been encouraged to avoid session notes, less they be accessed by school officials or parents. However, most licensure boards and current school practices require or at least encourage record keeping for students. Because educational records are accessible under federal law and because states have the authority to determine the definition of educational records, it is still recommended that school play therapists keep minimal notes, avoiding the details of specific play behaviors and verbalizations. The purpose of counseling notes in schools is to note delivery of services and mark progress; and this purpose can be met with short session entries. Table 12.2 presents examples of school play therapy session notes.

Table 12.2 Sample School Play Therapy Session Notes

3-15-10	Marcus participated in individual counseling for 30 minutes. He was quite agitated throughout the session. Counselor and student worked toward his goal of learning to cope with his aggressive behavior in more appropriate ways. (Bobo, dart, doll)
3-21-10	Marcus participated in individual counseling for 30 minutes. Marcus demonstrated a light affect and shared that his week was going well. Marcus appears to be integrating coping skills into his classroom experience. (doll, Bobo, sand)

There are four notable characteristics of school session notes. The first is that they should be factual, focused on the observed and concrete. Second, they are short, not providing unneeded detail. Third, they focus on the progress of the child, as determined by the match between educational goals and observable behaviors. And finally, there is an avoidance of interpretation, either verbal or play based. The final listing of play materials following each entry serves as a memory device for the play therapist to track continuity of play but will mean virtually nothing to a school administrator or legal reviewer. These types of notes serve to track attendance and progress of children who participate in play therapy but do not divulge confidential information that would be detrimental to the child or the child/therapist relationship.

Educational and behavioral plans are common devices used in schools. Because of the prevalent use of educational plans, the play therapist benefits from learning to integrate play therapy goals with school culture. Integration can be achieved without the abdication of child-centered philosophy and principles. Educational and behavioral plans require the play therapist to use language that is concrete, specific, and measurable. Although play therapy aspires to provide an environment where a child is free from evaluation and can develop the ability to self-evaluate, behavioral plans can reflect the outcome of providing this type of environment. Using what a play therapist knows about play therapy, behavioral plans that are not confining for the child can be developed. Table 12.3 provides an example of a written educational plan.

In the example in Table 12.3, Billy will participate in weekly play therapy with the counselor over the evaluation period of 1 year. During this year, the first objective requires that Billy express negative emotions such as anger appropriately with the counselor. In CCPT, appropriate expression of anger may entail hitting the bop bag, screaming in the session, tearing up a painting, and many other expressive outlets. The probability that the child can meet this objective is high and sets up the child for success while providing

Table 12.3 Sample Educational/Behavioral Plan

Short-Term Objectives	Level of Mastery	Evaluation Procedures
Billy will appropriately express negative emotions 1 time a week with counselor over evaluation period (1 year).	80%	Counselor observation; student conference
Billy will appropriately express anger through assertive statements in the classroom 3 times over evaluation period (1 year).	80%	Teacher observation

the child with the appropriate intervention of play therapy. For the second objective, Billy must express anger in an assertive statement three times over a year. Again, the probability of achieving this objective is good, recognizing that Billy probably already expresses himself appropriately on occasion. This objective requires the teacher's observation of the behavior, which encourages the teacher to notice positive behaviors displayed by Billy. Learning to speak the behavioral language can help a play therapist integrate play therapy intervention into the standard operations of the behavioral school culture, providing humanistic options to children under setting constraints.

Conclusion

Play therapy in schools can be challenging but also offers an opportunity rarely available to play therapists in which children in need are accessible for intervention throughout the day. The school play therapist does not rely on the parent's ability to consistently attend play therapy, or participate in parent consultation. Instead, school play therapy utilizes the natural setting of a child, a place where she spends 6 to 8 hours a day, to provide necessary mental health intervention. Schools provide a team approach to helping children in which a play therapist can integrate beliefs and practices into a systemic method of delivering educational, psychological, behavioral, and emotional support. In schools, children can participate in a play therapy program that facilitates their development of self-regard in the context of the school environment. School play therapists are in the unique position of supplying the necessary and sufficient conditions for change through the primacy of the therapeutic relationship within a setting that, at times, disregards the needs of the individual child.

References

American Counseling Association, American School Counselor Association, National Association of School Psychologists, & School Social Work Association of America. (2006). *Removing barriers to learning and improving student outcomes: The importance of school-based mental health services.* Retrieved from American Counseling Association website: http://www.counseling.org/PublicPolicy/TP/ResourcesForSchoolCounselors/CT2.aspx?

American School Counselor Association. (2005). *The ASCA national model: A framework for school counseling programs* (2nd ed.). Alexandria, VA: American School Counselor Association.

Axline V. (1949). Mental deficiency: Symptom or disease? *Journal of Consulting Psychology, 13,* 313–327.

Blanco, P. (2010). Impact of school-based child-centered play therapy on academic achievement, self-concept, and teacher-child relationships. In J. Baggerly, D. Ray, & S. Bratton (Eds.), *Child-centered play therapy research: The evidence base for effective practice* (125–144). Hoboken, NJ: Wiley.

Bratton, S. (2010). Meeting the early mental health needs of children through school-based play therapy: A review of outcome research (17–58). In A. Drewes, & C. Schaefer (Eds.), *School-based play therapy* (2nd ed). Hoboken, NJ: Wiley.

Committee on School Health. (2004). School-based mental health services. *Pediatrics, 113*(6), 1839–1845.

Dulsky, S. (1942). Affect and intellect: An experimental study. *The Journal of General Psychology, 27,* 199–220.

Fall, M., Balvanz, J., Johnson, L., & Nelson, L. (1999). The relationship of a play therapy intervention to self-efficacy and classroom learning. *Professional School Counseling, 2,* 194–204.

Fall, M., Navelski, L., & Welch, K. (2002). Outcomes of a play intervention for children identified for special education services. *International Journal of Play Therapy, 11*(2), 91–106.

Foster, S., Rollefson, M., Doksum, T., Noonan, D., & Robinson, G. (2005). *School mental health services in the United States, 2002–2003.* DHHS Pub. No. (SMA) 05-4068. Rockville, MD: Center for Mental Health Services, Substance Abuse and Mental Health Services Administration.

Garza, Y., & Bratton, S. (2005). School-based child-centered play therapy with Hispanic children: Outcomes and cultural considerations. *International Journal of Play Therapy, 14,* 51–71.

Gilliam, W. (2005). *Prekindergartens left behind: Expulsion rates in state prekindergarten programs* (FCD Policy Brief Series 3). Retrieved from Foundation for Child Development website: http://www.fcd-us.org/usr_doc/ExpulsionCompleteReport.pdf

Landreth, G. (2002). *Play therapy: The art of the relationship* (2nd ed). New York: Brunner-Routledge.

Mellin, E. A. (2009). Responding to the crisis in children's mental health: Potential roles for the counseling profession. *Journal of Counseling & Development, 87,* 501–506.

Mundy, L. (1957). Therapy with physically and mentally handicapped children in a mental deficiency hospital. *Journal of Clinical Psychology, 13,* 3–9.

Muro, J., Ray, D., Schottelkorb, A., Smith, M., & Blanco, P. (2006). Quantitative analysis of long term play therapy. *International Journal of Play Therapy, 15,* 35–58.

National Center for Children in Poverty. (2006). *Children's mental health: Facts for policymakers.* Retrieved from National Center for Children in Poverty website: http://www.nccp.org/publications/pub_687.html

Newcomer, B., & Morrison, T. (1974). Play therapy with institutionalized mentally retarded children. *American Journal of Mental Deficiency, 78,* 727–733.

Ray, D. (2007). Two counseling interventions to reduce teacher-child relationship stress. *Professional School Counseling, 10,* 428–440.

Ray, D., Blanco, P., Sullivan, J., & Holliman, R. (2009). Child-centered play therapy with aggressive children. *International Journal of Play Therapy, 18,* 162–175.

Ray, D., & Bratton, S. (2010). What the research shows about play therapy: Twenty-first century update. In J. Baggerly, D. Ray, & S. Bratton (Eds.), *Child-centered play therapy research: The evidence base for effective practice* (3–33). Hoboken, NJ: Wiley.

Ray, D., Henson, R., Schottelkorb, A., Brown, A., & Muro, J. (2008). Impact of short-term and long-term play therapy services on teacher-child relationship stress. *Psychology in the Schools*, 45, 994–1009.

Ray, D., Schottelkorb, A., & Tsai, M. (2007). Play therapy with children exhibiting symptoms of attention deficit hyperactivity disorder. *International Journal of Play Therapy, 16*, 95–111.

Rones, M., & Hoagwood, K. (2000). School-based mental health services: A research review. *Clinical Child and Family Psychology Review, 3*(4), 223–241.

Schottelkorb, A., & Ray, D. (2009). ADHD symptom reduction in elementary students: A single case effectiveness design. *Professional School Counseling, 13*, 11–22.

Schumann, B. (2010). Effectiveness of child-centered play therapy for children referred for aggression. In J. Baggerly, D. Ray, & S. Bratton (Eds.), *Child-centered play therapy research: The evidence base for effective practice* (193–208). Hoboken, NJ: Wiley.

Shmukler, D., & Naveh, I. (1985). Structured vs. unstructured play training with economically disadvantaged preschoolers. *Imagination, Cognition, and Personality, 4*(3), 293–304.

Siegel, C. (1970). The effectiveness of play therapy with other modalities in the treatment of children with learning disabilities (Doctoral dissertation, Boston University, 1970). *Dissertation Abstracts International, 48*, 2112.

CHAPTER 13
Play Therapy in Community Agencies and Private Practice

Play therapy is a mental health modality practiced across a variety of settings. This chapter addresses limited aspects of working in community agency and private practice settings, as encompassing all aspects of such a diversity of venues would be beyond the scope of this book. Play therapists operate in settings that sometimes serve adults as well as children. Often, play therapy takes place in settings where multiple services are offered, such as legal and medical aid. A play therapist will be required to structure an environment and work within an organizational framework that provides children with an effective option for help. Child-centered play therapy (CCPT) is more philosophically aligned with settings in which the medical model does not drive intervention. However, reality dictates that CCPT therapists will practice in settings where they will be expected to diagnose, develop treatment plans, and monitor treatment according to behavioral outcomes. And although CCPT therapists may not believe in working from a medical model, they can ultimately advocate for children by figuring out how to integrate humanistically based principles and practice into a medically driven report format.

Setting

Chapter 5 described the necessary space and material needs for a playroom. The play therapist in the community setting thinks beyond the playroom and is responsible for structuring an environment for full practice, including waiting rooms, family therapy rooms, assessment rooms, access to bathrooms, and file storage. Numerous details are involved in setting up a play therapy practice, far beyond the considerations of setting up an adult-only office.

Waiting room. A waiting room is a basic feature of most mental health offices. Mostly designed for adults, waiting rooms typically include nice chairs, lamps, and magazines. When creating a waiting room for play therapy practice, there are several issues to consider. Simple rules apply, such as removing breakable or expensive items. Waiting rooms should provide some level of entertainment to engage a child prior to session or while the child is waiting during a parent consultation. Toys should be available for different age groups, from toddlers to preadolescents. However, toys should be limited in number and uniqueness. If the waiting room offers exciting materials unavailable in the playroom, the play therapist will have difficulty getting the child to the session. Televisions with playback capabilities can be helpful to subdue multiple children when the waiting room is busy. When available to children, televisions should not be on regular channel broadcasts, but should play shows that are specific to the age group of children. Having a television on news stations or certain commercials/television shows can be disturbing for children. Obviously, playback recordings should be labeled appropriately for children. Ideally, a play therapist can employ an office worker who will watch children as needed or provide babysitting for parent consultations. Realistically, play therapists do not usually have this option so they might invest in a two-way mirror from one counseling room to the waiting room where they could meet with a parent but supervise the child.

The size and structure of a waiting room is an important consideration for a play therapist. Rooms that are too small feel uncomfortable to both parent and child and also limit the child's movement. I would especially caution against large, open rooms. Often, children in play therapy are sensitive to movement, sound, and space. When they are placed in a large, open setting, they may begin to feel anxious, sensing chaos. If sounds are added such as television noise and people talking, along with multiple children arriving, children will sometimes respond with loud or defensive behaviors. Children with extreme sensitivity issues may respond aggressively, acting out on the environment or other children. Enclosed rooms with clear entrances and exits work best as waiting rooms.

A final issue involving the waiting room is that the length of time that a child is expected to operate without incident should be limited. Children have obvious needs for space and movement. When they are restricted for long periods of time, they will react negatively. In my clinic setting, we strive to offer an environment where parents and children feel comfortable, accepted, and welcome. As a result, parents will sometimes arrive early or find reasons to delay leaving after a session. Typical behaviors may include remaining on personal cell phone calls, reading a book while the child is playing in the waiting room, or chatting with administrative staff. In addition, play therapists may have scheduled sibling children back to back or parent education sessions following play therapy. In these cases, a child may be in the waiting room for over an hour or longer if the play therapist conducts a parent consultation. In my estimate, successful wait time for a child is about 30 minutes in a waiting room. Beyond this time period, they will start to get bored and restless, as would be developmentally appropriate. The play therapist works to minimize the time a child is left in a waiting room, emphasizing the importance of getting to and leaving the play session as the main purpose of coming to the office. When the play therapist recognizes a parent's need for extra support or downtime, this issue should be addressed in parent consultation.

Counseling rooms. Therapists who practice play therapy need multiple rooms for the multiple interventions necessary in child therapy. Playrooms that are adaptable to children as young as 3 and as old as 10 are recommended. Some play therapists are fortunate to have both playrooms for young children and activity rooms for older children. Having a room where assessment can be conducted is also recommended. Rooms that offer stimulating materials or wall art can be distracting for assessment purposes. There are times when a play therapist may conduct cognitive or psychological assessments, and a simple, small room with a table and chairs is recommended for this purpose. Play therapists also maintain at least one room that can be used for family counseling or parent education. A playroom may not be appropriate for family counseling because children will be distracted by toys from the structured activity being offered to the family. A larger therapy room that can provide chairs and floor space for sitting, and wall space for art activities works for family therapy. For play therapists who act as supervisors, a two-way mirror and digital recording capabilities are recommended for all therapy rooms.

Bathrooms. Unlike most forms of therapy, play therapy requires thoughtful consideration of bathrooms. Bathrooms must be near the play therapy room. Children are often unaware of their needs to go to the bathroom until the immediate need arises. Bathrooms must be easily accessible from the playroom. Optimally, a play therapist will choose a space that includes a bathroom as part of the office suite but sometimes hallway bathrooms are the only choice. In this case, the play therapist would choose office space nearest to the hallway bathroom. Fixtures in the bathroom should also be accessible to children. They need to be able to turn on the lights, wash their hands, and reach the soap and paper towels without adult help. Bathrooms should have stalls for the toilets so that play therapists can accompany the child into the bathroom. One room with a toilet and sink forces the therapist to wait outside, which may not be advisable when working with

3- to 5-year-olds. Play therapists will make individualized decisions on whether to involve the parent when a child needs to use the bathroom. In the middle of session, it can be disruptive to not only have to accompany the child to the bathroom, but also to reenact the greeting and separating from parent again. Involving the parent would most often occur when the play therapist is of the opposite sex of the child and appearance of propriety is best.

File storage. As is true for all mental health professionals, a play therapist must have a secure, confidential space for client records. Files must be able to be locked and inaccessible to others. In an office where maintenance staff routinely cleans outside of office hours, a play therapist must ensure that file cabinets are not left unsecured. A unique consideration in child therapy is that more file space might be needed than when dealing with adult files. Depending on state law, some therapists are required to keep records for a certain number of years past the child's 18th birthday. For many child therapists, this translates into keeping files for possibly more than 20 years, creating a potential space problem. Many technologically advanced play therapists have moved to digital records, which is helpful in the file storage problem but carries a different set of considerations, including file protection from access or digital destruction.

Marketing Play Therapy Practice

Marketing play therapy practice involves educating the public regarding what play therapy is and how it is beneficial. Technology now offers multiple tools to help a play therapist share information in frugal or expensive ways. Play therapists will want to utilize tried and true methods of local presentations and advertising, as well as modern tools of Internet marketing and social networking sites.

Presentations and workshops. Perhaps the best way to build a local practice is to present locally. Presentations allow for personal interaction between the play therapist and potential clients. They also offer the opportunity for the play therapist to be perceived as an expert in the field of child therapy. There are endless organizations that regularly look for knowledgeable speakers, especially in the area of parenting. I recommend that a play therapist who is seeking presentation prospects compile a written list of speaker topics with a brief explanation of each. As play therapists meet community members who are involved in organizations, they can disseminate the topic list for consideration. Organizations such as churches, schools, mom groups, men's clubs, chambers of commerce, plus many more are potential speaker venues. Creativity is critical to marketing. For example, in a weight loss support group, a play therapist may choose to offer a brief seminar on how to reduce parenting stress that leads to overeating.

Personal networking. When building a play therapy practice, play therapists will want to take the initiative to meet community members who are affiliated with children. Gift baskets to local pediatrician offices are a nice way to meet the doctor's staff and a good excuse to drop by for a chat. Other community members associated with children include daycare workers, school staff, toy store managers, dentists, orthodontists, occupational therapists, video game retailers, etc. An especially helpful group of people for referrals to play therapy are local school counselors. School counselors are in constant need of referral sources. If they feel that a play therapist is a reputable professional, they will energetically send parents in the therapist's direction.

Brochures and paper marketing tools. Play therapists invest a considerable amount of money in brochures. Although the use of Internet resources is a less expensive method of advertising, brochures provide a tangible marketing tool that can be pinned up or taped to a refrigerator—still a common way for parents to remember materials. In brochures or other hard-copy methods, play therapists will want to specify the scope of practice. CCPT therapists will provide not only a definition that fits the child-centered philosophy, but they will also add specificity that is helpful to parents. Because the culture is dominated by labels and diagnoses, the CCPT therapist needs to ensure that parents understand that her services are applicable to the parent's main concern. For example, a successful brochure will list concrete presenting symptoms such as attention difficulties, aggression, and depression for which the therapist offers effective intervention. The Association for Play Therapy (APT) provides a resource explaining the purpose of play, how play therapy works, and specific problems for which play therapy has been beneficial on their website (http://www.a4pt.org/ps.playtherapy.cfm). Although the APT is not child-centered based, play therapists can use this resource to develop their own materials for marketing.

Video and website marketing. Current technology allows for play therapists to utilize digital tools to promote practice and explain play therapy. A large number of therapy clinics and offices operate a website to market their practice and possibly provide further resources to potential clients. At my clinic, we struggled with educating administrative staff, as well as some therapists, to explain play therapy and needed a way to introduce play therapy to children and parents. I developed and filmed two short segments for the purpose of explaining play therapy and realized it would be a helpful tool in marketing play therapy in general. These films were created with a short script, reasonable artistic ability of my husband, use of a hand-held video recorder, and software already loaded onto my computer. The first one is the *Introduction to Play Therapy for Parents*, which explains in simple language what happens in child-centered play therapy and how it is helpful to children. *Introduction to Play Therapy for Parents* is

Table 13.1 Introduction to Play Therapy for Parents Video Script

Hi! My name is Dr. Dee Ray. I'm a play therapist and I'm here to tell you a little about play therapy.
You might be worried about your child right now. Maybe they're sad, angry, or confused.
Or maybe they do things that you just don't understand.
We believe that children express their feelings or worries through play. Just as you talk out your feelings, kids play out their feelings.
In play therapy, your child will be given a play therapist who will meet with you to talk about your concerns and explain play therapy.
Then, your child's play therapist will meet with your child each week in the playroom.
In the playroom, the play therapist will reflect your child's feelings, help your child develop positive self-direction, and set limits for inappropriate behavior to build coping skills.
By saying these things, your play therapist is helping your child learn to express his or her feelings in acceptable ways that actually benefit your child. In time, you'll probably see your child's behavior change.
There is no way to know how long play therapy will be needed. Each child is different. Your play therapist will keep you updated to let you know how things are going and what progress is being made.
You can always ask to meet with your play therapist to talk about your concerns or situations in which you would like help.
If you have any questions, make sure to ask your play therapist.
And we look forward to seeing you in play therapy soon.

located at http://www.youtube.com/watch?v=Onn_qF4pZ9Q. The second one is the *Introduction to Play Therapy for Children*, which is intended for use by play therapists to introduce play therapy to children following a first parent consultation and directly before the initiation of play therapy. *Introduction to Play Therapy for Children* is located at http://www.youtube.com/watch?v=fmKxvTtSWoc. I have included a script from both videos in Tables 13.1 and 13.2. There were two purposes for including discussion of these videos in this chapter. The first goal was to demonstrate that technology could be used to market play therapy without vast resources and with little technological savvy. Second, the videos are available to practicing play therapists who would like to link them to their own websites for help with introducing play therapy. The APT has also produced a professional video that play therapists will find supportive of practice and can be used to promote practice. It can be found at http://www.a4pt.org/why.cfm.

Internet networking. Networking websites have become a valuable resource for play therapists. They provide a way to market practice with

Table 13.2 Introduction to Play Therapy Video Script for Children

Hi! My name is Dee. I'm a play therapist. I want to tell you a little about play therapy.
You know, sometimes you feel happy, or you feel sad, or you may feel mad.
Sometimes you do things you get in trouble for and you don't even know why.
And when you play, sometimes you feel better.
In play therapy, you will come to a place that's for kids.
You will meet a grown-up who will be your play therapist.
With your play therapist, you will go to a room with a lot of toys.
In the playroom, you can play with the toys in lots of the ways you like.
Your play therapist is there with you to play or talk. It's up to you.
We call your time in the playroom "special playtime."
I think play therapy makes you feel better because you get to play, you get to be with someone who cares about you, and you get to choose what you do.
Sometimes playing will be fun and sometimes it will be serious but you get to decide.
I think you'll feel safe in play therapy. If you don't understand something, make sure to ask your play therapist.
See you soon in play therapy!

minimal resources. Many potential clients or referral sources have access to the Internet and use social and professional networking sites to communicate. There appear to be an endless number of potential sites for a play therapist to market credentials and practice. Psychology Today (http://www.psychologytoday.com) provides a directory for therapists that allows the therapist to state credentials and personal approach to therapy. A popular site for professionals to use for networking, and one that has been embraced by therapists and seems appropriate for professional contact is LinkedIn (http://www.linkedin.com). Social networking is represented by the popular Facebook site (www.facebook.com), and many businesses use Facebook for marketing purposes. Play therapists should consider limited use of social networking as it might promote communication between client and counselor that would not be protected by confidentiality.

Administrative Tasks

Diagnosis. Because diagnosis is a method designed to label the client and thereby limit the client's potential as a person, seeing him only as a conglomeration of symptoms, CCPT does not support the use of diagnosis. As mentioned, CCPT therapists do not operate in a dream world that denies the current reality of the medical model pervasively used in mental health. Therefore, CCPT therapists will likely be required to diagnose in some settings. It should be noted that many CCPT therapists opt out of the medical model and set up practice to serve clients outside the reimbursement system. Although they may be very successful and this option fits the belief system of the therapist, reality dictates that affluent clients typically access mental health services without using insurance, resulting in impoverished clients left with few choices but to seek help through third-party insurers.

A CCPT therapist approach to diagnosis is to diagnose only when required to enable services for the client, thereby categorizing diagnosis as an administrative task with little impact on the therapeutic relationship. Even if play therapists are opposed to diagnosis, they must be knowledgeable when they work in a setting that requires diagnosis. The approach to diagnosis is to find the least restrictive but most descriptive diagnosis available for each case. When working with children, therapists look toward more developmentally appropriate diagnoses such as adjustment disorders and other conditions that may be a focus of clinical attention. There should be an assumption of growth in working with children that underlies the selection of diagnosis. For example, I work in a training setting where we prepare counselors to enter the mental health field. Diagnosis is required as part of the training and is used with every client, but I encourage my supervisees to use diagnosis accurately. If a child is in play therapy because the parent is worried about how the child might react to her father's imprisonment but the child demonstrates no reported problematic symptoms, then there is a "no diagnosis" code listed on Axis I and II. There is no need to diagnose the individual child for concerns of the parent, although the parent should be commended for seeking preventive care.

Treatment planning. As with most medical model tasks, treatment planning can present a problem for the CCPT therapist. Therapists are expected to develop a treatment plan that provides a diagnosis, prediction of therapy length, reported symptoms, and objectives for the client. In working with adults, a person-centered counselor could approach this task with some semblance of respect to the client by collaboratively working with the client on the plan. In working with children, this is a task that is performed without the child's knowledge and understanding, and with little feedback from the child involved. A play therapist develops a treatment plan by reporting parental concerns, setting objectives that are assumed to be easily attainable by the child, and providing a rationale for CCPT as the most appropriate intervention. Figure 13.1 provides an example treatment plan for a 7-year-old boy. The format of the treatment plan was revised from a form provided in Wiger (2009).

In the example treatment form of Figure 13.1, Joseph Morales was referred to therapy after the recent death of his sister, which occurred 3

Treatment Plan

Child's Name: *Joseph Morales* DOB: *02/04/2004* Date: *03/09/2011*

Presenting Problem: *Death of sister, Frustration Leading to Harm to Self* Therapist: *Dee Ray*

Axis I: *V62.82 Bereavement* Axis II: *None*

Services Needed:

Anticipated Number of Sessions

Intervention	1-2	3-7	8-10	11-20	21-40	41+
Assessment						
X Individual					X	
X Parent Consultation			X			
Filial Therapy						
X Family		X				
Group						
Other						

Problems/Parental Concerns	**Goals/Objectives**	**Interventions**
Repetitive talk of sister's death	• *Participate non-verbally in play activity* • *Interact with therapist through verbalization or play* • *Express perception of sister's death beyond repeating death story through verbalization or play*	*Individual child centered play therapy*
Low Frustration Level	• *Increase ability to tolerate failure in activity as evidenced by* o *Extending the length of activity by measurable number of minutes in play session* o *Decrease yelling or throwing item to 1 time per week at home*	*Individual child centered play therapy* *Parent consultations to teach response skills to parent such as reflection and problem-solving*
Banging head against wall when frustrated	• *Decrease incidents of head banging to zero* o *Current Level – 3 times per week* o *3 month objective – 1 per week* o *6 month objective – 0 incidents*	*Individual child centered play therapy* *Parent consultations to engage in limit-setting and reflection* *Family activity sessions to provide alternate forms of communication between family members*

I have discussed the intervention plan above with my therapist, understand the recommended strategies, and agree to participate as an active member in my child's intervention plan.

Patent/Guardian Signature: *Jessica Morales* Date: *03/09/2011*

Therapist Signature: *Dee Ray, Ph.D., LPC-S, NCC, RPT-S* Date: *03/09/2011*

Figure 13.1 Sample treatment plan for play therapy.

months prior to therapist contact. Joseph's mother was concerned about him because he repeatedly tells the story of his sister's death to everyone he greets on a daily basis. Since her death, he demonstrates a low tolerance for frustration. If a toy does not work as he wants it to, he quickly becomes angry and gives up, usually yelling or throwing the toy. He also engages in banging his head against the wall several times a week when he becomes frustrated. Each of these reported problems is reflected as a problem or concern on the treatment planning form. The therapist listed repetitive telling of the death story as a reported concern. However, there is an acknowledgment that this might be Joseph's natural way of grieving and should not be conceptualized as a problem. Because of this acknowledgment, the treatment plan reflects an objective that Joseph will extend his expression, not eradicate the behavior of repetitive verbal storytelling. For the other two concerns, easily accessible objectives are listed. The CCPT therapist realizes that such a simplistic approach to goal setting is for administrative purposes only. The genuine goal for Joseph is to provide an environment where he can explore the environmental crisis that has occurred for him and integrate this experience into his overall view of self, emerging with an experience that has been allowed into awareness and not denied or distorted. Each treatment strategy involves the use of CCPT, which will serve the objectives of the plan but more importantly will serve the genuine goal of therapy. In addition, the CCPT therapist recognizes the powerful influence of the parent/child relationship and will provide consultations to help the parents respond to Joseph in relationally beneficial ways. Family sessions will allow the play therapist to operate within the dynamics of the family, providing an environment of safety for their grief process.

Session summaries. The level of activity within a play therapy session is high with multiple strands of verbal and nonverbal communication. When a play therapist engages in numerous play therapy sessions weekly, session notes can be difficult to maintain in a timely manner or with accuracy. A session summary that uses prompts as reminders to play therapists can be a helpful tool for administrative record keeping. Figure 13.2 provides a sample play therapy session summary that can be modified to fit most play therapy settings. It should be noted that Dr. Linda Homeyer at Texas State University and Dr. Sue Bratton at the University of North Texas originated the concept of a play therapy session summary that used prompts to guide the therapist through note keeping. The sample summary follows the DAP approach to progress notes, an acronym that stands for Data, Assessment, and Plan (Wiger, 2009). Data includes expression of current concerns by parent, which may include any new environmental stressors or recent behavioral concerns. Data also includes identification of intervention and the therapist's observation of session events. For play therapy, session events include verbalization and play behaviors of the child. Assessment includes the therapist's assessment of session or therapy dynamics, along with client progress toward objectives. For play therapy purposes, assessment is also addressed through conceptualization of session dynamics. Finally, the Plan section addresses further recommendations from the therapist and plans for the time period following the session.

Figure 13.3 is an example of a completed play therapy session summary for Joseph Morales, the child recorded on the previous sample treatment plan. As can be seen in the example, the session summary is easily matched

PLAY THERAPY SESSION SUMMARY

Date________ Session #______ Time started: _____ Time finished:_____ Duration: _____

Child/Age________________/_____ Counselor ________________

Diagnosis/Presenting Problem ________________________

I. Data

Intervention:________________ **Current Concerns:** ________________

SIGNIFICANT VERBALIZATION:

LIMITS SET:

Protect Child (Physical & Emotional Safety):

Protect Therapist and/or Maintain Therapist Acceptance/Relationship:

Protect Room/Toys:

Structuring:

Reality Testing:

TOYS/PLAY BEHAVIOR:

__ hammer/log/woodworking
__ sandbox/water/sink
__ theater/puppets
__ kitchen/cooking/food
__ easel/paint/chalkboard
__ bean bag/pillows/sheet/blanket
__ bop bag/foam bats/etc.
__ dress up: clothes/fabrics/shoes/jewelry/hats/masks/wand
__ crafts/day/markers/etc.
__ doll house/doll family/bottle/pacifier/baby
__ cash register/money/phone
__ camera/flashlight
__ medical kit/bandages
__ musical instruments
__ games/bowling/ring toss/balls/etc.
__ cars/trucks/bus/emergency vehicles/planes/boats/riding car
__ animals: domestic/zoo/alligator/dinosaurs/shark/snake
__ soldiers/guns/knife/sword/handcuffs/rope
__ constructive toys/blocks/barricade
__ sandtray/miniatures
__ Other:____________

DESCRIPTION OF PLAY: Describe the play behavior, sequence of play and child's affect during play.

II. ASSESSMENT

PLAY THEMES: *Circle predominate theme(s).*

EXPLORATORY
POWER/CONTROL
DEPENDENCY
REVENGE
SAFETY/SECURITY
MASTERY
RELATIONSHIP
NURTURING
GRIEF & LOSS
ABANDONMENT
PROTECTION
SEPARATION
HELPLESS
REPARATION
RESILIENCY
CHAOS/INSTABILITY
PERFECTIONISM
INTEGRATION
POWERLESS
HOPELESS
ANXIETY
OTHER:______

CONCEPTUALIZATION AND PROGRESS:

III. PLAN/RECOMMENDATIONS: ***Circle Recommendations***

Play Therapy Next Appointment Date/Time:
Parent Consultation Next Appointment Date/Time: ________
Family Session
Sibling Play Therapy
Group Play Therapy
Final Therapy
Parent Counseling
Parent Resources
Medical Evaluation
Psychological Assessment
School Consultation
Professional Consultation
Request Records

________________________/______
Play Therapist Signature (with credentials) Date

Figure 13.2 Play therapy session summary.

to the treatment plan through an address of diagnosis and behaviors of concern. Under Data, CCPT is listed as the session intervention, and the mother's concerns about Joseph's head banging that were shared with the therapist that day are also recorded. Significant verbalization is recorded as any talk that is engaged in during session that appears to be of importance to the child, therapist, or the relationship. In this example, Joseph told the story of his sister's death while playing with the sand but exhibited no affect in his delivery. Following verbalization, the therapist records limits that were set during session. For this session, no limits were set until the end of the session when Joseph refused to leave the playroom because he

PLAY THERAPY SESSION SUMMARY

Date _04/14/11_____ **Session #** __5_____ **Time started:** 4:30 pm **Time finished:** 5:20 pm **Duration:** 50 min

Child/Age: Joseph Morales/7 **Counselor:** Dee Ray

Diagnosis/Presenting Problem: V62.82 Bereavement/ Death of sister

I. Data

Intervention: CCPT **Current Concerns:** Mother reported she stopped J. from banging head three times last week when he was upset

SIGNIFICANT VERBALIZATION:
J. casually related story of sister's death "She fell in swimming pool and couldn't get out. She's in heaven now. She makes sure that I don't die." Did not respond to pt's reflection.

LIMITS SET:
Protect Child (Physical & Emotional Safety):
Protect Therapist and/or Maintain Therapist Acceptance/Relationship:
Protect Room/Toys:
(Structuring) Reality Testing: J. would not leave session at end. He wanted to make a picture for dad. Limit set 5x. Finally left when finished picture.

TOYS/PLAY BEHAVIOR:

_X_ hammer/log/woodworking
_X_ sandbox/water/sink
__ theater/puppets
__ kitchen/cooking/food
_X_ easel/paint/chalkboard
__ bean bag/pillows/sheet/blanket
__ bop bag/foam bats/etc
__ dress up: clothes/fabrics/shoes/jewelry/hats/masks/wand
__ crafts/clay/markers/etc.
__ doll house/doll family/bottle/pacifier/baby
__ cash register/money/phone
__ camera/flashlight
__ medical kit/bandages
__ musical instruments
__ games/bowling/ring toss/balls/etc.
__ cars/trucks/bus/emergency vehicles/planes/boats/riding car
_X_ animals: domestic/zoo/alligator/dinosaurs/shark/snake
__ soldiers/guns/knife/sword/handcuffs/rope
__ constructive toys/blocks/barricade
__ sandtray/miniatures
__ Other: ____________

DESCRIPTION OF PLAY: Describe the play behavior, sequence of play and child's affect during play.
J. played in sandbox. Built walls and buried horse. Different animals would come to bite the horse. The horse had a broken tail and broken legs. Fire truck and ambulance both came but could not help the horse. J. told story of sister while playing out the scene. Affect was light throughout sandplay. J. hammered log and seemed really happy. At 5 minute warning, J. seemed anxious and quickly wanted to make a picture for his dad.

II. ASSESSMENT

PLAY THEMES: *Circle predominate theme(s).*

EXPLORATORY	RELATIONSHIP	(HELPLESS)	
POWER/CONTROL	NURTURING	REPARATION	POWERLESS
DEPENDENCY	GRIEF & LOSS	RESILIENCY	HOPELESS
REVENGE	ABANDONMENT	CHAOS/INSTABILITY	ANXIETY
SAFETY/SECURITY	PROTECTION	PERFECTIONISM	OTHER: ______
MASTERY	SEPARATION	INTEGRATION	

CONCEPTUALIZATION AND PROGRESS:
J.'s play continues to be very relational. He seems to be working through his grief by verbalizing the death story repetitively. His play indicates a sense of helplessness with outside factors coming to hurt but no one is able to help. He appears to be struggling with a developing sense of capable self apart from his sister and other events. He also continues to display a high need for pleasing his father, a possible condition of self worth.

III. PLAN/RECOMMENDATIONS: *Circle recommendations*

Play Therapy Next Appointment Date/Time: 04/21/11 4:30 pm
Parent Consultation Next Appointment Date/Time: 04/21/11 4:00 pm
Family Session
Sibling Play Therapy
Group Play Therapy
Filial Therapy
Parent Counseling

Parent Resources
Medical Evaluation
Psychological Assessment
School Consultation
Professional Consultation
Request Records

Dee Ray, PhD., LPC, NCC, RPT-S
Play Therapist Signature (with credentials)

Figure 13.3 Play therapy example session summary form.

wanted to make a picture for his dad. The number of times the limit was set is recorded. Under Toys/Play Behavior, all toy groupings available in the playroom are listed. This section would be modified according to setting. For Joseph, each toy is marked with an X, prompting the therapist's memory about events that took place in playroom.

Under Description of Play, the therapist records a brief synopsis of actual events that took place in play session. In this session, Joseph's play centered on the horse in the sandbox. He buried the horse, and other animals would come to bite the horse to hurt him. When the fire truck and ambulance came to the horse, they could not help him and left. The horse was stuck in the sand for the whole session. His affect was descriptively happy throughout the sandplay. At the 5-minute warning in session, Joseph panicked because he wanted to make something for his dad but did not have time. He broke the structuring limit of ending the session to finish the picture for his dad. He was anxious during this play behavior. The session summary then progresses to Assessment, where the play therapist is asked to identify play themes exhibited in session. For this session, the play therapist identified "helpless" as a theme because the horse could not help himself, could not find anyone else to help him, and was thus stuck in the sand. The theme is explained in the Conceptualization section of the summary and tied to the child-centered conceptualization that Joseph is working on integrating the experience of his sister's death into his view of self. His panic at the end of the session was observed by the therapist as a way of pleasing his father by giving him gifts, making him happy, a possible condition of worth for Joseph. Finally, the summary Plan provides a list of possible recommendations following the session. The play therapist records plans for a play therapy session next week, along with a parent consultation directly before the scheduled session.

Custody papers. Child therapy requires a clear understanding on the part of the therapist regarding who is legally allowed to make decisions for the child. Play therapists should be intimately aware of state laws related to parental standing. Of particular concern in cases of single or limited parenting is the legal status of each biological parent. Child client files must include custody agreement documents when parental standing is in question. The therapist's acquisition of custody documents is necessary prior to the initiation of play therapy. In cases of divorce, there should be no reason that the papers cannot be provided to the therapist. Separations sometimes present problems because no legal action may have been taken; and in these cases, the therapist will make a decision based on the individual case about the initiation of therapy. In some cases, one parent has never been involved in the child's life and the whereabouts of that parent are unknown. Again, the therapist will have to use discretion in making a decision about initiating therapy when one parent is not legally represented in paperwork. Custody is often an issue when children have been left with other caretakers, such as grandparents, without any legal agreement. In most of these cases, I will require the grandparent to gain a signature of the parent on an informed consent and a release of information giving approval to the therapist to communicate with the grandparent or custodial guardian prior to the first play therapy session. Also, it is not enough to just file custody documents; therapists should also read all legal documents related to their clients, becoming familiar with how legal rights or limitations might impact therapy decisions.

Release of information. Working with children involves communication among multiple parties who are systemically involved with the child. At intake, a play therapist will attempt to discover possible consultation partners for a holistic intervention. School staff, psychiatrists, pediatricians, occupational therapists, attorneys, and caretakers not having legal rights such as grandparents or estranged parents are just a few of the possibilities for a play therapist's consideration. Play therapists anticipate the need for communication and seek parental approval for contact as quickly as possible. A release of information or parent approval for outside communication with others is required prior to any therapist contact with a third party.

Program Evaluation

For several reasons, program evaluation is essential to successful play therapy practice. Program evaluation is the review of play therapy practices based on quantitative and qualitative data for a particular setting. Program evaluation assesses the level at which play therapy is beneficial to children and under what structure. Program evaluation provides a roadmap for the play therapist by highlighting weak areas of a play therapy program and pinpointing directions for growth. Successful findings based on thorough program evaluation can serve as support for the acquisition of funding on a private and public level. Funding sources prefer to give to agencies that provide evidence of therapeutic outcome. Positive evaluation outcome can also be used to market services and new initiatives.

Because program evaluation is based on data collected from assessments, tests, and other sources of hard data, CCPT therapists may be hesitant to engage in such concrete and limited ways of assessing value. However, program evaluation can also encompass qualitative methods of interviewing parents, therapists, and others involved in play therapy. Anecdotal stories from clients can serve as powerful indicators of outcome. A mix of qualitative and quantitative methods of evaluation will serve agencies, as well as private practitioners, well.

I highly recommend the collection of data to support the practice of play therapy. Over 70 years of consistent play therapy research (see Chapter 15) substantiates that CCPT can facilitate behavioral changes in children who are sensitive to traditional forms of assessment. Chapter 8 presented data collection methods to support therapeutic decision making. These methods can also be used for program evaluation. And although behavioral change is less important to CCPT therapists than the emergence of the self-actualizing tendency in each child, these phenomena often progress at similar rates. At this point in assessment development, we are relegated to the measurement of behavioral change due to a lack of ability to measure internal processes of change. Fortunately for play therapy, behavioral change has served as a sensitive variable influenced by CCPT.

Reference

Wiger, D. (2009). *The clinical documentation sourcebook* (4th ed.). Hoboken, NJ: Wiley.

CHAPTER 14
Supervision of Play Therapy

> Distinctions between professional development and personal growth are at best arbitrary and meaningless; at worst they are insidious and lead to a level of incongruence which I cannot see as healthy or effective. (Worrall, 2001, p. 207)

The goal of a child-centered play therapy (CCPT) supervisor is to provide an environment that facilitates the growth of a play therapist leading to higher levels of personal congruence necessary for the elevated experience and communication of unconditional positive regard and empathy for children. The supervisor structures supervision sessions to focus on the experience of the play therapist as a counselor in relationship with a client or clients. Although counselor skills and client conceptualization are addressed in supervision, emphasis is placed on the play therapist's capacity to be in an effective therapeutic relationship with a child. The more a play therapist is able to experience and provide therapeutic attitudinal qualities, the more effectiveness will be demonstrated in play therapy.

Supervisor Qualifications

Just as a play therapist needs specific experiences and education, a play therapist supervisor should possess certain qualifications prior to moving into the role of supervisor. Chapter 4 listed the knowledge, skills, and experiences recommended for practicing play therapists. Supervisors should have accumulated these experiences as an advanced play therapist in preparation for becoming a play therapist supervisor. In addition to the qualifications listed for play therapists, a supervisor needs further attention to attitudinal qualities, education, and experience.

Congruence. The play therapist supervisor should operate from a place of congruence or maintain awareness regarding his accessible level of congruence at any given time. As discussed in Chapter 4, congruence is most likely a characteristic that might be limited for new play therapists. It becomes of particular importance that play therapist supervisors experience congruence for the purposes of modeling and facilitating growth in the area of congruence for new play therapists.

Unconditional positive regard. Just as counselors with clients, supervisors need to experience a high level of unconditional positive regard for supervisees. Because one duty of a supervisor is to evaluate the therapeutic effectiveness level of a play therapist, unconditional positive regard can be seen as a problematic characteristic of supervision. However, unconditional positive regard encourages the supervisor to accept the supervisee unconditionally as a person, beyond skill level. The supervisor is constantly sending the message to the supervisee, "I respect and accept you as a person. I assess your skills as a professional. These are two different role dynamics and only interfere with each other when you see the external acknowledgment of your skills as a condition of your personal worth." Naturally, and frequently, a supervisee is going to associate the supervisor's evaluation of skills with an evaluation of the supervisee as a person, especially with novice, externally focused supervisees. When supervisees can perceive positive regard, they will more likely be able to grow in their skills. Unconditional positive regard will remain a challenge to supervisors due to the belief in unconditional positive regard as necessary for change juxtaposed with the ethical duty of the supervisor to the field to protect future clients.

Empathic understanding. Communication of empathy from the supervisor to the supervisee is critical to the supervisee's ability to lower anxiety, explore demanding parts of therapy, and express self-doubts. Fortunately, unlike relationships with most clients, supervisors have lived through the similar experience of supervision and a built-in predisposition for empathy is likely. There are times when the supervisor struggles with empathy, especially when supervisees demonstrate a doubtful match with play therapy. At these times, the supervisor is encouraged to consult with supportive colleagues for the purposes of increasing empathic understanding and deciding if and when the supervisee should terminate pursuit of becoming a play therapist.

Supervision education. To become a supervisor, a play therapist needs to participate in training on supervision. There are many supervision models and approaches. Supervision is based in theory and research, which is heeded by the advanced play therapist and integrated into a personal model of supervision.

Theory and practice education. A play therapist supervisor needs to be educated in all theoretical orientations for which he or she will be providing play therapy supervision. If a supervisor is willing to engage in supervision with a supervisee of a different theoretical orientation, the supervisor should have prior education and experience in that orientation. Of course, the supervisor should also have a belief in the effectiveness of the play therapy theory orientations of which he or she supervises.

Supervision of supervision. Although education on supervision is readily accessible to many play therapists, supervision of supervision is less available. Typically, a 3-hour university course will provide some level of supervision of a new supervisor. This type of training is recommended for new supervisors. If a full university course is not an option for a new supervisor, the supervisor should pursue a supervision relationship with an experienced supervisor and meet for regular supervision. This type of supervision relationship should be extended until the supervisor has gained a sense of competence. Supervision is a new therapeutic experience and is characterized by unique attributes and challenges different from counseling that requires initial supervision.

Play therapy experience. Although it may seem obvious to mention, the play therapist supervisor should have extensive experience in facilitating play therapy. I hesitate to identify specifically how many hours or years are needed, but play therapy practice should have provided a breadth and depth of experience. Play therapist supervisors rely on their experiences in seeing a diversity of clients with a diversity of presenting problems for short and extended lengths of time. A final note is that supervisors who have never facilitated play therapy should never supervise play therapists for play therapy. This is an ethical violation (providing a therapeutic service for which there is no training) and should not be tolerated in the mental health field.

Ongoing play therapy experience. Over time, the mental health field changes, client concerns change, and the systemic culture surrounding the field changes. For a play therapist supervisor to be of maximum help to supervisees, current practice is needed. A play therapist supervisor maintains his or her knowledge and skills by continuing with professional growth through the ongoing facilitation of play therapy.

Supervision as Collaboration

From a person-centered perspective, supervision involves a collaborative effort between supervisor and supervisee who attempt to develop an equal relationship within the external power constraints that supervision entails. Merry (2001) conceptualized supervision as a collaborative inquiry predicated upon five principles:

1. Humans are self-directing and capable of responsible, self-enhancing behavior when operating from the self-actualizing tendency.
2. Supervisor and supervisee contribute equally to discovering meaning when a democratic relationship is established.
3. Supervision as collaborative inquiry encourages a deeper level of engagement with therapy issues because all forms of knowledge are respected and considered meaningful, including knowledge such as intuition.
4. Supervisee need for defensiveness is lessened due to lack of personal evaluation of worth.
5. Supervisor and supervisee see each other as collaborators in a cooperative experience.

These principles form the base of the play therapist supervision relationship. The root of a meaningful supervision relationship is a search for equal partnership between supervisor and supervisee. When both participants feel that they contribute equally, the relationship will reveal deeper levels of meaning and enriched exploration for the supervisee.

Process of Supervision

The process of supervision is recognized as a developmental process that involves a conscious matching of supervisor with supervisee based on a supervisee's level of experience, worldview, and perception of counseling. Borders and Brown (2005) summarized the various developmental models of supervision by describing three phases that appear commonly among approaches to supervision. In the first phase of supervision, supervisees present as concrete and prefer structure and direction. Supervisors are primarily instructional and focus on concrete skills demonstrated in session. Supervisors engage in teaching while also providing great amounts of support and encouragement. Middle phases of supervision are characterized by a shift in focus to the person of the supervisee. Supervisees are more open to exploration of relationship dynamics between counselor and clients, as well as personal reactions to clients. Supervisors may engage in confrontation and can share genuine reactions to supervisees, leading to more immediacy in the supervisory relationship. Supervisors and supervisees engage in discussions regarding generalizing of knowledge gained from a few clients to overall practice. The supervisor encourages the need for independence that is slowly being experienced by supervisee. In later phases of supervision, supervisors operate as colleagues or consultants to the supervisee. There is an assumption that supervisees will identify areas of growth and initiate supervision discussion. The supervisee moves from a focus on external evaluation to the valuing of internal evaluation.

Discussions may center on the supervisee's integration of personal growth and professional identity.

The general trajectory of the supervision process involves a move for supervisees from an external need for approval and feedback to an internal locus of evaluation involving personal and professional characteristics. Concurrently, the supervisor moves from a directive, concrete teacher to an equal collaborator in the supervisee's journey to become an effective counselor. Research in supervision has supported the observation of this developmental process and the need for varying roles of the supervisor.

Developmental Process in CCPT Supervision

CCPT supervision requires a grounded practice in person-centered philosophy, requiring that the supervision process mirrors the therapy process in which the supervisor operates from a place of congruence to provide unconditional positive regard and empathic understanding to the supervisee. General supervision literature has observed the varying levels of supervisee growth and the need for a differential role from the supervisor. For a CCPT supervisor, integration of the person-centered approach and supervision process observations is necessary to provide effective supervision. In an attempt to initiate the integration of these concepts, I have developed a description and stage model for CCPT supervision that may also be applied to most play therapy supervision. Table 14.1 presents a short synopsis of the model and fuller descriptions are presented in the following paragraphs.

Stage 1: Skill focused. In the initial stages of play therapy supervision, supervisees will focus on skills and rules. They typically arrive with a list of close-ended questions such as, "Is it okay to get up from my chair?" "What are the definite limits in the room?" They have a tendency to generalize the supervisor's answer to one case and attempt to apply it to all cases without critical thinking. They are very sensitive to supervisor evaluation and often seek praise. If they are not praised, they are typically disappointed and interpret a lack of praise as criticism. They are also overly self-critical or overly confident, operating from a defensive position (e.g., "I'll criticize myself before you do" or "I performed all the right responses so there's nothing to criticize me for").

In play therapy sessions, supervisees in the first phase will often respond to the child in rote, memorized speech, using categorical responses such as content reflection, returning responsibility, etc. They may lack affect or be overly animated, not matching the affect or energy level of child. They are easily distracted by their own internal processes. They might not respond to a child because they are trying to think of a "correct" response, or they might be distracted by internally criticizing their previous response. They

Table 14.1 Process of Play Therapy Supervision

Stage	Supervisee Dynamics in Supervision	Supervisee Dynamics in Play Therapy Session	Supervisor Attitudinal Qualities
1: Skill focused	Concrete, rule-bound Seek definitive answers Tendency to generalize specific cases Sensitive to evaluation Seek praise Overly self-critical or overly confident Anxious	Rote responses Lack affect Inability to match child affect Easily distracted by internal processes Anxious Possible panic responses	Intense levels of communicated empathic understanding involving the provision of some definitive answers to lower anxiety Limited expression of unconditional positive regard and congruence
2: Experimentation and questioning	Question person-centered philosophy Possible attraction to directive methods Seek evidence for effectiveness but lack experience in seeing it Defensive to reflections of feelings by supervisor	Experimentation of new methods without supervisor knowledge Possible lack of limits to support permissiveness Most likely stage for harm to occur	Communication of empathic understanding remains high Growth in congruence regarding supervisor relationship and confrontation Unconditional positive regard is experienced but still limited due to possible misinterpretation by supervisee that “anything goes”

3: Philosophical decision making transformed into practice	Comes to terms with belief system Rejects or embraces CCPT philosophy If embrace CCPT, exploration of process, patterns, and themes Openness to personal exploration of feelings in relationship to play therapy If reject CCPT, emerge with respect for nondirectiveness	Greater comfort level in session Able to reach new levels of congruence Able to experience in the moment If not CCPT, practicing techniques from new philosophy with knowledge of supervisor	Equal levels of expression of congruence, unconditional positive regard, and empathic understanding Congruence highly valued by supervisee
4: Person of play therapist emerges as professional	Supervision transitions into consultation Initiated by supervisee Led by supervisee concerns typically related to person of play therapist or specific play therapy relationship Unconditional positive self-regard becomes a focus If non-CCPT, supervisee seeking training or supervisor experiences aligned with new current philosophy; uses previous CCPT supervisor as consultant	Regular encounters of being in the moment in session Empathic understanding and unconditional positive regard expressed in an uncensored way Conceptualization stems from accurate empathic understanding Confidence emerges from sense of authenticity	Intense levels of mutual expression of congruence, unconditional positive regard, and empathic understanding by both supervisor and supervisee Recognition of the effect of limited unconditional positive self-regard on offering unconditional positive regard for clients

may display varying levels of anxiety, from extreme incongruence (laughing through every response) to a slight delay of response to the child's verbalizations or actions. Frequently, play therapists in this initial stage will panic when a child exhibits unexpected behaviors that have not been previously addressed in training or supervision. The consequence of panic may be exemplified in setting an unnecessary limit, raising their voice, jumping up, or possibly abruptly ending a session.

The supervisor's approach to supervisees in the first stage is to provide empathic understanding at a maximum level. In this stage, a supervisor reflects feelings consistently and provides extra time with the supervisee. Part of communicating empathic understanding at this stage is to provide some level of concrete answers to the supervisee's questions. Although the supervisor will want to balance this approach to empathy with a level of unconditional positive regard, denying the supervisee certain answers, where there are answers, will only increase the supervisee's level of anxiety and limit the supervisee's growth. For example, providing the supervisee with the typical definitive limits for the setting's playroom will help the supervisee feel less anxious when in the playroom. Although the supervisor seeks to experience unconditional positive regard and congruence throughout the supervision process, the communication of unconditional positive regard and congruence is limited for the supervisor at this stage. By giving concrete answers to communicate empathy, the supervisor is giving up some level of unconditional positive regard, which would alternately encourage the supervisor to allow the supervisee to struggle with the unknown in order to develop a personal approach. Communication of congruence may also be limited due to the supervisee's limited ability to constructively hear supervisor concerns at this stage. It may be of some solace to play therapist supervisors to note that the supervisee will almost assuredly be moving to the next level of development where expression of the conditions will increase in their effectiveness.

Stage 2: Experimentation and questioning. In the second stage, the play therapist begins to question the child-centered way of working. Because permissiveness is culturally rejected in current society, a CCPT play therapist is often working against the dominant culture of limitations and behaviorism. After initial demonstration of skills in early play therapy experiences, the play therapist will often begin to explore his or her *thoughts* about child-centered philosophy. I emphasize the word "thoughts" because at this stage, the play therapist is still demonstrating little exploration of self in relation to feelings about the process. Supervision discussion in this stage will often concentrate on whether CCPT is effective due to its nondirective nature or whether more directive methods are needed. Supervisees who quickly embrace the CCPT philosophy will sometimes question the need for limits or structure to play sessions. The supervisee will seek evidence for effectiveness but lacks experience in understanding the process of play, identifying themes, and noting progress based on sessions. The supervisee may be defensive to the supervisor's reflections of feelings and deny evident feelings of anxiety, incompetence, and unworthiness to personal awareness.

In play therapy sessions, supervisees at Stage 2 often experiment in play sessions without the supervisor's knowledge. At this stage, the supervisor is often surprised to hear about a therapist action or verbalization after the fact. On some occasions, supervisees will hide their new actions, revealing them only if there is a serious negative consequence. For example, one of my supervisees allowed a child to pour multiple buckets of water on the floor so that the child could run and slide (an action I would have placed a limit on). In the third session of this occurrence, the child fell, bumped his head, and had to be taken to the emergency room. As the supervisor, I was unaware of this behavior in the playroom because the supervisee had chosen to show me other clients in supervision during this period of time. On the other hand, I had a supervisee who engaged in problem solving with a 5-year-old in which she asked the child to draw how he felt in a specific situation and then asked what he could do the next time to avoid feeling that way. Although this is not egregious play therapist behavior, it was clearly not aligned with CCPT, and the play therapist had not discussed with me a new way of working with the child prior to initiating this session. I have found these types of play therapist behaviors to be common at this stage. In the process of supervisee development, I would acknowledge this stage as the one where harm is most likely to be incurred between therapist and child.

In Stage 2, the supervisor extends the communication of congruence to the supervisee. The supervisor will engage in genuine expression of self related to a felt sense of the supervisee. An example of such an expression would be, "I get the sense that you feel anxious about allowing children so much freedom." The supervisor will also probably engage in confrontation at this stage, such as, "I see that you are feeling the need to experiment but when you changed methods without talking to me, I felt distrusted." Expression of empathic understanding remains high as in Stage 1 and may be more of a challenge for the supervisor if the supervisee engages in extreme independence. The supervisor's recognition and acceptance of the supervisee's need for independence is critical at this stage. For any theoretical orientation, a growing play therapist will question assumptions and practices, which should be embraced as part of healthy therapist development. Unconditional positive regard is demonstrated through the acceptance of the therapist's independence. However, communication of unconditional positive regard can be misinterpreted at this stage by novice play therapists as permission to engage in any behavior in the playroom. The supervisor needs to be aware of this possible misinterpretation.

Stage 3: Philosophical decision making transformed into practice. Following a skills focus and experimentation period, the supervisee emerges to a new stage in which a philosophical way of working is embraced. In supervision, the supervisee adopts a play therapy belief system that may accept or reject CCPT philosophy. If the play therapist rejects the philosophy of CCPT, and the supervisor has been supportive of this personal growth influencing professional practice, the play therapist usually emerges with a respect for a nondirective way of being and its place in working with children. Play therapists initially trained as CCPT therapists typically value nondirectiveness on some level, concluding that the conditions were necessary but not sufficient for their belief systems. If their supervisors are open and accepting, non-CCPT therapists emerge with vigor for integrating their newly embraced theory with practice. For those play therapists who embrace CCPT at this stage, supervision focuses on understanding process, patterns, and themes in CCPT. They are energized and curious regarding how they can better facilitate the healing factors of CCPT. Supervision becomes a collaborative approach to exploring CCPT for each child who is served. Supervisees at this stage also engage in personal reflection as it relates to play therapy, often integrating new awareness into practice.

In play sessions, CCPT therapists at this stage have a new comfort level in session, allowing them to bring the person as therapist into the playroom. They reach new levels of experiencing each of the attitudinal qualities, especially congruence, while in session. At this stage, they experience "in-the-moment" events in sessions where the relationship between therapist and child flows therapeutically and uncensored. If the supervisees have rejected CCPT and moved toward a new philosophy, they use this stage to practice techniques from their new orientation, seeing what fits for them. Unlike Stage 2, the supervisees will now initiate the discussion of using new techniques with the supervisor prior to their use.

In Stage 3, the supervisor is able to access and communicate all attitudinal qualities to a relatively equal degree. The supervisee values the supervisor's ability to be congruent and models after the supervisor in this respect. Empathic understanding is felt and communicated between supervisor and supervisee. The supervisor can now fully express an intense level of unconditional positive regard, allowing the supervisee to explore various avenues of philosophy and practice in a collaborative and equal way.

Stage 4: Person of play therapist emerges as professional. In the fourth stage of supervision, supervision sessions now occur as consultation sessions. Supervision is initiated by the supervisee, typically with a personal focus on how the play therapist as a person affects practice or a focus on a specific play therapy relationship. The supervisee uses the supervisor as a sounding board by communicating deeper-level feelings of self in relationship to play therapy. The supervisee will often explore limited feelings of unconditional positive self-regard and its effect on the play therapist's practice. At this stage, non-CCPT supervisees will seek new supervision or training experiences aligned with current philosophy. They may use their previous CCPT supervisor as a consultant on a continued, regular basis.

In session, a CCPT supervisee is regularly encountering congruent experiences of being in the moment. The expression of empathy and unconditional positive regard feel genuine and go unnoticed as processes in play therapy sessions. Following play therapy sessions, there is a natural inclination to conceptualize clients based on accurate empathic understanding. Confidence is rooted in an authentic way of being and expressing self to child, as well as to parents and caretakers.

At this stage, both the supervisor and supervisee are operating from elevated levels of congruence, unconditional positive regard, and empathic understanding. Unconditional positive regard in the supervisor and supervisee is only limited by unconditional positive self-regard. There is mutual understanding and acknowledgment that both the supervisor and supervisee are equal partners in the consultation/supervision process.

Each supervision stage requires that the supervisor operate from an experience of congruence, with high levels of verbally communicated empathy and unconditional positive regard for the person of the play therapist at early stages. In middle stages, supervisees are able to perceive and subceive empathy and unconditional positive regard in less overt interactions with the supervisor. In the latter stages, both the supervisee and supervisor are feeling reasonable levels of congruence and are able to send messages of empathy and unconditional positive regard to each other.

Moustakas (1959) probably best summarized the development of a play therapist through the following description:

> It takes a long time for a person with concentrated, formal training to stop trying to act like the professor in the classroom or clinic, to stop repeating the abstract concepts in the book and the dictates of a preconceived expert, and to start living the fresh, unique experience of a relationship in child therapy. It is sometimes a difficult, painful process for the 'trained' student to come to see that even in a professional capacity the most significant dimension is his own spontaneous self. (p. 317)

Additional Issues in Supervision

Use of video recordings. CCPT supervision is predicated on the review of video recording of play therapy sessions. Self-report is notoriously inaccurate and audio recording limits the supervisor's ability to experience the child's nonverbal communication. Video recording allows the supervisor to observe factors affecting the play therapy process, as well as allowing the supervisee to re-experience the session in the presence of the supervisor. Review of video recordings in supervision sessions may prompt a connection with feelings experienced by the play therapist during session. Emotional connections may allow deeper exploration of the supervisee's state of congruence, promoting a growth experience in supervision.

Personal growth focus in supervision. CCPT supervision places a decidedly strong emphasis on personal growth of the play therapist. Bryant-Jeffries (2005) warned that as the modern approach to therapy training moves more and more into knowledge and doing, there is a shift away from facilitating would-be counselors into becoming congruent persons offering unconditional positive regard and empathic understanding to clients. CCPT supervision addresses the basics of skill acquisition in order to reduce play therapist anxiety and ensure client safety in the initial stages of play therapist development. As supervisees progress in development, supervision sessions become increasingly focused on a supervisee's integration of personal values, feelings, and previous experiences into effective play therapy practice. Merry (2001) suggested that attention to performance at the expense of exploring attitudes and values strengthens the supervisee's external locus of evaluation and dependence on the supervisor. It is the supervisor's responsibility to assess the supervisee's level of development and offer supervision that is conducive to growth. Some supervisors focus particularly on the client, avoiding the potential intensity that arises from relational contact and emphasis on supervisee personal growth. Mearns (1995) noted that some supervisors engage in a game labeled CAP: Conceptualize the client's behavior, Analyze client personality dynamics, and Predict client's future behavior. This game avoids a meaningful encounter between supervisor and supervisee, resulting in the minimization of the client's experience and uniqueness as an equal person in the relationship. Emphasis on the person of the supervisee respects the client's person and role as perceived by the supervisee, not as an external object to be dissected. Through supervision that explores personal awareness of the play therapist, issues are likely to arise concerning the therapist at a deeply personal level. A CCPT therapist addresses the supervisee's need for personal counseling when there is a sense that the supervisee's issues are beyond the scope of the supervision relationship.

Previous experience of therapist. A unique feature in supervising new play therapists is that they are typically not new therapists. Because play therapy is a modality, not represented by licensure or a specific degree track, supervisees are likely to have been operating as mental health professionals prior to interest in or practice of play therapy. Whereas supervisees who are entering the mental health field arrive in supervision with unshaped beliefs systems, play therapist supervisees will often have set belief systems or habitual practices that may or may not align with the supervisor's approach to play therapy. This situation can be maneuvered by a supervisor's informed consent with clear expectations for supervisee participation. A supervisee should be informed of a supervisor's theory of orientation, accompanied by a full explanation of the theory. In addition, the supervisor should define expectations of the supervisee, including expectations for the supervisee's openness to new ways of working and personal exploration.

Supervision notes. Another issue involved in play therapy supervision is the use of supervision notes. Current practices encourage the use of supervision notes written by the supervisor. As described in this chapter, CCPT supervision involves a combination of reviewing client cases and personal exploration by the supervisee. Client files of supervisees should reflect any supervision regarding the specific case. Supervisors will want to also maintain separate files on each supervisee, noting the focus of supervision sessions when they concentrate on personal growth.

Conclusion

Play therapy supervision offers an environment where the supervisee can initiate, explore, and integrate thoughts, feelings, values, and previous experiences into an organized approach to practice. CCPT supervisors seek a high level of personal congruence communicating intense levels of unconditional positive regard and empathic understanding. The modeling of the necessary therapist attitudinal qualities is essential to the growth of supervisees. As supervisees perceive and receive the qualities provided by the supervisor, they will access the internal self-actualizing tendency available to them. In addition, as they perceive the supervisor's communicated empathy and unconditional positive regard, supervisees will experience a parallel process where they can provide the same qualities to their clients. Effective supervision inevitably facilitates the personal development of the play therapist (Worrall, 2001). CCPT supervision demands extensive personal resources from the supervisor for the purposes of extending the necessary therapist conditions to clients through the training of supervisees.

References

Borders, L. D., & Brown, L. L. (2005). *The new handbook of counseling supervision.* Mahwah, NJ: Lawrence Erlbaum Associates.

Bozarth, J. (2001). Congruence: A special way of being. In G. Wyatt (Ed.), *Congruence Rogers' therapeutic conditions: Evolution, theory and practice* (Vol. 1, 184–199). Ross-On-Wye: PCCS.

Bryant-Jefferies, R. (2005). *Person-centred counseling supervision: Personal and professional.* Abingdon: Radcliffe Publishing.

Mearns, D. (1995). Supervision: A tale of the missing client. *British Journal of Guidance & Counselling, 23*(3), 421–427.

Merry, T. (2001). Congruence and the supervision of client centred therapists. In G. Wyatt (Ed.), *Congruence Rogers' therapeutic conditions: Evolution, theory and practice* (Vol. 1, 174–183). Ross On-Wye: PCCS.

Moustakas, C. (1959). *Psychotherapy with children: The living relationship.* New York: Harper & Row.

Worrall, M. (2001). Supervision and empathic understanding. In S. Haugh & T. Merry (Eds.), *Empathy Rogers' therapeutic conditions: Evolution theory and practice* (Vol. 2, 206–217). Ross-On-Wye: PCCS.

CHAPTER 15
Evidentiary Research in Child-Centered Play Therapy

Child-centered play therapy (CCPT) research spans over 60 years, providing evidence of effectiveness across a diversity of generations, ages, ethnicities, settings, and presenting problems. Between the years of 1947 and early 2010, 63 studies were conducted on the effectiveness of CCPT. Table 15.1 provides a breakdown of the number of publications per decade.

This chapter includes a lengthy description categorizing 62 CCPT studies by research issue and standard of rigor. Criteria for inclusion included (a) child-centered play therapy was clearly used as the research intervention signified by the terms nondirective, self-directive, following procedures of Axline, Rogers, Landreth, etc., or child-centered; (b) study was published in journal, dissertation, or book venue; (c) play therapy is a child-centered intervention and not a parent or family intervention; and (d) study utilized aspects of experimental design. Each study is classified to differentiate between levels of rigor applied to experimental research. Using Rubin's (2008) conceptual framework, I applied his evidentiary hierarchy for evidence-based practice to the identification of individual research studies. Specifically, studies are categorized into three labels: experimental, quasi-experimental, and evidentiary. The experimental label describes studies meeting the most stringent criteria for research design, including random assignment of subjects, comparison to a control group or another treatment group, clear methodology and treatment descriptions, and attention to internal and external validity threats. The quasi-experimental label represents studies that used comparison or control groups with clear methodology and attention to internal and external validity threats but not

Table 15.1 CCPT Publications Per Decade

Decade	No. of Studies
1940	5
1950	8
1960	3
1970	13
1980	7
1990	8
2000	17
2010	2
Total	**63**

random assignment. The evidentiary label was applied to studies that provided evidence of play therapy effectiveness through pre/post assessment and clear methodology but typically did not use a comparison or control group. Of the 62 CCPT studies, 29 were classified as experimental, 20 as quasi-experimental, and 13 as evidentiary.

Table 15.2 is presented to briefly describe research results related to play therapy categorized by research issue. Research issues included multiculturalism (n = 5), externalizing/disruptive behaviors (n = 12), attention-deficit hyperactivity disorder (n = 1), internalizing behavior problems (n = 7), anxiety (n = 8), depression (n = 2), self-concept/self-esteem (n = 9), social behavior (n = 12), parent/teacher relationship (n = 5), sexual abuse/trauma (n = 6), homelessness (n = 2), identified disability/medical condition (n = 11), academic achievement/intelligence (n = 14), and speech/language skills (n =5). Some studies are listed in multiple categories due to outcomes related to more than one area.

Table 15.2 CCPT Research Studies Categorized by Research Issue

Authors	Research Classification	Participants	Findings
		Research Issue: Multiculturalism	
Garza & Bratton (2005)	Experimental	29: Ages 5–11 years	Authors randomly assigned Hispanic children identified by teachers as demonstrating behavioral problems to an individual CCPT for guidance curriculum intervention. Each group received 30 minutes of the assigned intervention once per week for 15 weeks. Results demonstrated that children receiving play therapy showed statistically significant decreases in externalizing behavioral problems and moderate improvements in internalizing behavior problems as reported by parents.
Post (1999)	Quasi-experimental	168: Ages 10–12 years	Author found at-risk children (82% were African-American) who participated in a mean of 4 nondirective play therapy sessions maintained same level of self-esteem and internal locus of control, while control group dropped at a statistically significant level as measured by the Coopersmith Self-Esteem Inventory and Intellectual Achievement Responsibility Scale-Revised.
Shen (2002)	Experimental	30: Ages 8–12 years	Author randomly assigned child participants from a rural elementary school in Taiwan following an earthquake to a CCPT group or control group. All children were scored at high risk for maladjustment. The CCPT groups received ten 40-minute group play therapy sessions over 4 weeks. Results indicated that the CCPT group demonstrated a significant decrease in anxiety, as well as a large treatment effect, and significant decrease in suicide risk as compared to the control group.

Continued

Table 15.2 (*Continued*) CCPT Research Studies Categorized by Research Issue

Authors	Research Classification	Participants	Findings
Trostle (1988)	Experimental	48: Ages 3–6 years	Author found after 10 sessions of nondirective group play therapy that bilingual Puerto Rican children showed significant improvement compared to control group on self-control, and the higher developmental level play behaviors of make-believe and reality as measured by Self-Control Rating Scale and Play Observation Scale. Boys who participated in the experimental group became more accepting of others than boys or girls in the control group, as measured by Peer Rating Scale. The control group participated in unstructured free play sessions as opposed to group play therapy sessions.
Wakaba (1983)	Evidentiary	3: Ages 4–8 years	Author found that three Japanese boys who stuttered and participated in 1 hour of nondirective group play therapy once a week for 5 months improved their stuttering symptoms.
Research Issue: Externalizing/Disruptive Behavior Problems			
Dogra & Veeraraghavan (1994)	Quasi-experimental	20: Ages 8–12 years	Authors found that children diagnosed with aggressive conduct disorder and their parents who received 16 sessions of nondirective play therapy and parental counseling showed significantly lesser extrapunitive responses and significantly higher impunitive and need-persistence responses as compared to the control group. According to the Picture-Frustration Test and Child Behavior Rating Scale, the treatment group showed significant positive change on adjustment to self, home, school, social, physical, and personality total adjustment. Aggression in the experimental group was reduced in fighting and bullying, violence against adults, obedience, temper tantrums, parental use of corporal punishment, parental neglect, and child's strong dislike for school.

Dorfman (1958)	Quasi-experimental	17: Ages 9–12 years	Author found that maladjusted children who received an average of 19 client-centered play therapy sessions showed improvement as compared to a control group on Rogers Test of Personality Adjustment, and maintained the improvement at follow-up. They also scored a significant improvement on Mean Adjustment Rating on Sentence Completion Test during therapy and at follow-up.
Fall, Navelski, & Welch (2002)	Experimental	66: Ages 6–10 years	Authors randomly assigned children identified with a special education label to 6 sessions of weekly 30-minute individual CCPT or a no-intervention control condition. Results demonstrated no difference between the groups in self-efficacy, but teacher ratings showed decreased problematic behavior and fewer social problems for the experimental group as compared to the control group.
Fleming & Snyder (1947)	Quasi-experimental	7: Ages 8–11 years	Authors found that after 12 nondirective group play therapy sessions, the girls' group showed significant improvement in personality adjustment according to the Rogers Personality Test as compared to control group.
Garza & Bratton (2005)	Experimental	29: Ages 5–11 years	Authors randomly assigned Hispanic children identified by teachers as demonstrating behavioral problems to an individual CCPT for guidance curriculum intervention. Each group received 30 minutes of the assigned intervention once per week for 15 weeks. Results demonstrated that children receiving play therapy showed statistically significant decreases in externalizing behavior problems and moderate improvements in internalizing behavior problems as reported by parents.

Continued

Table 15.2 (*Continued*) CCPT Research Studies Categorized by Research Issue

Authors	Research Classification	Participants	Findings
Muro, Ray, Schottelkorb, Smith, & Blanco (2006)	Evidentiary	23: Ages 4–11 years	Authors conducted a repeated measures, single group design for children identified by teachers as exhibiting behavioral and emotional difficulties. Children participated in 32 sessions of individual CCPT across the duration of a school year. Ratings over 3 points of measure indicated statistically significant improvement of total behavioral problems, teacher/child relationship stress, and ADHD characteristics.
Ray (2008)	Evidentiary	202: Ages 2–13 years	Author statistically analyzed archival data on children referred to a university counseling clinic and receiving weekly individual CCPT over a 9-year period. Children were assigned to data groups according to presenting problem and length of therapy as the independent variable and parent child relationship stress as the dependent variable. CCPT demonstrated statistically significant effects for externalizing problems, combined externalizing/internalizing problems, and nonclinical problems. Results also indicated that CCPT effects increased with the number of sessions, specifically reaching statistical significance at 11 to 18 sessions with large effect sizes.

Ray, Blanco, Sullivan, & Holliman (2009)	Quasi-experimental	41: Ages 4–11 years	Authors assigned children identified by teachers as demonstrating aggressive behaviors to a CCPT condition or a waitlist control condition. Children in CCPT condition participated in 14 sessions of 30-minute individual play therapy conducted twice a week. Children in CCPT showed a moderate decrease in aggressive behaviors over children in the control group according to parent report. Post hoc analysis revealed that children assigned to CCPT had a statistically significant decrease in aggressive behaviors, and children assigned to control group demonstrated no statistically significant difference.
Schmidtchen, Hennies, & Acke (1993)	Quasi-experimental	28: Ages 5–8 years	Authors found that in comparing a treatment group of children with behavioral disturbances who participated in 30 sessions of nondirective play therapy with a nonplay therapy control group receiving social education welfare in a large group, the treatment group showed a decrease in behavioral disturbance and an increase in person-centered competencies.
Schumann (2010)	Quasi-experimental	37: Ages 5–12 years	Author assigned children identified by teachers as demonstrating aggressive behaviors to an individual CCPT condition or an evidence-based guidance curriculum condition. The CCPT condition received 12 to 15 weekly play therapy sessions and the guidance condition received 8 to 15 group guidance sessions. Participation in either CCPT or evidence-based guidance curriculum resulted in significant decreases in aggressive behavior, internalizing problems, and externalizing problems.

Continued

Table 15.2 (*Continued*) CCPT Research Studies Categorized by Research Issue

Authors	Research Classification	Participants	Findings
Seeman, Barry, & Ellinwood (1964)	Experimental	16: 2nd & 3rd graders	Authors found that children maladjusted on aggression and withdrawal who participated in a median length of 37 nondirective play therapy sessions showed marginal significant improvement on teacher rating scale and by follow-up; all children in aggressive group rated below the average child, as compared to a control group. On the Tuddenham Reputation Test, experimental group showed favorable changes in sociometric gains.
Tyndall-Lind, Landreth, & Giordano (2001)	Quasi-experimental	32: Ages 4–10 years	Authors compared a sibling group play therapy condition to an intensive individual play therapy condition and a control condition for children living in a domestic violence shelter. Sibling group CCPT consisted of 12 sessions of 45 minutes over 12 days. Results indicated that sibling group play therapy was equally effective as intensive individual play therapy. Children in sibling group play therapy demonstrated a significant reduction in total behavior, externalizing and internalizing behavior problems, aggression, anxiety, and depression, and a significant improvement in self-esteem.

		Research Issue: Attention-Deficit Hyperactivity Disorder	
Ray, Schottelkorb, & Tsai (2007)	Experimental	60: Ages 5–11 years	Authors randomly assigned children meeting criteria for ADHD to a play therapy treatment condition or a reading mentoring active control condition. Children in both conditions participated in 16 individual 30-minute sessions over 8 weeks. The play therapy condition received individual CCPT. Results indicated that both conditions demonstrated statistically significant improvement in ADHD, student characteristics, anxiety, and learning disability. Children in CCPT demonstrated statistically significant improvement over reading mentoring children on student characteristics, emotional lability and anxiety/withdrawal.
		Research Issue: Internalizing Behavior Problems	
Baggerly & Jenkins (2009)	Evidentiary	36: Ages 5–12 years	Authors conducted a pretest/posttest single-group design with children who were homeless. Children received 45-minute individual CCPT sessions once per week ranging from 11 to 25 sessions with an average of 14 sessions over the academic year. Results indicated that children demonstrated statistically significant improvement on the developmental strand of internalization of controls and diagnostic profile of self-limiting features.
Brandt (1999)	Quasi-experimental	26: Age 5 years	Author found that young children with behavioral adjustment difficulties who participated in 7 to 10 play therapy sessions improved significantly on internalizing behaviors as measured by the Child Behavior Checklist, in comparison to a matched control group. Internalizing symptoms included withdrawn behavior, somatic complaints, and anxiety/depression. Improvement in parental stress approached significance for the experimental group. No differences were found between the experimental group and control group on self-concept.

Continued

Table 15.2 (*Continued*) CCPT Research Studies Categorized by Research Issue

Authors	Research Classification	Participants	Findings
Dorfman (1958)	Quasi-experimental	17: Ages 9–12 years	Author found that maladjusted children who received an average of 19 client-centered play therapy sessions showed improvement, as compared to a control group, on Rogers Test of Personality Adjustment and maintained the improvement at follow-up. They also scored a significant improvement on Mean Adjustment Rating on Sentence Completion Test during therapy and at follow-up.
Fleming & Snyder (1947)	Quasi-experimental	7: Ages 8–11 years	Authors found that after 12 nondirective group play therapy sessions, the girls' group showed significant improvement in personality adjustment according to the Rogers Personality Test, as compared to the control group.
Garza & Bratton (2005)	Experimental	29: Ages 5–11 years	Authors randomly assigned Hispanic children identified by teachers as demonstrating behavioral problems to an individual CCPT or guidance curriculum intervention. Each group received 30 minutes of the assigned intervention once per week for 15 weeks. Results demonstrated that children receiving play therapy showed statistically significant decreases in externalizing behavior problems and moderate improvements in internalizing behavior problems as reported by parents.

Tyndall-Lind, Landreth, & Giordano (2001)	Quasi-experimental	32: Ages 4–10 years	Authors compared a sibling group play therapy condition to an intensive individual play therapy condition and a control condition for children living in a domestic violence shelter. Sibling group CCPT consisted of 12 sessions of 45 minutes over 12 days. Results indicated that sibling group play therapy was equally effective to intensive individual play therapy. Children in sibling group play therapy demonstrated a significant reduction in total behavior, externalizing, and internalizing behavior problems, aggression, anxiety, and depression, and significant improvement in self-esteem.
Wall (1979)	Experimental	33: Ages 3–9 years	Author found that in dividing emotionally maladjusted children with one parent each into 3 treatments of traditional nondirective play therapy, guided play therapy (parent guided by therapist to provide play therapy), and free play condition of parent-child dyad, there were no significant improvements except in one area. After 8 weekly sessions, children in guided play therapy improved adjustment by increasing their ability to acknowledge negative feelings in their families.
			Research Issue: Anxiety
Baggerly (2004)	Evidentiary	42: Ages 5–11 years	Author conducted a pretest/posttest single-group design for children living in a homeless shelter. Children participated in 9 to 12, 30-minute CCPT sessions once or twice a week. Results revealed significant improvement in self-concept, significance, competence, negative mood and negative self-esteem related to depression, and anxiety.
Clatworthy (1981)	Experimental	114: Ages 5–12 years	Author found that children who received daily individual self-directive play therapy during hospitalization exhibited significantly less anxiety than control group as measured by the Missouri Children's Picture Series.

Continued

Table 15.2 (*Continued*) CCPT Research Studies Categorized by Research Issue

Authors	Research Classification	Participants	Findings
Post (1999)	Quasi-experimental	168: Ages 10–12 years	Authors found that at-risk children who participated in 4 nondirective play therapy sessions showed no change in anxiety as compared to the control group, as measured by State-Trait Anxiety Inventory.
Rae, Worchel, Upchurch, Sanner, & Daniel (1989)	Experimental	61: Ages 5–10 years	Authors found that hospitalized children receiving 2 nondirective CCPT sessions showed a significant reduction in hospital fears as measured by Fear Thermometer. The play therapy treatment group was compared to a verbally oriented support condition, diversionary play condition (allowed to play with toys), and control group. A reduction in fears was not evidenced in any other group.
Ray, Schottelkorb, & Tsai (2007)	Experimental	60: Ages 5–11 years	Authors randomly assigned children meeting criteria for ADHD to a play therapy treatment condition or a reading mentoring active control condition. Children in both conditions participated in 16 individual 30-minute sessions over 8 weeks. The play therapy condition received individual CCPT. Results indicated that both conditions demonstrated statistically significant improvement in ADHD, student characteristics, anxiety, and learning disability. Children in CCPT demonstrated statistically significant improvement over reading mentoring children on student characteristics, emotional lability, and anxiety/withdrawal.
Schmidtchen & Hobrucker (1978)	Quasi-experimental	50: Ages 9–13 years	Authors found that after receiving client-centered play therapy, children made significant improvement in social and intellectual flexibility as well as decrease in anxiety and behavior disorders as compared to two untreated control groups.

Shen (2002)	Experimental	30: Ages 8–12 years	Author randomly assigned child participants from a rural elementary school in Taiwan following an earthquake to a CCPT group or control group. All children were scored at high risk for maladjustment. The CCPT groups received 10 40-minute group play therapy sessions over 4 weeks. Results indicated the CCPT group demonstrated a significant decrease in anxiety, as well as a large treatment effect, and significant decrease in suicide risk as compared to the control group.
Tyndall-Lind, Landreth, & Giordano (2001)	Quasi-experimental	32: Ages 4–10 years	Authors compared a sibling group play therapy condition to an intensive individual play therapy condition and a control condition for children living in a domestic violence shelter. Sibling group CCPT consisted of 12 sessions of 45 minutes over 12 days. Results indicated that sibling group play therapy was equally effective as intensive individual play therapy. Children in sibling group play therapy demonstrated a significant reduction in total behavior, externalizing, and internalizing behavior problems, aggression, anxiety, and depression, and a significant improvement in self-esteem.
Research Issue: Depression			
Baggerly (2004)	Evidentiary	42: Ages 5–11 years	Author conducted a pretest/posttest single-group design for children living in a homeless shelter. Children participated in 9 to 12, 30-minute CCPT group play therapy sessions once or twice a week. Results revealed significant improvement in self-concept, significance, competence, negative mood and negative self-esteem related to depression, and anxiety.

Continued

Table 15.2 (*Continued*) CCPT Research Studies Categorized by Research Issue

Authors	Research Classification	Participants	Findings
Tyndall-Lind, Landreth, & Giordano (2001)	Quasi-experimental	32: Ages 4–10 years	Authors compared a sibling group play therapy condition to an intensive individual play therapy condition and a control condition for children living in a domestic violence shelter. Sibling group CCPT consisted of 12 sessions of 45 minutes over 12 days. Results indicated that sibling group play therapy was equally effective as intensive individual play therapy. Children in sibling group play therapy demonstrated a significant reduction in total behavior, externalizing, and internalizing behavior problems, aggression, anxiety, and depression, and a significant improvement in self-esteem.
Research Issue: Self-Concept/Self-Esteem			
Baggerly (2004)	Evidentiary	42: Ages 5–11 years	Author conducted a pretest/posttest single-group design for children living in a homeless shelter. Children participated in 9 to 12, 30-minute CCPT group play therapy sessions once or twice a week. Results revealed a significant improvement in self-concept, significance, competence, negative mood and negative self-esteem related to depression, and anxiety.
Crow (1990)	Quasi-experimental	22: 1st graders	Author found that poor readers who received 10 nondirective individual play therapy sessions improved significantly in their self-concept as measured by the Piers-Harris Children's Self-Concept Scale and also improved their internal locus of control as measured by Intellectual Achievement Responsibility Questionnaire in comparison with a nonintervention control group. Both the experimental and control groups made gains in reading ability as measured by Gates-MacGinite Reading Test.

Gould (1980)	Experimental	84: Elementary school age	Author found that when comparing children identified as having a low self-image who participated in 12 sessions of nondirective group play therapy and those who participated in a placebo of 12 discussion groups showed positive change on the Piers-Harris Children's Self-Concept Scale as compared to no change in the nonintervention control group. The strongest positive change was noted for the group play therapy participants.
House (1970)	Experimental	36: 2nd graders	Author found after 20 sessions of CCPT, socially maladjusted children significantly increased their self-concept according to the Scamin Self-Concept Scale, while members of the control group decreased in self-concept.
Kot, Landreth, & Giordano (1998)	Quasi-experimental	22: Ages 3–10 years	Author found that after 12 nondirective play therapy sessions over 2 weeks, child witnesses of domestic violence, in comparison with a control group, demonstrated significant improvement in their self-concept as measured by the Joseph Pre-School and Primary Self-Concept Screening Test, significant reduction in their externalizing behavior problems and significant reduction in their total behavior problems as measured by the Child Behavior Checklist, and significant improvement in the play behaviors of physical proximity and play themes as measured by Children's Play Session Behavior Rating Scale.

Continued

Table 15.2 (*Continued*) CCPT Research Studies Categorized by Research Issue

Authors	Research Classification	Participants	Findings
Pelham (1972)	Experimental	52: Kindergarteners	Author found that in comparing socially immature kindergartners participating in 6 to 8 individual self-directive play therapy sessions, 6 to 8 group self-directive play therapy sessions, or a control group, children in both treatment groups made positive gains in social maturity when compared to control group as measured by Missouri Children's Picture Services and Children's Self-Social Constructs Tests. Teacher ratings on the Behavior Problem Checklist indicated that children participating in play therapy improved significantly in classroom behavior when compared to control group.
Perez (1987)	Experimental	55: Ages 4–9 years	Author found that in comparing sexually abused children participating in 12 sessions of individual relationship play therapy, 12 sessions of group relationship play therapy, or a control group, self-concepts of children in treatment groups increased at a significant level while those in control group actually scored lower at posttest as measured by the Primary Self-Concept Inventory. The self-mastery scores of children in play therapy rose significantly while those in the control group dropped as measured by Locus of Control Scale. No differences occurred between individual and group play therapy.
Post (1999)	Quasi-experimental	168: Ages 10–12 years	Author found that at-risk children who participated in a mean of 4 nondirective play therapy sessions maintained same level of self-esteem and internal locus of control, while the control group dropped at a statistically significant level as measured by the Coopersmith Self-Esteem Inventory and Intellectual Achievement Responsibility Scale–Revised.

Tyndall-Lind, Landreth, & Giordano (2001)	Quasi-experimental	32: Ages 4–10 years	Authors compared a sibling group play therapy condition to an intensive individual play therapy condition and a control condition for children living in a domestic violence shelter. Sibling group CCPT consisted of 12 sessions of 45 minutes over 12 days. Results indicated that sibling group play therapy was equally effective as intensive individual play therapy. Children in sibling group play therapy demonstrated a significant reduction in total behavior, externalizing, and internalizing behavior problems, aggression, anxiety, and depression, and significant improvement in self-esteem.
Research Issue: Social Behavior			
Cox (1953)	Quasi-experimental	52: Ages 5–13 years	Author found that after 10 weeks of individual play therapy and a 13-week follow-up period, young children (3 yrs.) showed significant improvement in social adjustment. Older children (13 yrs.) showed significant improvement on sociometric measure as compared to the control group.
Elliott & Pumfrey (1972)	Experimental	28: Ages 7–9 years	Authors found that after 9 sessions of nondirective group play therapy, boys rated no differences on social adjustment or reading attainment, as measured by Bristol Social-Adjustment Guide Burt Word Reading Test, and Ballard One-Minute Reading Test, than a control group receiving no intervention. However, interaction was demonstrated between improvement and selection criteria such as IQ; emotional disturbance, which improved on social adjustment with therapy; and restlessness, which deteriorated in social adjustment with therapy.

Continued

Table 15.2 (*Continued*) CCPT Research Studies Categorized by Research Issue

Authors	Research Classification	Participants	Findings
Fall, Navelski, & Welch (2002)	Experimental	66: Ages 6–10 years	Authors randomly assigned children identified with a special education label to 6 sessions of weekly 30-minute individual CCPT or a no-intervention control condition. Results demonstrated no difference between the groups in self-efficacy but teacher ratings showed decreased problematic behavior and less social problems for the experimental group as compared to the control group.
Fleming & Snyder (1947)	Quasi-experimental	46: Ages 8–11 years	Authors found that after 12 nondirective group play therapy sessions, the girls' group showed significant improvement in personality adjustment according to the Rogers Personality Test, as compared to the control group.
House (1970)	Experimental	36: 2nd graders	Author found that after 20 sessions of CCPT, socially maladjusted children significantly increased their self-concept according to the Scamin Self-Concept Scale, while members of the control group decreased in self-concept.
Hume (1967)	Quasi-experimental	20: 1st–4th graders	Author found that after 6 months of weekly child-centered individual and group play therapy sessions with or without teacher in-service focusing on creating growth conditions in the classroom, play therapy participants showed considerable improvement in their behavior in school, at home, and in play therapy by end of school year and at follow-up. Play therapy appeared to be most effective when combined with teacher in-service, yet in-service appeared to be only partially helpful without play therapy.

Oualline (1976)	Experimental	24: Ages 4–6 years	Author found that deaf children participating in 10 individual nondirective play therapy sessions demonstrated a significant increase in mature behavior patterns as measured by the Vineland Social Maturity Scale, compared to children participating in 10 sessions of free individual play. No differences were demonstrated according to the Child Behavior Rating Scale and Behavior Problem Checklist.
Pelham (1972)	Experimental	52: Kindergarteners	Author found that both 6 to 8 individual self-directive play therapy sessions and 6 to 8 self-directive group play therapy sessions resulted in positive gains in the social maturity of kindergartners as measured by Missouri Children's Picture Services and Children's Self-Social Constructs Tests. In addition, teacher ratings of behavior indicated that children participating in play therapy improved significantly in classroom behavior as compared to control group.
Schmidtchen & Hobrucker (1978)	Quasi-experimental	50: Ages 9–13 years	Authors found that after receiving client-centered play therapy, children made significant improvement in social and intellectual flexibility as well as decreased anxiety and behavior disorders as compared to two untreated control groups.
Thombs & Muro (1973)	Experimental	36: 2nd graders	Authors found that after 15 sessions of relationship theory-based group play therapy, children showed a greater positive change in social position than those who participated in the alternate verbal group counseling experimental group. Both experimental groups made significant gains in sociometric status as compared to control group.

Continued

Table 15.2 (*Continued*) CCPT Research Studies Categorized by Research Issue

Authors	Research Classification	Participants	Findings
Trostle (1988)	Experimental	48: Ages 3–6 years	Author found that after 10 sessions of nondirective group play therapy, bilingual Puerto Rican children showed significant improvement compared to the control group on self-control, and the higher developmental level play behaviors of make-believe and reality as measured by Self-Control Rating Scale and Play Observation Scale. Boys who participated in the experimental group became more accepting of others than boys or girls in the control group as measured by Peer Rating Scale. The control group participated in unstructured free play sessions as opposed to group play therapy sessions.
Yates (1976)	Quasi-experimental	53: 2nd graders	Author found that when comparing children who participated in 8 weeks of a nondirective play therapy experimental group, structured teacher consultation experimental group, or control group, there were no statistically significant differences between experimental groups or control group. An overall trend toward gain in sociometric status was apparent in all groups.
Research Issue: Parent/Teacher Relationship			
Dougherty & Ray (2007)	Evidentiary	24: Ages 3–8 years	Authors statistically analyzed archival data on children referred to a university counseling clinic and receiving weekly individual CCPT over a 3-year period. Children were assigned to two data groups according to age (preoperational or operational) as the independent variable and parent/child relationship stress as the dependent variable. For both total stress and child domain scores, CCPT demonstrated statistically significant decreases in parent/child relationship stress with strong practical effects. Children in the concrete operations group experienced more change as a result of intervention than did children in the preoperational group.

Muro, Ray, Schottelkorb, Smith, & Blanco (2006)	Evidentiary	23: Ages 4–11 years	Authors conducted a repeated measures single-group design for children identified by teachers as exhibiting behavioral and emotional difficulties. Children participated in 32 sessions of individual CCPT across the duration of a school year. Ratings over 3 points of measure indicated statistically significant improvement on total behavioral problems, teacher/child relationship stress, and ADHD characteristics.
Ray (2007)	Experimental	93: Ages 4–11 years	Author randomly assigned students who were identified as experiencing emotional and behavioral difficulties in the classroom into one of three treatment groups: (1) play therapy only, (2) play therapy and consultation, or (3) consultation only. Children in the play therapy condition received 16 sessions of 30-minute individual CCPT over 8 weeks. Teachers in consultation group received one 10-minute person-centered consultation per week for 8 weeks. Results demonstrated significant decreases in teacher/child relationship stress with large effects sizes in total stress for all three treatment groups.
Ray (2008)	Evidentiary	202: Ages 2–13 years	Author statistically analyzed archival data on children referred to a university counseling clinic and receiving weekly individual CCPT over a 9-year period. Children were assigned to data groups according to presenting problem and length of therapy as the independent variable and parent/child relationship stress as the dependent variable. CCPT demonstrated statistically significant effects for externalizing problems, combined externalizing/internalizing problems, and nonclinical problems. Results also indicated that CCPT effects increased with the number of sessions, specifically reaching statistical significance at 11 to 18 sessions with large effect sizes.

Continued

Table 15.2 (*Continued*) CCPT Research Studies Categorized by Research Issue

Authors	Research Classification	Participants	Findings
Ray, Henson, Schottelkorb, Brown, & Muro (2008)	Experimental	58: Ages Pre-K–5th grade	Authors randomly assigned children identified by teachers as exhibiting emotional and behavioral difficulties into one of two treatment groups (short-term and long-term). Children in the short-term condition participated in 16 sessions of 30-minute individual CCPT sessions over 8 weeks. Children in the long-term condition participated in 16 sessions of 30-minute individual CCPT sessions over 16 weeks. Results indicated that both intervention groups demonstrated significant improvement in teacher/student relationship stress. Post hoc analyses indicated that the short-term intensive intervention demonstrated statistical significance and larger effect sizes in overall total stress, and teacher and student characteristics.
Research Issue: Sexual Abuse/Trauma			
Kot, Landreth, & Giordano (1998)	Quasi-experimental	22: Ages 3–10 years	Author found that after 12 nondirective play therapy sessions over 2 weeks, child witnesses of domestic violence, in comparison with a control group, demonstrated significant improvement in their self-concept as measured by the Joseph Pre-School and Primary Self-Concept Screening Test; a significant reduction in their externalizing behavior problems, and significant reduction in their total behavior problems as measured by the Child Behavior Checklist; and significant improvement in the play behaviors of physical proximity and play themes as measured by Children's Play Session Behavior Rating Scale.

Perez (1987)	Experimental	55: Ages 4–9 years	Author found that in comparing sexually abused children participating in 12 sessions of individual relationship play therapy, 12 sessions of group relationship play therapy, or a control group, self-concepts of children in treatment groups increased at a significant level while those in the control group actually scored lower at posttest as measured by the Primary Self-Concept Inventory. The self-mastery scores of children in play therapy rose significantly while those in control group dropped as measured by Locus of Control Scale. No differences occurred between individual and group play therapy.
Saucier (1986)	Quasi-experimental	20: Ages 1–7 years	Author found that after 8 sessions of nondirective or directive play therapy sessions, abused children scored significantly higher on personal-social development than the control group as measured by Minnesota Child Development Inventory.
Scott, Burlingame, Starling, Porter, & Lilly (2003)	Evidentiary	26: Ages 3–9 years	Authors conducted a pretest/posttest single-group design with children referred for possible sexual abuse. Children completed between 7 and 13 sessions of CCPT. Results indicated an increased sense of competency over the course of therapy. No improvement was reported in other group comparisons.
Shen (2002)	Experimental	30: Ages 8–12 years	Author randomly assigned child participants from a rural elementary school in Taiwan following an earthquake to a CCPT group or control group. All children were scored at high risk for maladjustment. The CCPT groups received 10, 40-minute group play therapy sessions over 4 weeks. Results indicated that the CCPT group demonstrated a significant decrease in anxiety, as well as a large treatment effect, and a significant decrease in suicide risk as compared to the control group.

Continued

Table 15.2 (*Continued*) CCPT Research Studies Categorized by Research Issue

Authors	Research Classification	Participants	Findings
Tyndall-Lind, Landreth, & Giordano (2001)	Quasi-experimental	32: Ages 4–10 years	Authors compared a sibling group play therapy condition to an intensive individual play therapy condition and a control condition for children living in a domestic violence shelter. Sibling group CCPT consisted of 12 sessions of 45 minutes over 12 days. Results indicated that sibling group play therapy was equally effective as intensive individual play therapy. Children in sibling group play therapy demonstrated a significant reduction in total behavior, externalizing, and internalizing behavior problems, aggression, anxiety, and depression, and a significant improvement in self-esteem.
Research Issue: Homelessness			
Baggerly (2004)	Evidentiary	42: Ages 5–11 years	Author conducted a pretest posttest single group design for children living in a homeless shelter. Children participated in 9-12, 30-minute CCPT group play therapy sessions once or twice a week. Results revealed significant improvement in self-concept, significance, competence, negative mood and negative self-esteem related to depression, and anxiety.
Baggerly & Jenkins (2009)	Evidentiary	36: Ages 5–12 years	Authors conducted a pretest/posttest single-group design with children who were homeless. Children received 45-minute individual CCPT sessions once per week ranging from 11 to 25 sessions, with an average of 14 sessions over the academic year. Results indicated that children demonstrated statistically significant improvement on the developmental strand of internalization of controls and diagnostic profile of self-limiting features.

		Research Issue: Identified Disability/Medical Condition	
Cruickshank & Cowen (1948) and Cowen & Cruickshank (1948)	Evidentiary	5: Ages 7–9 years	Authors found that of five physically handicapped children identified as having emotional problems in school who received 13 nondirective group play therapy sessions, three children showed considerable improvement in behavior at home and at school, one showed some slight evidences of gain, while the fifth gave no indication of any improvement. All five reported positive feelings toward experience.
Danger & Landreth (2005)	Experimental	21: Ages 4–6 years	Authors randomly assigned children qualified for speech therapy to one of two conditions: group play therapy condition or regularly scheduled speech therapy session condition. Children assigned to the play therapy condition received 25 sessions of group CCPT concurrently with speech therapy over 7 months. Results revealed that children in play therapy demonstrated increased receptive language skills and expressive language skills with large practical significance.
DeGangi, Wietlisbach, Goodin, & Scheiner (1993)	Experimental	12: Ages 36–71 months	Authors found that in comparing a child-centered activity therapy to structured therapy for children with sensorimotor dysfunction, structured sensorimotor therapy was more useful in promoting gross motor skills and functional skills, as well as sensory integrative skills. Child-centered activity was more useful in improving fine motor skills. Children rated as having an easy temperament and children who received treatment for the first time responded better to child-centered therapy in regard to behaviors and play.

Continued

Table 15.2 (*Continued*) CCPT Research Studies Categorized by Research Issue

Authors	Research Classification	Participants	Findings
Dudek (1967)	Evidentiary	20: Ages 4–13 years	Author found in comparing two treatment groups in which one group received therapeutically oriented play each week combined with a threat to cut off warts in the following week and a second group receiving therapeutically oriented play without any threats, five children from the group that was threatened were discharged with no curative change, two had complete cures within 3 weeks, and three had partial cures within 3 to 4 weeks. Of those in the unthreatened treatment, six showed curative changes within 2 weeks, two within 4 weeks, and one developed more warts. Within 5 to 11 weeks, eight were complete cures, one was a partial cure, and one showed no change.
Fall, Navelski, & Welch (2002)	Experimental	66: Ages 6–10 years	Authors randomly assigned children identified with a special education label to 6 sessions of weekly 30-minute individual CCPT or a no-intervention control condition. Results demonstrated no difference between the groups in self-efficacy but teacher ratings showed decreased problematic behavior and less social problems for the experimental groups as compared to the control group.
Jones & Landreth (2002)	Experimental	30: Ages 7–11 years	Authors randomly assigned children diagnosed with insulin-dependent diabetes mellitus to an experimental or nonintervention control group. The experimental group participated in 12 sessions of CCPT over a 3-week camp. Both groups improved anxiety scores; the experimental group showed a statistically significant increase in diabetes adaptation over the control group.
Mehlman (1953)	Quasi-experimental	32: Ages 86–140 months	Author found that when comparing 29 sessions of group play therapy, movie group, and nonintervention group, mentally challenged children showed no changes in intelligence among any group as measured by Stanford Binet.

Miller & Baruch (1948)	Evidentiary	7 children	Authors found that of 22 patients, including 7 children who had been unsuccessfully treated for severe allergies thus far, who participated in nondirective therapy for adults and nondirective play therapy for children, marked improvements were measured in 19 of 22 subjects; 21 of 22 showed improvement and 6 subjects were completely cleared of symptoms.
Morrison & Newcomer (1975)	Experimental	18: Ages less than 11 years	Authors found that when comparing 11 sessions of directive play therapy, 11 sessions of nondirective play therapy, and nonintervention control group, mentally challenged children in both treatment groups made greater gains on Fine Motor-Adaptive and Personal-Social scales on the Denver Developmental Screening Test than the control group. There was no evidence that directive or nondirective was more effective.
Newcomer & Morrison (1974)	Experimental	12: Ages 5–11 years	Author found that when comparing individual play therapy with directive and nondirective leadership to group play therapy with directive and nondirective leadership, the mean scores of both treatment groups comprised of mentally challenged children increased continuously over 30 weeks as measured by the Denver Developmental Screening Test. A beneficial effect on social and intellectual functioning was shown as compared to the control group. There were no differences between group versus individual, or between directive versus nondirective.
Oualline (1976)	Experimental	24: Ages 4–6 years	Author found that deaf children participating in 10 individual nondirective play therapy sessions demonstrated a significant increase in mature behavior patterns as measured by the Vineland Social Maturity Scale, compared to children participating in 10 sessions of free individual play. No differences were demonstrated according to the Child Behavior Rating Scale and Behavior Problem Checklist.

Continued

Table 15.2 (*Continued*) CCPT Research Studies Categorized by Research Issue

Authors	Research Classification	Participants	Findings
		Research Issue: Academic Achievement/Intelligence	
Axline (1947)	Evidentiary	37: 2nd graders	Author found that subjects placed in a classroom led by child-centered trained teacher and receiving 8 nondirective play therapy sessions showed a noteworthy IQ increase as measured by the Stanford Binet.
Axline (1949)	Evidentiary	15: Ages 6–7 years	Author found that children receiving 8 to 20 individual nondirective play therapy sessions demonstrated higher IQ scores. She concluded that the child was freed from emotional constraint and could thus express his/her capacities more adequately.
Bills (1950a)	Quasi-experimental	18: 3rd graders	Author found that emotionally maladjusted children receiving 6 individual child-centered play therapy sessions and 3 group play therapy sessions showed significant improvement on reading ability and maintained improvement 30 days after intervention as compared to a control group.
Bills (1950b)	Evidentiary	8: 3rd graders	Author also found that well-adjusted children who received nondirective individual and group play therapy failed to make statistically significant gains in reading ability following nondirective play therapy. He concluded from these two studies that reading gains noted in maladjusted slow readers followed a nondirective treatment of the maladjustment present in the children.

Blanco (2010)	Experimental	43: 1st graders	Author randomly assigned 1st graders labeled at-risk by state academic standards to an experimental treatment group or waitlist control group. Children in experimental group participated in 16 sessions of 30-minute individual CCPT sessions over 8 weeks. Children in the CCPT treatment group demonstrated statistically significant improvement on academic achievement composite score over children in control group.
Crow (1990)	Quasi-experimental	22: 1st graders	Author found that poor readers who received 10 nondirective individual play therapy sessions improved significantly in their self-concept as measured by the Piers-Harris Children's Self-Concept Scale, and also improved their internal locus of control as measured by the Intellectual Achievement Responsibility Questionnaire in comparison with a nonintervention control group. Both the experimental and control groups made gains in reading ability as measured by Gates-MacGinite Reading Test.
Elliott & Pumfrey (1972)	Experimental	28: Ages 7–9 years	Author found that after 9 sessions of nondirective group play therapy, boys rated no differences on social adjustment or reading attainment, as measured by Bristol Social-Adjustment Guide Burt Word Reading Test and the Ballard One-Minute Reading Test, than a control group receiving no intervention. However, interaction was demonstrated between improvement and selection criteria such as IQ, emotional disturbance that improved on social adjustment with therapy, and restlessness, which deteriorated in social adjustment.
Mehlman (1953)	Quasi-experimental	32: Ages 86–140 months	Author found that when comparing 29 sessions of group play therapy, movie group, and nonintervention group, mentally challenged children showed no changes in intelligence among any group as measured by Stanford Binet.

Continued

Table 15.2 (*Continued*) CCPT Research Studies Categorized by Research Issue

Authors	Research Classification	Participants	Findings
Morrison & Newcomer (1975)	Experimental	18: Ages less than 11 years	Authors found that when comparing 11 sessions of directive play therapy, 11 sessions of nondirective play therapy, and nonintervention control group, mentally challenged children in both treatment groups made greater gains on Fine Motor-Adaptive and Personal-Social scales on the Denver Developmental Screening Test than the control group. No evidence that directive or nondirective was more effective.
Newcomer & Morrison (1974)	Experimental	12: Ages 5–11 years	Author found that when comparing individual play therapy with directive and nondirective leadership to group play therapy with directive and nondirective leadership, the mean scores of both treatment groups comprised of mentally challenged children increased continuously over 30 weeks as measured by the Denver Developmental Screening Test. A beneficial effect on social and intellectual functioning was shown as compared to the control group. There were no differences between group versus individual, or between directive versus nondirective.
Quayle (1991)	Experimental	54: Ages 5–9 years	Author found that children participating in 20 sessions of individual CCPT and those participating in 20 sessions of individual tutoring showed improvement on the Child Rating Scale for Teachers, Associate, and Child as compared to the control group. Children in CCPT showed more positive growth in a greater number of areas, 6 of 15, while tutoring group showed gains in 4 of 15. The control group experienced negative results in 7 of 11 areas. Teachers rated children receiving CCPT as improving learning skills, assertive social skills, task orientation, and peer social skills.

Seeman & Edwards (1954)	Quasi-experimental	38: 5th–6th graders	Authors found that personally maladjusted children who received an average of 67 sessions of play groups led by a "teacher-therapist" maintaining a child-centered atmosphere made a significant reading gain of 7/10 of a year in 4 months as measured by Gates Reading Survey in comparison to a control group.
Winn (1959)	Experimental	26: Ages 7–10 years	Author found that low readers of average intelligence who participated in 16 sessions of nondirective/relationship play therapy showed a significantly greater improvement in personality than a control group. Children with the lowest personality scores made the greatest improvements in personality. The experimental group did not show significantly greater improvement in reading than the control group.
Wishon (1975)	Experimental	30: 1st graders	Author found that delayed readers with average IQs who participated in 32 nondirective play therapy sessions over 16 weeks did score significantly higher on achievement, self-concept, and self-constructs, as did the matched control group. Treatment group girls did perform significantly better than control group girls on the Identification/Friend subtest of the Long-Henderson Children's Self-Social Constructs Test.
		Research Issue: Speech/Language Skills	
Axline (1949)	Evidentiary	15: Ages 6–7 years	Author found that children who were emotionally disturbed with speech problems and behavior problems receiving 8 to 20 individual nondirective play therapy sessions demonstrated higher IQ scores. She concluded that the child was freed from emotional constraint and could thus express his/her capacities more adequately.

Continued

Table 15.2 (*Continued*) CCPT Research Studies Categorized by Research Issue

Authors	Research Classification	Participants	Findings
Bouillion (1974)	Experimental	43: Ages 3–6 years	Author compared children with a speech or language delay through treatment groups of nondirective group play therapy, individual direct speech therapy, group speech lessons, and physical-motor training that met 5 days a week for 14 weeks with a nonintervention control group. Children who participated in group play therapy achieved significantly higher scores than the other treatment groups in the areas of fluency and articulation. Play therapy group also showed the least improvement in remediating receptive language deficits.
Danger & Landreth (2005)	Experimental	21: Ages 4–6 years	Authors randomly assigned children qualified for speech therapy to one of two conditions, including group play therapy condition and regularly scheduled speech therapy session condition. Children assigned to the play therapy condition received 25 sessions of group CCPT concurrently with speech therapy over 7 months. Results revealed that children in play therapy demonstrated increased receptive language skills and expressive language skills with large practical significance.
Moulin (1970)	Experimental	126: 1st–3rd graders	Author found after 12 sessions of client-centered group play therapy, underachieving students made significantly greater gains in non-language intelligence than the control group, as measured by the California Short-Form Test of Mental Maturity and Illinois Test of Psycholinguistic Abilities. Treatment was effective in significantly increasing meaningful language usage, not automatic language. There was no effect on academic achievement.
Wakaba (1983)	Evidentiary	3: Ages 4–5 years	Author found that three Japanese boys who stuttered and participated in 1 hour of nondirective group play therapy once a week for 5 months improved their stuttering symptoms.

References

Axline, V. (1949). Mental deficiency-Symptom or disease? *Journal of Consulting Psychology, 13*, 313–327.

Baggerly, J. (2004). The effects of child-centered group play therapy on self-concept, depression, and anxiety of children who are homeless. *International Journal of Play Therapy, 13*, 31–51.

Baggerly, J., & Jenkins, W. (2009). The effectiveness of child-centered play therapy on developmental and diagnostic factors in children who are homeless. *International Journal of Play Therapy, 18*, 45–55.

Bills, R. (1950a). Nondirective play therapy with retarded readers. *Journal of Consulting Psychology, 14*, 140–149.

Bills, R. (1950b). Play therapy with well-adjusted retarded readers. *Journal of Consulting Psychology, 14*, 246–249.

Blanco, P. J. (2010). The impact of school-based child-centered play therapy on academic achievement, self-concept, and teacher-child relationship stress. In J. Baggerly, D. Ray, & S. Bratton's (Eds.), *Child-centered play therapy research: The evidence base for effective practice* (pp. 125–144). Hoboken, NJ: Wiley.

Bouillion, K. (1974). The comparative efficacy of non-directive group play therapy with preschool, speech- or language-delayed children (Doctoral dissertation, Texas Tech University, 1973). *Dissertation Abstracts International, 35*, 495.

Brandt, M. (1999). Investigation of play therapy with young children (Doctoral dissertation, University of North Texas, 1999). *Dissertation Abstracts International, 61*, 2603.

Clatworthy, S. (1981). Therapeutic play: Effects on hospitalized children. *Journal of Association for Care of Children's Health, 9*, 108–113.

Cowen, E., & Cruickshank, W. (1948). Group therapy with physically handicapped children. II: Evaluation. *The Journal of Education Psychology, 39*, 281–297.

Cox, F. (1953). Sociometric status and individual adjustment before and after play therapy. *Journal of Abnormal Social Psychology, 48*, 354–356.

Crow, J. (1990). Play therapy with low achievers in reading (Doctoral dissertation, University of North Texas, 1989). *Dissertation Abstracts International, 50*, 2789.

Cruickshank, W., & Cowen, E. (1948). Group therapy with physically handicapped children. I: Report of study. *The Journal of Educational Psychology, 39*, 193–215.

Danger, S., & Landreth, G. (2005). Child-centered group play therapy with children with speech difficulties. *International Journal of Play Therapy, 14*, 81–102.

DeGangi, G., Wietlisbach, S., Goodin, M., & Scheiner, N. (1993). A comparison of structured sensorimotor therapy and child-centered activity in the treatment of preschool children with sensorimotor problems. *American Journal of Occupational Therapy, 47*, 777–786.

Dogra, A., & Veeraraghavan, V. (1994). A study of psychological intervention of children with aggressive conduct disorder. *Indian Journal of Clinical Psychology*, 21, 28–32.

Dorfman, E. (1958). Personality outcomes of client-centered child therapy. *Psychological Monographs, 72 (3)*, No. 456.

Dougherty, J., & Ray, D. (2007). Differential impact of play therapy on developmental levels of children. *International Journal of Play Therapy, 16*, 2–19.

Dudek, S. (1967). Suggestion and play therapy in the cure of warts in children: A pilot study. *The Journal of Nervous and Mental Disease, 145,* 37–42.

Elliott, G, & Pumfrey, P. (1972). The effects of non-directive play therapy on some maladjusted boys. *Educational Research, 14,* 157–163.

Fall, M., Navelski, L., & Welch, K. (2002). Outcomes of a play intervention for children identified for special education services. *International Journal of Play Therapy, 11,* 91–106.

Fleming, L., & Snyder, W. (1947). Social and personal changes following nondirective group play therapy. *American Journal of Orthopsychiatry, 17,* 101–116.

Garza, Y., & Bratton, S. (2005). School-based child centered play therapy with Hispanic children: Outcomes and cultural considerations. *International Journal of Play Therapy, 14,* 51–80.

Gould, M. (1980). The effect of short-term intervention play therapy on the self-concept of selected elementary pupils (Doctoral dissertation, Florida Institute of Technology, 1980). *Dissertation Abstracts International, 41,* 1090.

House, R. (1970). The effects of nondirective group play therapy upon the sociometric status and self-concept of selected second grade children (Doctoral dissertation, Oregon State University, 1970). *Dissertation Abstracts International, 31,* 2684.

Hume, K. (1967). A counseling service project for grades one through four. (Doctoral dissertation, Boston University, 1967). *Dissertation Abstracts International, 27*(12A), 4130.

Jones, E., & Landreth, G. (2002). The efficacy of intensive individual play therapy for chronically ill children. *International Journal of Play Therapy, 11,* 117–140.

Kot, S., Landreth, G., & Giordano, M. (1998). Intensive play therapy with child witnesses of domestic violence. *International Journal of Play Therapy, 7,* 17–36.

Mehlman, B. (1953). Group play therapy with mentally retarded children. *Journal of Abnormal and Social Psychology, 48,* 53–60.

Miller, H., & Baruch, D. (1948). Patients as shown in group and individual psychotherapy. *Journal of Consulting Psychology, 12,* 111–115.

Morrison, T., & Newcomer, B. (1975). Effects of directive vs. nondirective play therapy with institutionalized mentally retarded children. *American Journal of Mental Deficiency, 79,* 666–669.

Moulin, E. (1970). The effects of client-centered group counseling using play media on the intelligence, achievement, and psycholinguistic abilities of underachieving primary school children. *Elementary School Guidance and Counseling, 5,* 85–98.

Muro, J., Ray, D., Schottelkorb, A., Smith, M., & Blanco, P. (2006). Quantitative analysis of long-term child-centered play therapy. *International Journal of Play Therapy, 15,* 35–58.

Newcomer, B., & Morrison, T. (1974). Play therapy with institutionalized mentally retarded children. *American Journal of Mental Deficiency, 78,* 727–733.

Oualline, V. (1976). Behavioral outcomes of short-term non-directive play therapy with preschool deaf children (Doctoral dissertation, North Texas State University, 1975). *Dissertation Abstracts International, 36,* 7870.

Pelham, L. (1972). Self-directive play therapy with socially immature kindergarten students (Doctoral dissertation, University of Northern Colorado, 1971). *Dissertation Abstracts International, 32,* 3798.

Perez, C. (1987). A comparison of group play therapy and individual play therapy for sexually abused children (Doctoral dissertation, University of Northern Colorado, 1987). *Dissertation Abstracts International, 48,* 3079.

Post, P. (1999). Impact of child-centered play therapy on the self-esteem, locus of control, and anxiety of at-risk 4th, 5th, and 6th grade students. *International Journal of Play Therapy, 8,* 1–18.

Quayle, R. (1991). The primary mental health project as a school-based approach for prevention of adjustment problems: An evaluation (Doctoral dissertation, The Pennsylvania State University, 1991). *Dissertation Abstracts International, 52,* 1268.

Rae, W., Worchel, E, Upchurch, J., Sanner, J., & Daniel, C. (1989). The psychosocial impact of play on hospitalized children. *Journal of Pediatric Psychology, 14,* 617–627.

Ray, D. (2007). Two counseling interventions to reduce teacher-child relationship stress. *Professional School Counseling, 10,* 428–440.

Ray, D. (2008). Impact of play therapy on parent-child relationship stress at a mental health training setting. *British Journal of Guidance & Counselling, 36,* 165–187.

Ray, D., Blanco, P., Sullivan, J., & Holliman, R. (2009). An exploratory study of child-centered play therapy with aggressive children. *International Journal of Play Therapy, 18,* 162–175.

Ray, D., Henson, R., Schottelkorb, A., Brown, A., & Muro, J. (2008). Effect of short-term and long-term play therapy services on teacher–child relationship stress. *Psychology in the Schools, 45,* 994–1009.

Ray, D., Schottelkorb, A., & Tsai, M. (2007). Play therapy with children exhibiting symptoms of attention deficit hyperactivity disorder. *International Journal of Play Therapy, 16,* 95–111.

Rubin, A. (2008). *Practitioner's guide to using research for evidence-based practice.* Hoboken, NJ: John Wiley & Sons.

Saucier, B. (1986). An intervention: The effects of play therapy on developmental achievement levels of abused children (Doctoral dissertation, Texas Woman's University). *Dissertation Abstracts International, 48,* 1007.

Schmidtchen, S., Hennies, S., & Acke, H. (1993). To kill two birds with one stone? Evaluating the hypothesis of a two-fold effectiveness of client-centered play therapy. *Psychologie in Erziehung und Unterricht, 40,* 34–42.

Schmidtchen, V.S., & Hobrucker, B. (1978). The efficiency of client-centered play therapy. *Praxis der Kinderpsychologie und Kinderpsychiatrie, 27,* 117–125.

Schumann, B. (2010). Effectiveness of child centered play therapy for children referred for aggression in elementary school. In J. Baggerly, D. Ray, & S. Bratton's (Eds.), *Child-centered play therapy research: The evidence base for effective practice* (pp. 193–208). Hoboken, NJ: Wiley.

Scott, T., Burlingame, G., Starling, M., Porter, C., & Lilly, J. (2003). Effects of individual client-centered play therapy on sexually abused children's mood, self-concept, and social competence. *International Journal of Play Therapy, 12,* 7–30.

Seeman, J., Barry, E., & Ellinwood, C. (1964). Interpersonal assessment of play therapy outcome. *Psychotherapy: Theory, Research, and Practice, 1,* 64–66.

Seeman, J., & Edwards, B. (1954). A therapeutic approach to reading difficulties. *Journal of Consulting Psychology, 18*, 451–453.

Shen, Y. (2002). Short-term group play therapy with Chinese earthquake victims: Effects on anxiety, depression, and adjustment. *International Journal of Play Therapy, 11*, 43–63.

Thombs, M., & Muro, J. (1973). Group counseling and the sociometric status of second grade children. *Elementary School Guidance and Counseling, 7*, 194–197.

Trostle, S. (1988). The effects of child-centered group play sessions on social-emotional growth of three- to six-year-old bilingual Puerto Rican children. *Journal of Research in Childhood Education, 3*, 93–106.

Tyndall-Lind, A., Landreth, G., & Giordano, M. (2001). Intensive group play therapy with child witnesses of domestic violence. *International Journal of Play Therapy, 10*, 53–83.

Wakaba, Y. (1983). Group play therapy for Japanese children who stutter. *Journal of Fluency Disorders, 8*, 93–118.

Wall, L. (1979). Parents as play therapists: A comparison of three interventions into children's play (Doctoral dissertation, University of Northern Colorado, 1979). *Dissertation Abstracts International, 39*, 5597.

Winn, E. (1959). The influence of play therapy on personality change and the consequent effect on reading performance (Doctoral dissertation, Michigan State University, 1959). *Dissertation Abstracts International, 22*, 4278.

Wishon, P. (1975). The impact of play intervention on word recognition skill and on aspects of personal-social development of first-grade children (Doctoral dissertation, Ohio State University, 1975). *Dissertation Abstracts International, 36*, 5030.

Yates, L. (1976). The use of sociometry as an identifier of research sample for psychological treatment and quantifier of change among second grade students. *Group Psychotherapy, Psychodrama, and Sociometry, 29*, 102–110.

Appendix: Child-Centered Play Therapy Treatment Manual*

Contents

Introduction

This manual is written to provide a resource for researchers examining the use of child-centered play therapy (CCPT). The reader will find an explanatory rationale for the CCPT perspective rooted in person-centered psychology and specific methods of how effective CCPT is facilitated with children. CCPT has been facilitated with children over seven decades since the 1940s, and methods are detailed in Axline (1947), Landreth (2002), and Wilson and Ryan (2005). These books offer an in-depth analysis of the explanation, beliefs, and workings of CCPT. Play therapists who are interested in facilitating CCPT are advised to use these more traditional sources for understanding CCPT. Play therapists are also encouraged to obtain extensive training and supervision on CCPT prior to independent delivery of this approach. The purpose of this manual is to outline a protocol that can be used in the delivery of individual and group CCPT as a component of research design. Because CCPT is a humanistic approach, play therapist practitioners might feel limited by the strict protocol of this manual, feeling that this manual may not meet the needs of individual clients. This is a valid concern related to the use of any therapeutic treatment manual and is recognized in the literature as a limitation of therapy manuals in practice (Nathan, Stuart, & Dolan, 2003). However, in order to ensure the consistent delivery of specific modalities such as CCPT, researchers highlight the need for manuals to include a description of techniques, a clear statement of therapist operations, and a measure of determining adherence to the technique. This manual is a step toward providing this type of operational protocol to aid the researcher in the delivery of CCPT. Notably, the specifics outlined in this manual serve as guidelines to follow but not dictates for therapist behavior. As in any therapeutic modality, therapists must sometimes abandon protocol and serve the client in a very individual, unique way guided by experienced therapeutic judgment and consultation.

Theoretical Rationale*

CCPT is a developmentally appropriate modality of facilitating therapy with children from a person-centered philosophy. Person-centered theory, also referred to as client-centered theory, was developed by Carl Rogers (1902–1987), who is cited as being the most influential counselor and psychotherapist in American history (Kirschenbaum, 2004). He was the founder and promoter of person-centered therapy, which made a significant impact on the counseling profession by transforming the perception of the client, the counselor, and the therapeutic relationship. Through a

* Selections of Theoretical Rationale were adapted from Ray & Schottelkorb (2008).

multitude of research, exemplary cases, and writings, Rogers demonstrated the need for and success of client-centered theory. Rogers promoted the basic principle of trust that individuals and groups can set their own goals and monitor their own progress in counseling (Raskin & Rogers, 2005).

Person-centered theory is based on 19 propositions listed in *Client-Centered Therapy* (Rogers, 1951) that describe personality and development. These 19 propositions show the personality to be a naturally evolving entity that is developed through a perceived understanding of reality influenced by self-created values mixed with introjected values. More simply explained, people experience life through a subjective perception of reality. As they experience life through their own lenses and understanding, they create a self that is a culmination of internal processes consisting of emotions and insights combined with external processes consisting of the influence of parental values and cultural norms. Emotions and behavior are then based on this perception, which leads to self-directed goals. When a child encounters experiences that are consistent with his or her concept of the self, there is no problem. However, when a child begins to encounter messages that differ from the self-concept, these inconsistent messages must be assimilated to form a new self-concept or psychological maladjustment will result. A child who learns to accept those experiences that are consistent and assimilate the ones that are inconsistent will evolve toward self-actualization, which leads to a deeper understanding and acceptance of self and others. Hence, human nature is positive, forward moving, constructive, realistic, and trustworthy (Rogers, 1957). Rogers was a firm believer in the wholeness of the individual. One part of the being does not act without an impact on all others. For significant growth, all parts of the being must move together.

Virginia Axline (1947), who was a student and colleague of Rogers, fully applied the philosophy and concepts of person-centered theory to her work in counseling children. Axline utilized person-centered theory in a developmentally responsive manner in her work with children by providing an environment conducive to their natural way of communicating. This environment consisted of a playroom of specific toys that allowed children to express their inner selves through play. The development of the relationship within the context of the playroom provided children with a safe environment in which to express themselves verbally and nonverbally.

Child-centered play therapists have a unique philosophy regarding the understanding of children. Children are seen as people who are capable of positive self-direction. Metaphorically, children are seen as flowers to bloom, not clay to be shaped. For flowers to bloom beautifully, the ideal conditions need to be provided: sun, food, water, etc. When these conditions exist, the flower blooms. When these conditions are lacking, the flower wilts and dies. In contrast, clay is poked, prodded, scraped, and molded until the creator produces a desired image. The image is a projection of the creator, not a representation of the initial clay.

Landreth (2002) offered 10 basic tenets about children that serve as a framework for child-centered play therapists:

1. Children are not miniature adults. As explained through developmental theory, children think and act differently from adults.
2. Children are people. They are capable of intense emotions and complicated thoughts.
3. Children are unique and worthy of respect. Each child possesses an individual personality and will.
4. Children are resilient. Although children experience some unfathomable situations, they are able to persevere beyond adult understanding.
5. Children have an inherent tendency toward growth and maturity. They are endowed with the will to strive for self-actualization.
6. Children are capable of positive self-direction. On their own, children are creative and able to develop ways to work positively in their world.
7. Children's natural language is play. Play is their safest and most comfortable way to express themselves.
8. Children have a right to remain silent. Because children operate most expressively in a nonverbal world, a child-centered counselor does not force them to communicate in an adult verbal world.
9. Children will take the therapeutic experience to where they need to be. There is no need for the counselor to direct the experience.
10. Children's growth cannot be sped up. Children operate on their own developmental time schedule that cannot be directed by an adult.

Goals of Child-Centered Play Therapy

In his own words, Rogers (1942) very clearly summarized the goal of person-centered counseling:

> It aims directly toward the greater independence and integration of the individual rather than hoping that such results will accrue if the counselor assists in solving the problem. The individual and not the problem is the focus. The aim is not to solve one particular problem, but to assist the individual to grow, so that he can cope with the present problem and with later problems in a better-integrated fashion. (p. 28)

The goal of CCPT is to establish conditions so that the child can experience growth and integration. It is postulated by Raskin and Rogers (2005) that if the counselor is successful in conveying genuineness, unconditional positive regard, and empathy, then the client will respond with a changed personality organization. Child-centered play therapists believe that a child's experience within the counseling relationship is the factor that is most meaningful and helpful in creating lasting, positive change.

Role of the Child-Centered Play Therapist and Play Therapy Relationship

As previously stated, there are specific conditions that a play therapist must provide in order to set up an environment for change. These are core conditions that must be provided by the play therapist, including (a) empathy—the play therapist must get within the child's world and seek to live the attitudes expressed; (b) unconditional positive regard—a warmth and acceptance of the child; (c) congruence—the play therapist is willing to express any personal feelings that exist in the relationship; and (d) implied conditions such as psychological contact between the play therapist and the child, the child experiencing incongruence, and the child experiencing conditions offered by the play therapist (adapted from Raskin & Rogers, 2005). These conditions are the "techniques" of person-centered counseling.

The fundamental "technique" of CCPT is the therapeutic relationship. Rogers (1942) described four aspects of the therapeutic relationship that can be applied to the CCPT play therapist. The play therapist provides warmth and responsiveness that makes rapport possible and gradually develops into a deeper emotional relationship. Second, there is permissiveness in regard to the expression of feeling. When the child recognizes the play therapist's acceptance of statements and actions, the child will express all feelings and attitudes. The third aspect is the setting of therapeutic limitations. Setting a structure for counseling, regarding timing and behavior, enables the older child to gain insight and the younger child to experience social reality. The final aspect of the relationship is the absence of pressure or coercion. The play therapist does not offer advice, suggestion, or pressure to follow one course of action over another.

Building on her developmental understanding of children, Axline (1947) identified eight basic principles that guide the CCPT play therapist. These basic principles are consistent with a person-centered philosophy of working with children by emphasizing the primacy of the counseling relationship. These principles insist that the counselor

1. Must develop a warm, friendly relationship with the child
2. Accepts the child unconditionally, without wishing the child were different in some way
3. Establishes a feeling of permissiveness in the relationship so that the child feels free to express self

4. Recognizes and reflects the feelings of the child to create understanding for the child
5. Respects the child's innate ability to solve his or her own problems and offers the opportunity to return responsibility to the child
6. Does not attempt to direct the child's actions or conversation, but allows the child to lead the way
7. Recognizes the gradual nature of the child's process and does not try to rush counseling
8. Establishes only those limitations that are necessary to anchor the child's counseling to the world of reality

Process of Change

According to Rychlak (1981), if a person's perception of experiences is incongruent with the perception of self, so that he or she holds to a self-concept that is not reflective of the underlying organic feelings, then there is increasing tension in the personality structure. More simply stated, Rogers found that clients with this degree of incongruence were found to suffer from low self-esteem (Raskin & Rogers, 2005). The incongruence between the self-concept and self-ideal causes a noticeable lack of self-regard.

Rogers (1942) clearly delineated the therapeutic process necessary to facilitate substantive personality reorganization and that can also be applied to children. The process begins when the child comes for help. The helping situation is defined as one in which the play therapist does not have the answers but will provide a place where the child can work out his or her own solutions. The play therapist encourages free expression as the play therapist accepts, recognizes, and clarifies negative feelings. When the child is able to fully express negative feelings, small movement toward the expression of positive impulses will occur. The play therapist accepts and recognizes positive feelings as well. The child gains understanding and acceptance of self, followed by an awareness of possible decisions or courses of action. The child will follow with small but significant positive actions, with broader understanding, leading to further positive action. As a result, the child experiences a decreasing need for help and a recognition that the counseling relationship will end.

Use of Play in Therapy

The use of play therapy is based on the developmental understanding of children. Piaget (1962) offered his theory of cognitive development that recognizes the differences between the way children understand and process information and the way that adults function. Most children at the elementary level function at the two stages identified as preoperational (2 to 7 years) and concrete operations (8 to 11 years). These stages are approximately identified with chronological ages, but it is relatively understood that development is specific to the individual. At the preoperational stage, a child is acquiring the skill of language where symbols are used to mentally represent objects. Also, in this stage, a child's thinking is rigid and limited to how things appear at the time. This is the stage of magical thinking in which children create implausible explanations for things that they do not understand. Regarding play, a child's play behaviors become increasingly imaginary, unassociated with reality, but will increase in complexity of make-believe play to encompass emerging cognitive patterns. Internally, the child is improving understanding and knowledge, but externally, the child lacks the ability to communicate this enhanced way of working within the world. Play is the child's most natural way of communicating this internal awareness of self and others.

The concrete operational stage offers children the ability to reason logically and organize thoughts coherently. They are able to manipulate ideas and accept logical society rules. However, they can only think about actual physical objects; they cannot maneuver abstract reasoning. They are unable to express certain complicated emotions, such as guilt or resentment, because of the need for abstract thought to understand such emotions. For those children operating in the concrete stage, play helps bridge the gap between concrete experience and abstract thought.

Other theorists recognized the need and purpose for play in children. Erikson (1963) believed that play offered a safe place for children to work through difficulties at an early age. In play, a child can initiate activity without the threat of real-life consequences. The child can act as the authority. Play allows the child to organize experiences, express feelings, and explore fantasies. Vygotsky (1978) theorized that play allowed the child to practice self-regulation and need fulfillment. Play offers an environment where a child can test fantasies. Going somewhat further than Piaget, Vygotsky believed that play led to the development of abstract thought for children.

In summary, play is an important medium for children for several reasons. Play is the natural language of children (Landreth, 2002). Developmentally, play bridges the gap between concrete experience and abstract thought. Play offers children the opportunity to organize their real-life experiences that are often complicated and abstract in nature. Children gain a sense of control through play and also learn coping skills.

Appropriate Client Populations for CCPT

Because CCPT treatment is based on person-centered philosophy, an approach that is child centered rather than problem centered, the same basic conditions are offered to all prospective clients (Raskin & Rogers, 2005). Hence, CCPT is appropriate for children who are labeled with specific diagnoses such as attention-deficit hyperactivity disorder, oppositional defiant disorder, anxiety disorder, etc., as well as with children who are experiencing normal difficulties related to development.

LeBlanc and Ritchie (2001) published their meta-analysis of play therapy outcomes summarizing the results of 42 controlled studies, with an effect size of 0.66 standard deviations. Using Cohen's (1988) guidelines for interpretation, an effect size of 0.66 denotes a moderate treatment effect, similar to effect sizes found in other child psychotherapy meta-analyses (Casey & Berman, 1985, ES = 0.71; Weisz, Weiss, Han, Granger, & Morton, 1995, ES = 0.71).

Bratton, Ray, Rhine, and Jones (2005) conducted the largest meta-analysis on play therapy outcome research. This meta-analysis included the review of 180 documents that appeared to measure the effectiveness of play therapy dated 1942 to 2000. Based on stringent criteria for inclusion designating use of a controlled research design, sufficient data for computing effect size, and the identification by the author of a labeled "play therapy" intervention, 93 studies were included in the final calculation of effect size. The overall effect size was calculated at 0.80 standard deviations, interpreted as a large effect and indicating that children receiving play therapy interventions performed 0.80 standard deviations above children who did not receive play therapy.

Bratton, Ray, Rhine, and Jones (2005) coded specific characteristics of play therapy that impacted or had no impact on play therapy outcome. Effect sizes for humanistic (ES = 0.92) and nonhumanistic play therapy (ES = 0.71) interventions were considered effective regardless of theoretical approach. However, the effect size reported for the humanistic approach was in the large effect category while nonhumanistic was in the moderate category. This difference in effect may be attributed to a larger number of calculated humanistic studies (n = 73) compared to nonhumanistic studies (n = 12). Treatment duration was a factor in the success of play therapy. Optimal treatment effects were obtained in 35 to 40 sessions, although many studies with fewer than 14 sessions also produced medium and large effect sizes. Age and gender were not found to be significant factors from which to predict the effects of play therapy. Play therapy appeared to be equally effective across age and gender. An effect size was not calculated for ethnicity due to the lack of specificity in the reporting of ethnicity in individual studies. In addressing presenting problems, the researchers encountered difficulty in distinguishing specific diagnoses and symptoms due to the variation of the studies. However, 24 studies were calculated as investigating internalizing problems with an effect size of 0.81; 17 studies were calculated as examining the effects of play therapy on externalizing problems with an effect size of 0.78; and 16 studies addressed a combination of internalizing and externalizing problems with an effect size of 0.93. These results indicated that play therapy had a moderate to large beneficial effect for internalizing, externalizing, and combined problem types.

In a meta-analysis of treatment for sexually abused children, Hetzel-Riggin, Brausch, and Montgomery (2007) found that play therapy seemed to be the most effective treatment for social functioning. Beelmann and Schneider (2003) found that nondirective play therapy was effective for children with mixed presenting problems. And in a more systematic review, Bratton and Ray (2000) found evidence to support the use of play therapy in the areas of self-concept, behavioral change, cognitive ability, social skills, and anxiety. Because play therapy has been in use across seven decades, individual study support for various presenting problems can be found in many peer-reviewed publications.

Historically, play therapy has been facilitated with clients of various ages from infancy to adulthood. Research supports the use of CCPT across age groups, most specifically focusing on 3- to 10-year-olds. However, research has also demonstrated that modifications to room, materials, and responses also provide an effective intervention for clients up to adulthood. For the purposes of this manual, CCPT focuses on early and middle childhood. Materials and responses are appropriately designed for children ages 3 to 10 years old.

Play Therapist Training

Facilitation of CCPT requires extensive training for the play therapist providing services to children. Minimal standards for CCPT education include a master's degree in a mental health field and a 40-hour course in the basics of play therapy, usually provided in a 3-credit-hour format at the university level. A course that prepares a therapist in CCPT would be based on the principles of child-centered philosophy, including the review and study of such resources as Landreth (2002), Axline (1947), Wilson and Ryan (2005), Guerney (2001), and Nordling and Guerney (1999). A course on the basics of CCPT would also include a clinical practice component where students are supervised in facilitating play therapy through the basic CCPT skills. These are seen as minimal requirements for the facilitation of CCPT at the research level. Typically, play therapists who provide CCPT within research projects optimally have extensive training and supervision in CCPT, including but not limited to a master's degree in mental health, two didactic courses in play therapy, and two semesters of supervised clinical practice in play therapy. If the primary investigator is unable to procure play therapists with this level of training, treatment protocol could be threatened and, hence, extensive supervision of the process would be a necessary part of the play therapy research design.

Structure of the Therapeutic Session

The beginning play therapist must first master the basic skills of the process. Basic skills include setting up a playroom, selecting materials, and the use of effective nonverbal and verbal ways of being with the child. This section serves as a blueprint for conducting CCPT in research settings. For more detailed information on the intricacies of play therapy, I refer the reader to more detailed descriptions by Landreth (2002). Before a play therapist can successfully progress to more advanced concepts in play therapy, forming a relationship with the child, in which the child is provided an environment of acceptance and understanding, is essential.

The Playroom

Before meeting a child, a play therapist prepares an environment in which the culture of childhood is addressed. This environment is the playroom. Because play is the developmental language of the child, a playroom is designed and filled with materials that help the child speak with clarity. The size of the playroom allows enough space for a child to move freely without becoming overwhelmed with too much space. Landreth (2002) suggests that an ideal playroom is 12 by 15 feet. Although this is an ideal size for playrooms, many therapists are restricted in their settings and compromise space for utility. Play therapy can be effective in different sizes of rooms. Essential features of a playroom include shelves for placing toys above the floor and allowing more room for movement and at least some space for free movement. Optimal features include access to water through a sink, noncarpeted floors, durable wall paint, and a two-way mirror for camera and observation possibilities. Figure A.1 is an example of the more ideal type of playroom.

Play Materials

Materials for the playroom include toys, craft materials, paints, easel, puppet theater, sandbox, and child furniture. In selecting toys, the most fundamental criterion is that the toy serves a purpose in the playroom. For each and every toy or play material in the playroom, a therapist should ask the following questions:

1. What therapeutic purpose will this serve for children who use this room?
2. How will this help children express themselves?
3. How will this help me build a relationship with children?

When a therapist chooses purposefully, appropriate selection becomes clear. This type of careful selection helps to focus the play therapist on what toys are essential to the process. Materials such as computerized games,

Figure A.1 Ideal type of playroom.

board games, puzzles, and books may meet the criteria for one or two of the above questions but they rarely meet the criteria for all three.

When setting up a playroom for the first time, a play therapist might become overwhelmed by the vast number of different toys and materials, especially if space is limited. Kottman (2003) provides categorization of materials in five general areas, including family/nurturing, scary toys, aggressive toys, expressive toys, and pretend/fantasy toys. For the family/nurturing category, materials provide the child with the opportunity to act in the role of an adult or a child, especially within family contexts, whether it be a meticulous role of sweeping and washing or the nurturing role of feeding and clothing. Scary toys include materials that typically solicit fear in larger society, such as spiders and snakes. Scary toys help children address their own fears and anxieties.

Expressive toys and materials include arts and crafts materials and allow for expression of creativity. They are used to express both positive and negative emotions in children, and most all children who enter a playroom with these materials will use them at some point in their therapy. Water is typically the most used material in the playroom while easel and paints are typically the second most used materials in the playroom. Both materials are considered expressive and are used creatively by children. Pretend/fantasy toys such as dress-up clothes, puppets, and medical kits allow children to deeply explore the adult world in a safe environment.

Table A.1 CCPT Playroom Toys

Sand	Puppet	Bean bag chair
Scoops/shovel/bucket	Puppet theater	Plastic domestic animals
Dramatic play clothes	Vehicles/planes	Plastic zoo animals
Masks and hats	Toy guns	Medical kit
Plastic dinosaurs	Baby dolls/clothes	Bandages
Knife/sword	Pacifier	Baby bottle
Rope	Cash register	Dart gun
Play kitchen/food items	Handcuffs/keys	Pillow/blanket
Pots/pans/dishes/utensils	Blocks	Paints/easel
Dollhouse/bendable family	Toy soldiers	Bowling pins/ball
Musical instruments	Bop bag/Bobo	Toy car/truck
Cell phones	Camera/binoculars	Play dough
Transparent tape	Vehicles/planes	Glue/scissors/paper

Although it is helpful to conceptualize toys categorically when designing a playroom, it should be noted that effective expressive toys in the playroom are used by children in a multiplicity of ways. Knives can be used to cut a therapist free for safety while baby bottles can be used to choke a baby doll. A cuddly stuffed bear can be used to suffocate a small cub while a bop bag can be used to hug for an entire session. The successful selection of a toy is confirmed when a play therapist sees that children are using it for varying purposes of expression. A detailed list of toys provided by Landreth (2002) can be found in Table A.1. Although it is not required to have all the toys that are listed, it is highly recommended that each category is represented in a playroom. For research purposes, if a research design requires several playrooms, each playroom should be set up similarly with the exact same list of toys for each room.

The playroom environment not only provides toys for expression, but also conveys a sense of order and consistency. As children participate in play therapy, they learn to depend on the consistency of the room and the therapist. Placing items in the room should make logical sense, grouping similar categories together. And most importantly, the materials are in the same place in the playroom every time the child enters. This helps send the message to children that this is a place they can truly know and feel safe. They have full mastery over their environment in the playroom so that they can progress to expression and resolution of difficulties in their lives. If toys are strewn carelessly in the playroom and in different places from session to session, the play therapist is reinforcing the child's experience of chaos in the home/external context. As they nervously search through a disorganized playroom to find the toy they need, children learn that they must "fight" to get their needs met, and this environment is just like all the others that have previously failed them.

Therapist Nonverbal Skills: A Way of Being

Just as the physical environment is designed as an inviting space for children, the play therapist must convey a way of being that is also inviting to a child. In play therapy, nonverbal skills are equally critical, if not more so, to verbal skills. Because children express themselves in the nonverbal world, play therapists are effective in using the same type of nonverbal expression. The use of nonverbal skills is heavily influenced by the genuineness and personhood of the play therapist. At the Center for Play Therapy (CPT) at the University of North Texas, certain skills are highlighted for the purposes of training new play therapists. Over decades of training and supervising play therapists at CPT, certain skills have emerged as essential to the play therapy process.

Structuring the session provides the child with a sense of consistency and mastery over the environment. CCPT sessions are typically 45 minutes in length, with a range from 30 to 50 minutes. For research purposes, the primary investigator should ensure that each session is of the same time duration. The play therapist facilitates the session to begin on time and provides a consistency to the ending of the session at the same time for each session. The child is not allowed to leave the playroom during the session time unless there is an unforeseen circumstance such as emergency bathroom trip or interruption by an external event. CCPT does not define the number of sessions required for the success of play therapy. Research has demonstrated that 35 to 40 sessions provides optimal results. However, this number of sessions is often prohibitive from a research stance and is unnecessary for marked growth/change in the child. Experience demonstrates that 15 to 20 sessions often yield significant, noteworthy changes that can be measured.

When the therapist enters the playroom with a child, great care is taken to provide an environment where the child is in the lead. The therapist sits in a designated chair in the room and does not enter the child's physical space or play without invitation. The therapist maintains an open stance toward the child, leaning forward toward the child and keeping arms and legs positioned to convey a sense of openness to the child. The therapist is attentive and appears interested in the child. The therapist actively works to remain connected to the present moment and avoids preoccupation with other thoughts. Although sometimes difficult for new therapists, a therapist seems comfortable with the child and the situation, remaining relaxed throughout the session.

Tone of voice communicates the therapist's ability to connect with the child on an emotional level. Two considerations emerge when addressing the tone of the therapist's voice. First, the therapist's tone matches the level of affect displayed by the child. Often, new play therapists will present themselves as overly animated to the child. This is generally the way that many adults relate to children. Therapists new to working with children often harbor the idea that their role is to make the child happy and use their tone of voice toward this end. Matching therapist tone to the tone of the child suggests that the therapist has a genuine understanding and acceptance of emotions expressed by the child. Second, the therapist's tone matches the therapist's own words and affect. Matching verbal response with nonverbal response communicates genuineness. The child experiences the therapist more fully as a person. For example, if a child accidentally hits the therapist with a toy, and the therapist experiences a flash of shock or anger but responds, "Sometimes accidents happen in here" with a flat affect, the child will experience the therapist as insincere, which can lead to mistrust in the relationship. A more effective and congruent response might be, "That really hurt but sometimes accidents happen in here."

Therapist Verbal Skills

CCPT has benefited from offering distinct categories of verbal responses that guide the play therapist in therapeutic communication. Delivery of therapeutic responses is also key to reaching a child effectively. Two delivery skills are of special note. Because play therapy recognizes the limited language ability of children, the importance of short therapeutic responses is helpful. Lengthy responses lose the interest of the child quickly, confuse the child, and often convey a lack of understanding on the part of the therapist. Second, the therapist's rate of responses should match the interaction of the child. If the child is quiet and reserved, then the play therapist will slow his responses. If the child is highly interactive and talkative, the play therapist will want to match this level of energy with an increased number of responses. In initial sessions with the child, play therapists often have a quicker rate of response because silence can be uncomfortable for the child in a new situation. In subsequent sessions, the therapist will learn to create a pace that matches that of the child.

There are eight categories of therapeutic verbal responses. Several of these are presented by Moustakas (1959), Ginott (1965), Axline (1947), and Landreth (2002), and others are from my own experiences in play therapy (Ray, 2004).

1. *Tracking behavior.* Tracking behavior is the most basic of play therapist responses. The therapist tracks behavior when he or she verbally responds to the behavior of the child simply by stating

what is seen or observed. Tracking behavior allows the child to know that the therapist is interested and accepting. It also helps the therapist immerse him or herself into the child's world. As a child picks up a dinosaur, the therapist might respond, "You're picking that up." As the child rolls the car across the room, "You're running that all the way over there."

2. *Reflecting content.* Reflecting content in play therapy is identical to reflecting content in adult talk therapy. To reflect content, the play therapist paraphrases the verbal interactions of children. Reflecting content validates children's perceptions of their experience and clarifies children's understanding of themselves (Landreth, 2002). As a child describes the movie that she saw over the weekend, the therapist responds, "You went to see James Bond and there was a lot of action."

Although tracking behavior and reflecting content are essential to the play therapy process, they are the most basic skills in play therapy. They help build a relationship with a child so that the child can benefit from higher-level skills. The following skills facilitate self-concept, development of self-responsibility, creation of awareness, and the building of the therapeutic relationship.

3. *Reflecting feeling.* Reflecting feeling is the verbal response to emotions expressed by children in play therapy. Reflecting feeling is considered a higher-level skill because children rarely communicate by verbally expressing emotion. However, they are quite emotive. In addition, the reflection of feeling can sometimes be threatening to children and should be presented carefully. Reflecting feeling helps children become aware of emotions, thereby leading to the appropriate acceptance and expression of such emotions. A child says, "This place is stupid and I want to go home." A therapist might respond, "You're angry about being here and you'd rather be at home."
4. *Facilitating decision making, returning responsibility.* One of the play therapist's goals is to help children experience a sense of their own capability and take responsibility for it. The therapist does not do for children what children can do for themselves (Landreth, 2002). Responses that facilitate decision making or return responsibility help children to experience themselves as able and empowered. A child might ask, "What am I supposed to do in here?" Instead of replying with an answer such as, "You can paint or play in the sand," which directs the child and places responsibility on the therapist, a more facilitative response of decision making would be, "In here, it's up to you." Another example

might be if a child attempts to open a glue bottle, quickly gives up, and then asks, "Can you do it?" The therapist returns responsibility by responding, "That looks like something you can do." Of course, a therapist would only return responsibility if it is determined that the child is capable of the action.

5. *Facilitating creativity, spontaneity.* Helping a child experience his own sense of creativity and freedom is another goal of play therapy. Acceptance and encouragement of creativity sends a message to the child that she is unique and special in her own way. Maladjusted children are often trapped in rigid ways of acting and thinking. Experiencing the freedom of expression allows a child to develop flexibility in thought and action. If a child asks, "What color should the flower be?" A therapist who wishes to encourage creativity might say, "In here, it can be whatever color you want it to be."
6. *Esteem building, encouraging.* Encouraging children to feel better about themselves is a constant objective for the play therapist. The use of esteem-building statements works to help children experience themselves as capable. As a child proudly finishes a painting, a therapist might respond, "You made that look just how you wanted." After a child spends several minutes trying to make the bullet fit in the gun and succeeds, a therapist might respond, "You did it. You figured it out."

   Initially, play therapists may struggle with the difference between praising and esteem-building responses. Esteem-building responses have a deeper therapeutic purpose of helping a child create an intrinsic sense of self rather than relying on praise for external evaluation. A praise response, such as "That's a pretty picture" or "I like the way you did that" encourages the child to perform for the therapist and continue to seek external reinforcement, thereby eroding a sense of self. An esteem-building response such as, "You're really proud of your picture" or "You made that just the way you wanted" encourages a child to develop an internal sense of evaluation leading to an internal sense of responsibility.
7. *Facilitating relationship.* Responses that focus on building the relationship between the therapist and child help the child experience a positive relationship. Because the therapy relationship serves as a model for all intimate relationships, the therapist should respond to any attempt by the child to address the relationship. Relational responses help the child learn effective communication patterns and express the therapist's care for the child. Relationship responses should always include a reference to the child and reference to self as therapist. A therapist sets a limit with

a child that she (the therapist) is not for shooting with the gun. The child responds, "I hate you. I'm going to put you in jail." To facilitate the relationship, the therapist acknowledges the child's direct anger at her by saying, "You're really mad at me that I'm not for shooting. You want to punish me." Another scenario might be a child who cleans up the entire room right before the end of the session and says, "Look, now you don't have to clean." The therapist would respond to this relational gesture by saying, "You wanted to do something to help me."

8. *Limit-setting.* Limits are used to set realistic boundaries in the playroom that provide safety and consistency for the child. Limits can be set in simple short directives or they can develop into complicated battles between the therapist and child. In an attempt to provide an environment for a child that allows self-direction and self-responsibility, minimal limits are encouraged in child-centered play therapy. The goal is to help the child move toward the ability to self-limit. Typically, limits are set when children attempt to damage themselves, another person, and certain expensive or irreplaceable toys, or if their behavior impedes play therapist acceptance. Landreth (2002) proposed a specific method for setting limits in play therapy. The ACT model of limit setting includes (a) Acknowledge the feeling, (b) Communicate the limit, and (c) Target an alternative. In this model, the play therapist recognizes and addresses the child's feelings in the moment: "You're really excited about the paint." Second, the counselor sets a short, concrete, definitive limit: "But it's not for throwing on the walls." Finally, the play therapist provides an alternative to the action: "The paper is for painting." When children have directed energy in the moment, it is important to provide them with an alternative for that energy so that they do not feel the need to act on impulse. Although there are other methods for setting limits, the ACT model is short, direct, and works effectively.

Ensuring Integrity of Protocol

In conducting research using CCPT, the investigator ensures the integrity of the CCPT protocol. Supervision of the use of skills is vital to the treatment protocol. All research sessions are video recorded and provided to the primary investigator. In order to provide the researcher with a method for ensuring integrity of treatment, Table A.2 offers the Play Therapy Skills Checklist (PTSC). The PTSC is used to supervise video recordings of sessions and marked according to therapist responses. Therapists' verbal responses should fall into one of the presented eight categories. Responses

Table A.2 Play Therapy Skills Checklist (PTSC)

Therapist: ____________________ Child/Age/Code: ____________________

Observer: ____________________ Date: ____________________

Therapist Nonverbal Communication:		**Too Much**	**Appropriate**	**Need More**	**None**	**Therapist Responses/Examples**	**Supervision Comments**
Lean Forward/Open							
Appeared Interested							
Relaxed Comfortable							
Tone/Expression Congruent with Child's Affect							
Tone/Expression Congruent with Therapist's Responses							
Succinct/Interactive							
Rate of Responses							
Therapist Responses:	**No. of Responses**	**Too Much**	**Appropriate**	**Need More**	**None**	**Therapist Responses/Examples**	**Other Possible Responses**
Tracking behavior							
Reflecting content							
Reflecting feelings							

Facilitating decision making/responsibility							
Facilitating creativity/spontaneity							
Esteem building/encouraging							
Facilitating relationship							
Limit setting							
Non-CCPT response							

Child Made Contact/Connectedness:

Identified Themes:

Therapist's Strengths:

Areas for Growth:

---

that cannot be categorized into one of the eight categories are considered non-CCPT responses and threaten the integrity of treatment. In addition, supervision of nonverbal skills should also be conducted and marked on the PTSC.

The PTSC can be a specific aid in supervision and consultation of play therapy (see Ray, 2004). When used as part of play therapy research, the use of the PTSC follows several specific steps, including

1. Every CCPT session is recorded on video.
2. If needed, the play therapist presents the recording in supervision/consultation session with investigator or clinical supervisor to help with case discussion.
3. The play therapist is required to present each recording to the primary investigator with the date and session number marked, as well as any other needed information.
4. The primary investigator randomly selects 10% to 20% of all recordings to review.
5. The recordings are then reviewed by an experienced CCPT play therapist using the PTSC. Typically, the reviewer will observe 5 to 10 minutes of each session and mark each response provided by the play therapist into one of the response categories, specifically marking non-CCPT responses.
6. The reviewer provides the marked PTSC protocols to the investigator.
7. The investigator analyzes the PTSC protocols and calculates an agreement percentage within the response categories. Optimal agreement would be that between 90 and 100% of responses fall into one of the CCPT verbal response categories.

Parent and Teacher Consultation

In CCPT, consultation with parents, parent education, or family therapy is typically part of the play therapy process. In addition, play therapy in the schools might often include consultation with teachers, school counselors, or administrators. The purpose of this treatment manual is to provide a protocol for conducting CCPT within an individual or group child session. If an investigator chooses to extend this protocol to work with parents, guardians, or school personnel, a specified way of working would need to be defined as part of the research design. Consultation or family interventions would need to be clearly outlined and follow the same procedures for all children and parents/teachers. Bratton, Landreth, Kellam, and Blackard (2006) provided a specific manual for conducting child/parent relationship therapy that can often be used in conjunction with CCPT. Ray (2007) provided a method of consulting with teachers as an adjunct to the CCPT process. These types of parent and school interventions have been shown to enhance the CCPT process, demonstrating a greater amount of play therapy effect. However, CCPT alone without parent and/or teacher intervention has also been shown to be effective from a research perspective.

Steps for Facilitation of CCPT as Part of Research Design

1. Primary investigator defines the specific population for CCPT intervention, and the specific number of sessions provided by research design.
2. Primary investigator identifies how to access the sample population and collects data to confirm the specificity of the population (e.g., screening assessments for ADHD, disruptive behaviors, etc.).
3. Informed consent is provided to and signed by the custodial guardian.
4. Additional data is collected according to research design.
5. Children are randomly assigned to research treatment group, with at least one treatment group following the protocol of CCPT.
6. Primary investigator schedules sessions for CCPT group with each session taking place for exactly the same amount of time (optimal time for sessions are from 30 to 45 minutes).
7. An experienced and well-trained CCPT play therapist is assigned to each child.
8. Play therapist conducts CCPT following given protocol for each session until research design criteria for session number are met.
9. Each play therapist is assigned a supervisor or consultant for weekly interaction regarding progress of cases.
10. Each session is recorded and submitted to the primary investigator.
11. Investigator ensures protocol integrity through PTSC.
12. Upon completion of required research play sessions, the play therapist and primary investigator decide upon termination readiness for the child. If the child is not ready for termination, the primary investigator provides a case plan to provide additional services to the child following completion of research design.
13. Follow-up or post data is collected according to research design.

References

Axline, V. (1947). *Play therapy.* New York: Ballantine Books.

Beelmann, A., & Schneider, N. (2003). The effects of psychotherapy with children and adolescents: A review and meta-analysis of German-language research. *Zeitschrift fur Klinische Psychologie und Psychotherapie: Forschung und Praxis, 32*, 129–143.

Bratton, S., Landreth, G., Kellam, T., & Blackard, S. (2006). *Child parent relationship therapy treatment manual: A 10 session filial therapy model for training parents.* New York: Routledge.

Bratton, S., & Ray, D. (2000). What the research shows about play therapy. *International Journal of Play Therapy, 9*, 47–88.

Bratton, S., Ray, D., Rhine, T., & Jones, L. (2005). The efficacy of play therapy with children: A meta-analytic review of treatment outcomes. *Professional Psychology: Research and Practice, 36*, 376–390.

Casey, R., & Berman, J. (1985). The outcome of psychotherapy with children. *Psychological Bulletin, 98*, 388–400.

Cohen, J. (1988). *Statistical power analysis for the behavioral sciences* (2nd ed.). Mahwah, NJ: Lawrence Erlbaum Associates.

Erikson, E. (1963). *Childhood and society.* New York: Norton.

Ginott, H. (1965). *Between parent and child.* New York: Avon.

Guerney, L. (2001). Child-centered play therapy. *International Journal of Play Therapy, 10*, 13–31.

Hetzel-Riggin, M., Brausch, A., & Montgomery, B. (2007). A meta-analytic investigation of therapy modality outcomes for sexually abused children and adolescents: An exploratory study. *Child Abuse & Neglect, 31*, 125–141.

Kirschenbaum, H. (2004). Carl Rogers's life and work: An assessment on the 100th anniversary of his birth. *Journal of Counseling and Development, 82*, 116–124.

Kottman, T. (2003). *Partners in play: An Adlerian approach to play therapy* (2nd ed.). Alexandria, VA: American Counseling Association.

Landreth, G. (2002). *Play therapy: The art of the relationship* (2nd ed.). New York: Brunner-Routledge.

LeBlanc, M., & Ritchie, M. (2001). A meta-analysis of play therapy outcomes. *Counseling Psychology Quarterly, 14*, 149–163.

Moustakas, C. (1959). *Psychotherapy with children: The living relationship.* New York: Harper & Row.

Nathan, P., Stuart, S., & Dolan, S. (2003). Research on psychotherapy efficacy and effectiveness: Between Scylla and Charybdis? In A. Kazdin (Ed.), *Methodological issues and strategies in clinical research* (3rd ed., pp. 505–546). Washington DC: APA.

Nordling, W., & Guerney, L. (1999). Typical stages in the child-centered play therapy process. *Journal for the Professional Counselor, 14*, 16–22.

Piaget, J. (1962). *Play, dreams, and imitation in childhood.* New York: Routledge.

Raskin, N., & Rogers, C. (2005). Person-centered therapy. In R. Corsini and D. Wedding, (Eds.), *Current psychotherapies* (7th ed.) (pp. 130–165). Belmont, CA: Brooks/Cole.

Ray, D. (2004). Supervision of basic and advanced skills in play therapy. *Journal of Professional Counseling: Practice, Theory, and Research, 32*(2), 28–41.

Ray, D. (2007). Two counseling interventions to reduce teacher-child relationship stress. *Professional School Counseling*, 10, 428–440.

Ray, D., & Schottelkorb, A. (2008). Practical person-centered theory application in the schools. In A. Vernon & T. Kottman (Eds.), *Counseling Theories: Practical Applications with Children and Adolescents in School Settings* (pp. 1–45). Denver, CO: Love.

Rogers, C. (1942). *Counseling and psychotherapy*. Boston: Houghton Mifflin.

Rogers, C. (1951). *Client-centered therapy*. Boston: Houghton Mifflin.

Rogers, C. (1957). The necessary and sufficient conditions of therapeutic personality change. *Journal of Consulting Psychology, 21*, 95–103.

Rychlak, J. (1981). *Introduction to personality and psychotherapy* (2nd ed.). Boston: Houghton Mifflin.

Vygotsky, L.S. (1978). *Mind and society: The development of higher mental processes.* Cambridge, MA: Harvard University Press.

Weisz, J., Weiss, B., Han, S., Granger, D., & Morton, T. (1995). Effects of psychotherapy with children and adolescents revisited: A meta-analysis of treatment outcomes studies. *Psychological Bulletin, 117*, 450–468.

Wilson, K., & Ryan, V. (2005). *Play therapy: A non-directive approach for children and adolescents* (2nd ed.). Edinburgh: Elsevier.

Index

R

S

U

V

W

CD Contents

CCPT Manual
Play Therapy Progress Worksheet
Sample School Counseling Consent Form
Sample School Counseling Brochure
Play Therapy Treatment Plan Sample
Play Therapy Session Summary
Play Therapy Session Summary Sample

Made in the USA
Thornton, CO
05/16/22 19:47:27

07fbdf0a-4823-4a0b-9cc0-13544be78d84R01